Caring for people with
DISABILITIES

Caring for people with
DISABILITIES

Alan Skelt

LONGMAN

Pearson Education Limited
Edinburgh Gate
Harlow, Essex CM20 2JE,
England and Assoiated
companies throughout the world.

© Longman Group UK Limited 1993

First published in Great Britain 1993
Second impression 1994
Third impression 1995
Fourth impression 1999

British Library Cataloguing in Publication Data
A catalogue record for this book is available from the British Library

ISBN 0 273 60089 3

Typeset by Avocet Typesetters, Bicester, Oxon

Transferred to digital print on demand 2001

**Printed and bound in Great Britain by Antony Rowe Ltd,
Eastbourne**

Contents

v

Introduction

In this book I hope to provide a general overview of the subject of physical disability at a practical level through the use of exercises, assignments, and case histories. Covering the whole range of disability has not been possible, but many of the situations described are directly transferable to a variety of different circumstances, and tutors should have no difficulty adapting material to specific requirements.

A major change in the way services are provided is contained in the NHS & Community Care Act 1989, which became law on 1 April 1992. A new world of Purchaser/Provider splits, mixed economies of care and Packages of Care is now with us.

The material here should be of particular use to students and teaching teams of BTEC, City & Guilds, CCETSW and other health and care courses, including those which are NVQ and GNVQ linked. For many of the assignments and exercises, the elements of BTEC Common Skills, GNVQ and NVQ competences which can be assessed have been identified.

Which ones are assessed, where the emphasis is placed and how the suggested exercises and assignments are interpreted depends upon individual tutors and teaching teams. The material is intended to be flexible; the assignments can be modified in any way required; pieces added or taken away, or used in part or as a whole.

The case histories (all of which are based on real people) can be used as they stand, or with the associated questions and exercises, or any other presentation which makes them appropriate for different courses, from level 2 NVQ to professional level nurse and social work training; the aim is for flexibility.

The main emphasis is toward adult life, as other Pitman texts cover Child Care and Elderly People. *A Practical Approach to Caring* by Kate Williams covers the general background to Caring and the Structure of the NHS and Local Authorities. This volume builds from there and concentrates on the specialist area of Caring for People with a Physical Disability. *Caring for the Elderly* by Veronica Windmill continues through the life span.

Inevitably, generalisations and prescriptive labels are used, and no excuse is made for this, as it enables information to be imparted with greater ease, and allows for simpler explanations. The reader should remember, however, that we are talking about *people* all the way through this book − not 'the handicapped', or 'the disabled', but people with disabilities, or disabled people.

The population of people with disabilities is just as much a mixture of people as is your neighbourhood, college, or town. Disability is no respecter of age or social circumstance. The majority of those so labelled do not need individual help, but help from society to make their environment more 'user-friendly', although the minority who do need personal attention are the people who will need carers, and will be the future employers of those using this book.

Every person that you will be helping during your caring career is an individual, with their own views, likes and dislikes, rights and expectations. Caring does not necessarily mean 'doing things for', it also encompasses the enabling role; helping people do things for themselves.

How do *you* like to be treated and spoken to by other people? Bear this in mind in all your dealings with others, both colleagues and people in your care for whatever reason.

Remember, it is quite possible to be efficient without being officious.

Alan Skelt
1992

With particular thanks to Geoff Thomason of the Winged Fellowship Trust and Don Melbourne of Dudley SSD for their help in the preparation of this book.

Part One

WHO CARES?

Chapter 1

WHO ARE THE CARERS?

You will probably know from your own experience that knowing where to get help is something you are vaguely aware of in general terms – that is, until the time arrives when you actually need it. This is just as true with disability as it is in any other sphere of life. It is always other people who need the help, not us or ours, isn't it?

However, you are now embarking upon a career in the caring services, so you will need to know what is available in a little more detail. Nobody will expect you to know everything straightaway, but they will expect you to be able to find out. If you do not know yourself, then you should know where to look or where to ask.

Sources of help

Where would you start if you were asked where help could be obtained from? Having a framework from which to start is the first requirement, and there are different ways of sub-dividing the sources of help.

One possible classification is into general providers and specific providers. General providers are organisations such as the National Health Service, the general practitioner services, or the Local Authorities via social, educational, and other services. Specific providers are the smaller organisations such as the Spastics Society, Royal National Institute for Deaf People, etc., who offer services very specific to a given disability. You must then find out the type of help which they are able to give, be it advice, cash or services.

Another way of looking at sources of help is to break them down into groups; for example informal; statutory; voluntary; and private.

Informal

This group is almost always the first involved, and comprises the immediate family; (e.g. wife, husband, parents, brothers and sisters, sons and daughters); the extended family (e.g. grandparents, aunts, uncles, nephews and nieces); and also neighbours and close friends.

The care provision may never go beyond this group, or only do so when a crisis occurs such as a carer becoming ill. Statistics in this area are obviously more guesswork than fact, as only those families who approach one of the three groups mentioned above for help will appear on registers or listings of any sort.

There are many families which fit into this group, looking after a disabled person and managing without recourse to any outside help.

Statutory

What this means is 'belonging to the state', that a law has been passed to ensure something is provided. The provider can be central government or local government.

The National Health Service Act of 1946 led to the NHS being created in 1948; this is the responsibility of central government, and includes not only hospitals, but also the family doctors, chemists (pharmacists), opticians, dentists, and provision of items for disabled people such as prostheses, wheelchairs, and footwear.

The Local Authority Social Services Act of 1970 created today's social services departments; they have a wide range of responsibilities, and these include services to disabled people. The NHS & Community Care Act is changing the emphasis of these services, and they will no longer have to be provided by the Local Authorities. An assessment will be made as to what is required, and this will then be provided from whatever source is felt to give the best quality service for the best price.

It will be more usual for the actual service to be bought from the voluntary or private sector rather than provided directly by the SSD when the act is fully implemented.

Housing Departments, Education Services and Leisure Services such as swimming pools, libraries and parks are also a part of Local Government provision.

The Department of Social Security (DSS) is a Central Government facility which helps with finance; a variety of benefits are available, but as the variety and the actual amounts involved vary greatly from year to year, a little research will be needed at the time the need arises.

Voluntary organisations

These are also referred to as Charities, Charitable Organisations, non-statutory, or non-profit making. They are not a part of the statutory provision of the country, but are often closely associated, and receive funding from the state. They are not bound by the same rules and regulations as Government bodies, and can be innovative and respond more quickly to perceived need.

The fact that they are voluntary organisations does not necessarily mean that they are run by volunteers. The major charities have large numbers of professional staff earning exactly the same salaries as their statutory counter-parts; for example the NSPCC and the Spastics Society, which are widely known. It is the organisation which is voluntary, not the people within it.

Having said that, however, there are groups which are totally voluntary, and nobody receives any pay whatsoever, although these tend to be localised rather than national. Some groups have a wide remit, such as RADAR, the Royal Association for Disability and Rehabilitation. Most have a narrower remit concerning specific disorders, e.g. the Friedreich's Ataxia Group.

Direct Services are the *raison d'etre* for organisations such as Crossroads (providing respite care schemes); advice and information giving for others (RADAR), and political pressure functions may be included (Age Concern).

3

Private sector

These are businesses set up to provide caring services as a commercial venture. Many of the people doing this have professional qualifications or a background of working within the caring services at some level, although this is not a necessity. Residential homes are often private concerns, run as a hotel would be. Residents are charged at a rate which provides a profit for the business.

Employment Agencies specialising in providing nurses, home carers, cooks, gardeners, etc. are on the increase. Meals delivery services from the private sector are replacing the voluntary meals-on-wheels deliveries in some towns. Private laundry and transport services (taxis, buses) have been with us for a long time. (*See* the exercise on pages 21–2 to consolidate this knowledge.)

Another way of categorising could be to isolate the type of help needed; for example:

- financial help;
- help with mobility;
- medical services;
- holiday provision;
- aids to daily living;
- dietary advice;
- specialist clothing;
- education; and so on . . .

Provision for these may be from one or more agencies in the statutory or voluntary sector, and for those able to pay, the private agencies and businesses are always available.

No matter which sector the assistance comes from, there are key groups of professionals involved; it is the employing agency which may be different.

The professionals

There are a variety of professionals which are useful to know about, and call upon as required.

Doctors

Doctors are found in many different guises and under many different names (physicians, surgeons, psychiatrists, paediatricians, etc.). The ones we all have the most contact with are listed below.

1 Family doctors. Also known as General Practitioners, or GPs, these are the most available of the medical profession. They are the first port of call when the need arises, and are also the key to much of the rest of the help which we may require in the UK. They can refer you on to the specialist branches of their profession, or to other paramedical services such as physiotherapists, dieticians, or social workers.

A selection of other branches of medicine are:

2 Physicians are doctors specialising in the treatment of diseases using methods other than surgery, e.g. medicines or diets.

3 Surgeons are doctors who specialise in direct intervention into the structure of the body. They also divide themselves into different specialisms, such as Orthopaedic, Ear Nose and Throat, Brain or Plastic (the reconstruction of damaged or deformed parts of the body).

4 Psychiatrists diagnose and treat mental illness and emotional problems. Their services may be required by both disabled people and carers.

Medical training is offered at a large number of universities, and entry is via the Universities Clearing House system (UCCA). Good 'A' level passes including sciences are required.

Nursing

Nurses mostly work in the statutory sector, in the NHS hospitals, but also increasingly in the community as District Nurses or Community Nurses. There is a growing number of private hospitals and Nursing Homes.

Nursing services can also be obtained privately, usually through nursing agencies, a list of which can be found in *Yellow Pages* or *Thomson's Local Directory*, although some nurses do work independently. Agencies can be either local or national; Reed Nurses and the British Nursing Association (BNA) are two of the larger organisations.

Community Nurses are arranged through the family doctor. They come into homes to provide nursing care such as changing dressings, bathing and giving injections, and will also show the disabled person and/or the main carer how to carry out routine tasks such as the prevention of pressure sores, changing colostomy/ileostomy bags, and lifting techniques.

Some voluntary organisations also employ nurses, the McMillan Cancer Fund, for instance. Their help may also be forthcoming via the Red Cross and St John Ambulance Brigade.

Health Visitors are nurses who have done further training, including having some experience of midwifery. They work exclusively in the community, and can be approached directly or through the family doctor. They work primarily with children up to the age of five years. This obviously includes all children with disabilities, but their role can be extended to any age group if felt to be appropriate. They can be an invaluable source of support, advice and guidance in routine medical/nursing matters, but do not have a 'hands-on' role. This is for the Community Nurses.

Community Psychiatric Nurses will also visit people at home; it should be remembered that mental illness is no respecter of persons, and disabled people are just as prone to emotional problems as anybody else.

Community Mental Handicap Nurses. They have specialist training in working with people with learning difficulties (RNMH or Registered Nurse for the Mentally Handicapped – a title which needs to change to keep up with changing terminology).

Further information on all branches of nursing can be obtained from the United Kingdom Central Council, 23 Portland Place, London, W1N 3AF.

GENETIC COUNSELLING

Introduction

The term 'genetic counselling' means different things to different people.

Some place emphasis on the counselling and supportive aspects and see it as an opportunity to talk over problems connected with having healthy children or passing on hereditary conditions.

Others see it more in terms of obtaining factual information about genetics, particularly the risks involved and tests available.

Perhaps the best approach is a combination of both these aspects, when not only is information exchanged but support and help can be offered in making what can often be difficult decisions.

People who have had a pregnancy terminated or have had a baby with an abnormality should have the opportunity of genetic counselling. Questions such as 'why me?', 'is the problem genetic?', 'could it happen again?', and 'are there any tests available during a future pregnancy?' are all points which can be discussed with a genetic counsellor.

The aim of genetic counselling

The aim of genetic counselling is not to make decisions for people but to enable them to have the necessary understanding of the situation so that they can decide for themselves.

There are rarely easy answers and each person has individual and special needs but it often makes things clearer when the issues involved are discussed with someone who has some experience and understanding of them.

The importance of accurate diagnosis

Sometimes, especially with conditions diagnosed before birth, what was thought to have been a neural tube defect (e.g. anencephaly and spina bifida) may, on closer examination, be a condition that is similar but linked to other problems with very different genetic implications for the future. It is therefore very important that the couple have accurate advice about this, and a post mortem examination of the baby may be necessary. An accurate diagnosis is vital for accurate genetic counselling.

Who gives genetic counselling?

A variety of people and agencies may offer genetic counselling but, at a specialist genetics centre, the counselling is usually done by someone with a medical background and further training in genetics. Referrals to such centres are often made by a GP or obstetric or paediatric staff, but anyone is entitled to ask for a referral if the matter has not been raised and s/he feels that s/he would benefit from genetic counselling.

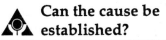 Can the cause be established?

Often parents feel guilty about their child's disability and it does help knowing that there was nothing which they could have done to prevent it. However, not all abnormalities are caused by genetic factors and often there may be no clear answer as to exactly what went wrong or why the disability occurred.

▶

Fig 1.1 The information sheet on genetic counselling published by the Association for Spina Bifida and Hydrocephalus

Reproduced with their kind permission

▲♀▲ Ante-natal tests

There are a growing number of conditions that can be diagnosed in pregnancy by tests such as amniocentesis, the earlier chorionic villus sampling test and improved ultrasound scans.

However, the recently developed test known as Chorionic Villus Sampling is not able to help with diagnosis of neural tube defects such as anencephaly or spina bifida.

The usefulness, availability and risks of such tests for each individual can be discussed with the genetic counsellor if it has not already been dealt with by the GP or obstetric staff. This is a rapidly developing field of medicine and it is important to get up-to-date information - see ASBAH's Information Sheet Number 3 for further details.

▲♀▲ How long does counselling take?

An appointment will last as long as necessary, which depends on the needs of each individual or couple.

The counsellor will usually spend some time drawing out a family tree to see if there are any relevant problems on either side of the family and, where appropriate, will discuss what happened during a pregnancy and after.

Any questions or worries that people may have can be covered and a further appointment arranged if more time or further information or tests are needed. Occasionally, couples may need to have their chromosomes checked. This involves a simple blood test, the results of which may not be known for several weeks. More complicated tests are not often required for genetic counselling.

▲♀▲ How can you get genetic counselling?

If you feel you could benefit from genetic counselling, ask your own GP or obstetrician to refer you to your nearest genetics centre. Some people find counselling helpful very soon after the birth as they have urgent questions which they feel cannot wait. Others prefer to leave it a little while until they may be thinking more clearly. Whichever you choose, the important thing is that you have an opportunity to discuss the issues at a time that feels right for both you and your partner.

Genetic counsellor

When parents have had a child with a disability, there are understandable concerns about what the chances are of any other children being similarly affected (*see* the ASBAH leaflet above). When another member of the family has a disability, there are similar concerns; and in families with a history of disorders such as Huntington's Chorea, which only starts to affect people in mid-life, individuals worry about their own chances of being affected.

Disabled people wanting to start a family of their own may also want to discuss fully the implications of this, and the chances of their children being similarly disabled. When this is the case, referral can be made to a Genetic Counsellor. S/he will discuss the mathematical likelihood of disorders being passed on, and talk through the anxieties associated with deciding whether to have children, or more children. Decisions will not be taken on other people's behalf, but full information and the implications of any decision will be fully explored and discussed.

Some doctors undertake genetic counselling as a part of their day-to-day work; other counsellors are drawn from the nursing, health visiting and social work professions. There are no specific training courses.

Physiotherapists

Once again, most 'physios', as they are commonly called, work within the Health Service. The majority are hospital based, but in some areas there is a domiciliary (or home visiting) service. They are also employed in some special schools, residential facilities, or operate privately on a commercial basis. Through the use of exercise and manipulation, and the application of heat and electricity, they help people maintain as much movement as possible.

Training lasts for three years, and the Chartered Society of Physiotherapy is at 14 Bedford Row, London, WC1R 4ED.

Remedial gymnasts

Do not have the same qualifications as physiotherapists, but work in a similar kind of way. They also encourage the use of exercises, but more particularly in a recreational way. They are likely to be involved in football, basketball and swimming teams. Employed by rehabilitation centres and some hospitals, the number of people employed in this capacity is relatively small. There are no specific training courses.

Occupational therapists

OTs, as they are commonly referred to, are to be found working in hospitals, schools and some other residential establishments. They also work in the community, employed by the social services departments, where they will probably be known as 'COTs', or Community Occupational Therapists. Some are employed by voluntary organisations such as the Spastics Society.

Initially they will carry out a full assessment of an individual's practical abilities, following which they will advise on the most appropriate techniques to use and the most effective specialist equipment available. This may be anything from structural alterations to the house to long-handled taps which can be turned on and off without gripping, or adapted eating utensils.

Some OTs specialise in working with children, and are hence known as Paediatric Occupational Therapists.

Occupational therapy is a three-year degree level course. The British Association of Occupational Therapists is at 20 Rede Place, Bayswater, London, W1 4TU.

Speech therapists

These are employed by Health Authorities in the main, although there are some in private practice. Overall, however, they are a somewhat scarce resource, and demand far outweighs the provision. Their role is to help improve speech difficulties, whatever the cause, whether from deafness to stroke, cerebral palsy, head injury or any other reason.

Speech therapy training is very specialist, and only available at a limited number of places. More information can be obtained from the College of Speech Therapists, 6 Lechmere Road, London NW2 5BU.

Social workers

The vast majority of social workers (or SWs) are employed by the social services departments (social work departments in Scotland) and this includes those working in hospitals. Others work for voluntary organisations, and a few are in private practice, although not many in the field of disability, it has to be said.

Anybody can ask for social work help, either by phoning, calling in, or writing to their local SSD or SWD. Most SWs now work for specialised teams dealing with a specific client group – although the specialism may be something like 'Elderly and Disability Team' or 'Disability and Learning Difficulties Team'. SWs normally make home visits to the people on their 'caseload' (jargon for the people they have been given responsibility for). They will initially make an assessment of need, and this may range from a sympathetic listener to calling in other services such as OTs, making arrangements for residential care on a respite or permanent basis, or liaising with other departments such as the DSS, NHS, or voluntary organisations. They may also be able to put you in touch with other people with disabilities, or carers' groups in the area, if these exist. If they do not, then it may be possible for them to instigate the formation of 'user-groups' or carers' groups.

Social work training is through a two-year Diploma in Social Work course, and places obtained via the Universities and Polytechnics Clearing House system (UCCA and PCAS).

Dieticians

Some disabilities require special diets for various reasons; the doctor will sometimes recommend a diet to prevent future problems, for example to control weight when a person has become less mobile. Individuals may have a dietary regime imposed as part of an overall treatment plan, e.g. with diabetes; and some may wish to have a vegetarian diet, but need special advice due to their personal circumstances. A dietician is the most appropriate person to speak to about these. What could otherwise be bland and boring meals may be greatly improved with expert advice.

Other diets are felt to be beneficial, but are as yet unproven. An example of this is the low sugar diet suggested for people with multiple sclerosis.

Most dieticians can be found working for the Health Service, occasionally for the Local Authority. Some do work in industry, such as for Electricity and Gas Boards, or food manufacturers, but then they are obviously not as accessible for this type of advice and guidance.

Some of the more usual diets you are likely to come across are:

- low fat;
- low sugar;
- salt free;
- gluten free;
- low residue;
- diabetic;
- high energy;
- low cholesterol or cholesterol-free;
- liquid;
- high fibre.

Dieticians invariably have degrees in Home Economics or Food Technology or an equivalent qualification.

Home care services

These used to be the Home Help Service of the Local Authority Social Services Departments. They have developed and extended their role, and now do much more than the cleaning and dusting. These services operate under a variety of names in different areas; e.g. Domiciliary care; Homemakers; Homecare, and still Home Helps in some places. Private organisations also exist to provide the same service, and most Local Authorities charge for the service on a sliding scale according to income.

Tasks which are undertaken by the homecare services include getting people up in the mornings, going shopping and collecting any allowances from the Post Office, preparing meals, doing the laundry, basic cleaning, and some childcare, bedmaking and washing up. Matters of a more personal nature, such as bathing and washing hair, changing dressings and colostomy bags, etc. are more in the province of the District Nursing Services.

There is no formal training for this work other than that provided by employers, and this should be increasingly linked with the competences expected with the National Vocational Qualification Scheme.

Home care organisers will in future be expected to have a formal relevant qualification; some are qualified social workers, others have management ceritificates of one kind or another, or have passed Home Economics examinations. Their role is likely to move further towards becoming care managers as the NHS and Community Care legislation extends.

Chiropodists

Chiropodists deal with problems associated with the feet and lower limbs, including the nails and skin. They may also be able to help with advice regarding specialist footwear.

There is a shortage of practitioners, and those that are available are in great demand. They can be arranged through the Health Service, but the wait may be quite a long one; alternatively the *Yellow Pages* lists the numbers of those in private practice. Both groups will arrange home visits where necessary.

There are two types of training available at present – college based and postal courses with practice placements– and the Society of Chiropodists is at 53 Welbeck Street, London W1M 7HE.

Disablement Resettlement Officers

Otherwise known as DROs, are employees of the Department of Employment. There are also BPROs, or Blind Persons' Resettlement Officers providing the same service for a more specialised group.

DROs have the power to register people as disabled for employment legislation purposes; they will obviously need medical evidence to do this. A person can be registered for periods of one year to ten years. This register is not the same as the Local Authority register of disabled people living in their area, and neither is it compulsory. What it may do is attract some extra benefits and more help in finding work. Employers of more than 20 people are required to give three per cent of their jobs to disabled people,

10

Fig 1.2 A selection of the types of job advertisements published in the Press

and this quota must be met from people on the DROs register. One role of the DRO is to check compliance with this.

Some jobs, such as car park attendants and lift attendants are reserved for those on the register.

DROs spend all their time looking after the needs of the disabled work force, either by individual interviews and assessments, or by creating links with employers and training agencies. They can also authorise aids to employment to enable a disabled person to do a job, e.g. modified control systems; flashing lights instead of audible signals, special seating, or braille labelling.

DRO training is provided 'in-house' by the Department of Employment, the address of which will be found in the telephone directory.

Teachers

Specialist training is required to teach special groups, such as hearing impaired and sight impaired. These courses follow the basic teacher training offered by colleges, polytechnics and universities. Employers are usually the Local Authority Education Departments, but with a growing trend toward direct employment by schools as they leave local authority control. Some teachers work for SSDs and SWDs, and in the voluntary sector. Others are private practitioners.

Information on training can be obtained from PCAS, UCCA and direct from the Teacher Training colleges.

Dentists

Dentists deal with problems affecting the mouth and jaws as well as the teeth. Orthodontists are a type of dentist who treat irregularities and developmental problems around the mouth. Training is university-based, and the profession regulated by the General Dental Council.

Audio technicians

These are also known as Audiologists. They measure the level of hearing in children as a developmental check, and in adults with hearing difficulties. In some noisy occupations, regular checks are made to detect problems early enough to prevent deafness.

Sign language interpreters

These have the task of translating speech into sign language for deaf and hearing impaired people. You may see them occasionally on television news bulletins, or at public meetings where matters concerning disability are on the agenda.

They will obviously also translate signing into speech when required.

There are other caring professions and jobs, and the best way to find out about them (and the ones mentioned above) is to speak to the people involved, either those who give the service or those who receive it. Shown on page 11 is a selection of jobs based on real posts advertised in the press.

Chapter 2

THE NEEDS OF CARERS

It should be remembered that only a small proportion of people with a physical disability need help with day-to-day living. Of those that do, the vast majority are looked after by care providers from the informal sector.

The pressures on these relatives and friends are undoubtedly considerably more than are the pressures on most 'professional' carers, who are responsible for the disabled person for an allotted length of time. They then go home and rest. This is not the case when you are living with a person needing constant attention. There is rarely any time off, the stress is there day and night, and can lead to the carer becoming cared for if they do not pay heed to their own health, and if help is not arranged to give some regular respite.

The following information was prepared for the use of informal carers, but nevertheless the advice given and the sentiments expressed apply equally to the vocational carer, and to professionals.

EXERCISE

Compare and contrast the two documents on pages 14 and 15.
(a) What are the similarities?
(b) What are the differences?
(c) Which purposes does each suit?
(d) Who is the target audience for each, do you think?
(e) Could you do better? Prepare a ten point plan for a *student* who is also a carer sharing responsibility with one parent for the other parent.

Read also the case histories of the Church family and Mr & Mrs Kelsall on pages 183−4 and 188−9.

Not to be outdone, some recipients of care have prepared their own list of Rights and Responsibilities, which is reproduced in Fig 2.2 on page 16, by kind permission of *FAX* (No. 93), the magazine of the Friedreich's Ataxia Group.

Carers' Needs

A 10 POINT PLAN FOR CARERS

Carers are people who are looking after elderly, ill or disabled relatives or friends who cannot manage at home without help. They may be the parents of a child with a mental handicap, a husband whose wife has a physical disability or a daughter looking after her frail elderly mother.

Carers come from all racial, ethnic and religious backgrounds. Their circumstances vary enormously, with the severity of the condition of the person cared for, their economic circumstances and the overall help and support available. The majority of carers are women and many carry out the tasks of caring completely on their own.

Carers are deeply concerned about the needs of the people they care for; services need to be planned for and with them.

CARERS NEED:

1 **Recognition of their contribution** and of their own needs as individuals in their own right

2 **Services tailored to their individual circumstances**, needs and views, through discussions at the time help is being planned

3 **Services which reflect an awareness of differing racial, cultural and religious backgrounds** and values, equally accessible to carers of every race and ethnic origin

4 **Opportunities for a break**, both for short spells (an afternoon) and for longer periods (a week or more) to relax and have time to themselves

5 **Practical help** to lighten the tasks of caring, including domestic help, home adaptations, incontinence services and help with transport

6 **Someone to talk to** about their own emotional needs, at the outset of caring, while they are caring and when the caring task is over

7 **Information** about available benefits and services as well as how to cope with the particular condition of the person cared for

8 **An income which covers the costs of caring** and which does not preclude carers taking employment or sharing care with other people

9 **Opportunities to explore alternatives to family care**, both for the immediate and long-term future

10 **Services designed through consultation** with carers, at all levels of policy planning

Fig 2.1(a) The 10 point plan for carers' needs

Originally published by the King's Fund Centre, Carers Unit, with financial support from the Health Education Authority and the Department of Health

YOU THE CARER

This chapter recognises that *you the carer* are the most important person in this book, that is why it comes first.

As the carer there are certain rules you should always try to keep.

1 Do not allow yourself to become isolated. Try at all times to maintain *your* interests, *your* hobbies, *your* lifestyle. If you have a job, don't give it up lightly.

2 Keep yourself fit. Studies have shown that if you are physically fit you are more able to deal with stress and cope with the hard work involved in caring.

3 Make time to be you. Make time to do the shopping or to enjoy leisure activities. Have a regular day or evening out.

4 Learn to relax. If you sit down, don't cross your legs. Cup your hands one inside the other with them resting gently in your lap.

5 Be Assertive − What does it mean? Well it doesn't mean being aggressive, that only puts people's back up. Being assertive means expressing yourself specifically, clearly and honestly, and sticking to it.

6 Keep things in perspective. You can only do so much. It may seem pretty awful but all you can do is your best. There may be times when something amusing will happen − HANG ON TO IT.

7 Set yourself limits. Decide what you are prepared to do. What you are taking on may last for a long time and it is better to do less rather than taking everything on and only being able to cope for a short time.

8 Always seek help and seek it early. Try and get regular breaks, and help around the house.

9 Try and bring the family in. I know it doesn't always work but the more you can share the burden of caring the better it will be.

10 A friendly neighbour near mum or dad, or next door to you if your elderly relative is living with you is a godsend. Don't put on them but keep them informed of what's going on. Give them a key if they will have one. Leave important information with them − doctor's name and telephone number, how to get hold of you (or your husband), a relative who will help, Day Centre, Social Worker or District Nurse's telephone number.

11 Maintain your feelings of self worth. Be positive in your outlook. You are doing a smashing job.

Fig 2.1(b) An extract taken from the Brierley Hill and Kingswinford branch of Age Concern's *Guide for Carers*

Reproduced by kind permission of Age Concern

RIGHTS AND RESPONSIBILITIES

*Following the "Declaration of Self Esteem" in FAX 92, **Trevor Whitehead** has provided the following list:*
(courtesy of Derbyshire Social Services Department's course notes)

Rights

I have the right to be treated with respect.

I have the right to make decisions for myself.

I have the right to set limits and to say No.

I have the right to prioritise my needs some of the time.

I have the right to express my views and opinions.

I have the right to make mistakes.

I have the right to ask for help or information when I need it.

I have the right to have time and space for myself.

I have the right to change my mind sometimes.

I have the right to control my own life.

I have the the right to own these rights.

Responsibilities

I have the responsibility to treat others with respect.

I have the responsibility to allow others to make decisions for themselves.

I have the responsibility to accept the limits others have set and to accept other people's right to say no to me.

I have the responsibility to prioritise other people's needs some of the time.

I have the responsibility to let other people express their views and opinions.

I have the responsibility to accept that other people make mistakes.

I have the responsibility to listen when others ask for help or information.

I have the responsibility not to invade other people's time and space.

I have the responsibility to accept that others can change their minds sometimes.

I have the responsibility not to control the lives of other people.

I have the responsibility to accord these rights to others.

Fig 2.2

Chapter 3

CARE IN THE COMMUNITY

The National Health Service and Community Care Act was passed by Parliament in June 1990. As it was such a complicated and costly piece of legislation, it has not been introduced all at once, but parts of it are being chosen to implement from different dates. The changes in the NHS have happened more quickly than the changes in Social Services. By 1994, the majority of the changes should have taken place.

The basis behind the changes was explained in a speech by a Conservative Government Minister (Virginia Bottomley) in November 1991 . . .

> 'Our approach to the provision of community care is based on the principle that the decision about what care is needed and the form it should take should, wherever possible, be discussed and agreed with the individual in need of care and with his or her carers.
>
> Local Authorities are being given the freedom, in consultation with colleagues in health authorities and with the voluntary and private sectors, to devise flexible and innovative care packages to fit in with these identified needs. But in order to achieve this aim considerable change will be needed.
>
> Our community care reforms will be a major step forward, but there is a great deal to be done to effectively implement them.'

The diagram below shows how a Social Services Department could be organised to provide care in the community.

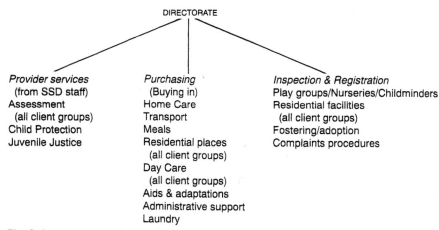

Fig 3.1 A possible Social Services Department organisation for the provision of care in the community

So what is Community Care? It is the provision of support services to people who need help to live as independently as is possible in the setting of their own choice, be it their own homes or in sheltered housing provided by the Local Authority, voluntary organisations, or private providers. Residential care (which includes nursing homes) is still an option if this is what is required, but is more likely to be in establishments run by the private or voluntary sector than in statutory provision.

The legislation covers all potential user groups from childhood to old age, and whether the help required is to be permanent or temporary. The Health Services and Social Services are expected to be working together very closely.

There are six identified 'key objectives':

1 To promote domiciliary, day and respite services to enable people to live in their own homes wherever feasible and sensible.
2 To ensure that service providers make practical support for carers a high priority.
3 To make proper assessment of need and good care management the cornerstone of high quality care.
4 To promote the development of a flourishing independent sector alongside good quality public services.
5 To clarify the responsibilities of agencies and so make it easier to hold them to account for their performance.
6 To secure better value for taxpayers' money by introducing a new funding structure for social care.

A package of care

This is the name given to all the different aspects of help arranged for a given individual or family. The elements involved can come from any or all available sources – informal, statutory, voluntary and private.

Before a package of care can be arranged, there has to be an assessment undertaken. This is to decide what the needs of the person (or family) being assessed actually are. This is the responsibility of the Local Authority Social Services Department (SSD) under Section 47 of the NHS & Community Care Act 1990. Having decided upon the needs, the next step is to ascertain how these needs can best be met, from whatever source is felt to be most appropriate.

The co-ordination and management of the package of care is the responsibility of the care manager. They may be from any of the caring professions depending upon the particular needs in any given case, or another person appointed by them. In some areas, it will not be a person, but a care management process shared by a team.

Inevitably there will be costs involved; and you should not assume that because an organisation is a voluntary one that they do not charge for their services, as many of them do. Even elements from the informal sector may require payment; a neighbour may be given an allowance to call in a few times a day to check on somebody, or fares paid for a relative to visit.

Packages of care will have to be arranged according to a fixed budget, and the task of care management will be to obtain value for money as well as meeting client need.

Care management

Some clients may need more than the straightforward provision of services; they have complex needs requiring co-ordinated, flexible services, and help to guide them through the 'maze'. The care manager should be the primary point of contact for both clients and their carers, assisting them to gain access to services which meet their individual needs.

Through discussion with all the people involved, a package of care should be devised based on an individual's abilities, the help they get from family and friends, and the suitability of their living accommodation. When the assessment has been completed, the services are arranged from the most appropriate provider; the care manager is the purchaser, and also responsible for adjustments to the plan as needs change.

Making it work

For a package of care to work, it may be necessary to purchase some specialised equipment, or make structural modifications. The assessment for these will probably be made by an occupational therapist, or another person trained to undertake the task. The equipment may be supplied by Social Services or the Health Service; adaptations to houses or flats are matters for the SSD and Housing Departments. Sometimes the Department of Social Security will be involved in providing funds.

More information will be found in Chapter 10 on Housing on pages 87–108. *See also* the package of care section for Mr and Mrs Dale in case study 5 (page 182) and the care scheme for Robert Taylor in case study 7 (pages 184–5).

Now you have some idea of what a package of care involves; but in addition to the daily and weekly elements, some people may wish to take advantage of respite care or holidays, so there may be monthly, quarterly, or annual elements to include. Respite care is when a carer is given a rest from their responsibilities for a short period of time. This can be achieved by another carer moving in with the cared for, or the cared for moving out to another care setting, either a residential establishment, hospital or a private home. One weekend per month could be spent in a residential placement, or covered by volunteers through Crossroads (a voluntary organisation set up to provide respite carers who go into private houses, usually for a day or two, but also provides 'sitting' services, so the carers can go out for an evening's entertainment, for example), or similar schemes to allow respite for the carer.

One week per quarter may be spent at a holiday centre or other residential place, again on a respite basis; or this may be an annual arrangement for two weeks every summer.

The Social Services Department

The role of a Social Services Department has moved on from being a monopolistic provider of services to that of an enabler and purchaser. They must provide the assessment service, but once needs have been identified, they should put the contract out to the most appropriate provider(s). This may be their own in-house service, NHS provision, taxi companies, home care agencies, meal delivery services, day care providers, residential care providers, building companies or any other appropriate service. In short, there will be a 'mixed economy of care' from which to arrange packages to meet individual need, and a distinct purchaser/provider split.

NB: Compare this system with that required for the 'Statementing' process under the Education Act 1981 in Chapter 14 Education (pages 123–33).

Quality control

Once the packages of care have been finalised and are operating, there should then be a system of checks to ensure that the services contracted for are actually being delivered, and being delivered to the required standard.

There are three ways that this is achieved; first by the regular feedback from recipients themselves to care managers; second, and more formally, having access to an established Complaints Procedure which is easy to feed into; and third by the work of the Inspection and Registration Units.

Obviously, the first part of the process of contracting work out to independent providers should include agreements about what is expected, and the level and quality of service required in each particular case, group of cases, or particular service. If this is identified and written down, then all parties have agreed expectations, and can always refer back to these original documents when disputes arise. The initial specifications, then, are of prime importance for what follows.

If all parties live up to the agreed contract, then there should be no difficulties. There is potential for dispute, however, when the original requirements change. Input from a Home Care Service, for example, may be based upon the fact that a carer lives with the recipient of the service. If that carer can no longer help due to illness, then the home care cover may need to increase. Before this can be done, a new contract will have to be agreed or the provider risks losing payment for services provided. In a commercially driven environment, this is unlikely to be allowed to happen. Will this mean a delay and consequent risk to the client, or is there sufficient flexibility in agreements to cater for the unexpected?

Where service users are not satisfied with the assessment of need, and feel that they require more than is being offered, there should be access to an appeals or complaints procedure to examine this. Details of how to invoke this should be given to users and their carers at the outset of any assessment.

Once they are in receipt of the service, but they feel that it does not come up to standard, then Complaints Procedures may come into play. These may be through the SSD, but in the case of contracted providers, may be through their own systems; for example, if the recipients of services from the Spastics Society wish to complain, they would do so through the Society's procedures, even if funding was from the SSD.

The first stage is obviously to discuss matters with the care manager, who will speak with the direct providers either with or on behalf of the recipient. Hopefully, most situations will be resolved at this level. The second stage will come into play when stage one has failed to achieve a satisfactory result. This will then involve the care manager's supervisor if they are from the SSD or the NHS, or a professional from one of these organisations if the care manager is an appointee of the disabled person. An investigation will be conducted and the complaints addressed as necessary.

If the problem persists, then the third stage is to ask the Inspection Unit to undertake an independent review of the whole case, and feed back their findings to all parties concerned.

Inspection Units

The establishment of independent Inspection Units by Social Services Departments is a requirement of the NHS and Community Care Act. They are involved in the initial registration of new residential homes (for all groups of people requiring care), and the regular inspections of such premises plus day centres and other facilities such as playgroups and nurseries.

The Units will also be involved in checking the quality of services provided to people assessed by Social Services, and receiving services contracted by them. Quality in this case means ensuring that the service is suitable for the purpose for which it was intended; for example, is the laundry collected at the agreed time each week, and has it been cleaned satisfactorily when it is returned? Do the night attendants arrive on time, and do they do what the contracted agreement says they should do when they are there? Are the meals of the required quality, delivered at a resonable time and at the agreed temperature?

EXERCISE

Contact the Inspection and Registration section of your local SSD and ask if they could provide a speaker for your group (*see* the 'Assignments' section in Part Four on pages 202–3 for guidelines).

Obviously every individual service and contract cannot and will not be checked, but random sampling and the following up of all complaints and comments received will give an overall idea of the level of service being provided. Where this falls short of requirements and expectations, action can be taken to have it improved, or award the contracts elsewhere. However, a problem with more specialist services will be whether there are sufficient alternative providers.

EXERCISE

The new NHS & Community Care Act is moving the provision of services into the Private Sector; this exercise is intended to increase student familiarity with what is available in that sector, and how to access it. It should be useful in emphasising the new purchaser/provider split introduced into the Health and Social Services from April 1993. (*See also* comments on pages 2–4 about knowing where to get help.)

Look in the *Yellow Pages* or *Thomson's Local Directory* under the following headings:

- 'Social Service and Welfare Organisations';
- 'Disabled';
- 'Charitable Organisations';
- 'Nursing (Agencies, Homes, and Supplies)';
- 'Orthopaedic goods';
- 'Therapists';
- 'Chiropodists'; and
- 'Physiotherapists'.

Can you think of any other relevant categories? Before long, a new one may have to be added – 'Care Agencies'.

Many nursing agencies are expanding their operations to include the wider caring role, and employing more home care staff rather than qualified (and more expensive) nurses. They are able to undertake the basic day-to-day tasks of caring which the relatives, who are probably themselves unqualified in professional terms, would normally do. This could be a growing area of employment in the 'care industry' for those who are interested.

There are also social care agencies; they advertise in the local press, and others can be found on the back pages of the professional magazines such as *Community Care* and *Care Weekly*. They tend to be based in the large towns.

EXERCISE

Using the information you have obtained, prepare a directory of what is available in your area to help people looking for a service provider.

- Make it as 'user-friendly' as you can, with easy to find references. Consider the use of large print, and perhaps a Braille version for some or all of the information.
- How would you go about preparing an audio version?
- How much would it cost to produce and distribute? Calculate the costs of the printed version, Braille pages, and bulk audiotapes, or even video cassettes.
- Who would it be distributed to? Which organisations are most likely to have a need for this kind of information?
- What advice would you give to people wishing to use your directory? Are you recommending any of the services included, or is it just for information?

BTEC Common Skills: 1, 2, 3, 4, (5, 6, 7 if group work), 8, 9, 10, (11 if group work), 12, 13, 14, 15, 16 if word-processed, audio-taped or video-taped, 17, 18.
GNVQ Level 2: 5, 6.
GNVQ Level 3: 6, 8.

SELF-CHECK QUESTIONS

1 What are the four groups of care providers?
2 What is the purpose of the assessment process?
3 Who co-ordinates a package of care?
4 Who is the care manager for Robert Taylor (*see* case study 7 on pages 184–5)
5 What are the three ways in which quality of service can be checked?
6 Why are social care agencies more likely to be found in large towns?
7 When was the NHS and Community Care Act passed by Parliament?
8 Who is responsible for assessing structural changes to houses?

Residential care

The decision to opt for residential care as opposed to living a more independent life is, in theory, one taken by the individual. In practice, however, there are many pressures involved in the process of reaching that decision.

The realisation that one can no longer cope alone may take some time in coming or it may be a bolt out of the blue. One of the most common reasons is the death or incapacity of the main carer. This may be sudden, as with accidental death or a debilitating heart attack, or gradual as with old age or a progressive disease.

It may be that dependency is increasing, and the carer can no longer cope with the increased demands. This may be very difficult for both parties to accept, and is a good example of where a counsellor could be of help. It is a traumatic time, and the feelings of guilt on the part of the carer and rejection on the part of the cared for need reconciling for the sake of a future relationship. If the parting is on bad terms, then the relationship may suffer irretrievably. If both realise that it is an inevitability, and that neither is either to blame or being personally rejected, then a future relationship on new terms becomes much more possible.

There may, of course, be no carer, but a deterioration in an individual living alone to such a degree that no matter what help is provided, the quality of life will still be very poor without constant care and attention. At the other end of the spectrum, it may be somebody who has just become disabled, and the aim of the residential care is to teach the skills necessary to be able to live independently once again. Figure 3.2 on page 24 describes the Five Oaks Centre run by ASBAH. (*See* case study 4 on Jason Young on pages 179–80.)

ASBAH Services

Wedded bliss - thanks to Five Oaks!

Five Oaks Centre

ASBAH runs a residential centre called Five Oaks at Ben Rhydding, near Ilkley in Yorkshire, where children and young people attend courses designed to encourage and promote greater independence. Respite care and activity holidays are also available.

The staff skills developed over the years has made Five Oaks one of the leading centres of its type. With patience, understanding and specific knowledge of the learning difficulties experienced by people with hydrocephalus, they are able to help young people reach their full potential. Their expertise was recognised internationally with a top award two years ago in the European Community's HELIOS programme.

In the summer of 1991, staff and residents were interviewed about the centre's independence training courses for the Radio 4 programme 'Does He Take Sugar?'

An extended training course can last up to two years. Students progress through stages towards independent living. They can try living by themselves in a training flat in Denton View.

Young adults wishing to experience greater independence may be offered a chance to take one of the four flats in Wharfedale, either by themselves or sharing. Their tenancies are secure, and a housing support worker is there when needed.

Denton View and Wharfedale are attractive, modern buildings in the grounds of Five Oaks and were built by the Sanctuary Spiral Housing Association.

Modern homes at the Five Oaks Centre

Two marriages among residents were celebrated at Five Oaks during 1991, with the centre being the chosen venue for the wedding breakfasts. Several residents moved on to independent living with housing associations around the country.

Education authorities are using Five Oaks as a resource in assisting pupils with disabilities from mainstream schools to achieve greater independence. These pupils are given the space to explore their own needs, widen their physical horizons and understand more their own problems. This is particularly valuable in preparation for, and transfer from, primary to senior school, and from school to college.

Five Oaks runs a series of successful activity weeks and courses for people with spina bifida and/or hydrocephalus. They come from Britain and throughout Europe. Driving instruction, fashion design, outdoor and recreational activities, and wildlife courses are among the most popular.

Fig 3.2 The Five Oaks Centre, run by the Association for Spina Bifida and Hydrocephalus (ASBAH)

Taken from the ASBAH Annual Report 1991 and reproduced with their kind permission

Chapter 4

PERSONAL CARE AND DAILY LIVING

As has been stated previously, there are only a small proportion of people with disabilities who will actually need help from another person, but as carers, this is the group with which you will be involved.

Exactly what you will need to provide help with is going to differ from individual to individual, but it is wise to remember that we all have the same basic needs, no

Fig 4.1 © John Birdsall Photography

matter what our physical condition. What you need is exactly what those people in your care will need. These were put into a logical and understandable list by Maslow in 1970:

- Sufficient appropriate food and drink
- To eliminate waste products
- To breathe properly
- To have the body at a comfortable temperature
- Sleep and rest
- To keep clean and maintain health
- Communication and interaction with others
- To wear suitable clothing
- To be free from discomfort and pain
- To feel safe.

If the basic physiological needs are not being met, you will become aware of that fact by feeling hungry, thirsty, cold, constipated, breathless, dirty, uncomfortable, anxious, or in pain. So will people in your care, but they may not be able to communicate that fact directly, and you will have to read the signs from body language.

Once a daily routine has been established, all these requirements should be catered for automatically; a change in this routine is going to cause some anxiety to the recipient, and require some help and understanding from any carer to help adjustment to a new situation. The change may be the loss of a carer and the arrival of a new one, (possibly you) or a change in environment, such as admission to hospital or residential care.

You should always remember that people with disabilities are not ill, but can become ill in just the same way as anyone else. It may be a little more difficult to diagnose and treat the illness, and carers should be aware of any indications that things are not as they should be, particularly where there are communications difficulties.

So how do you establish a daily routine for somebody you will be caring for? Catering for someone else's needs may be a new experience for you, and will demand more thought and consideration than meeting your own needs. The first thing to do, then, is to consult the expert. Where do we find the expert? The expert is the person with a disability who requires your assistance – the client/patient/recipient/service user/disabled person/person with a disability/guest, or whatever is the agreed form of address in your particular workplace, be it a private house, residential centre, hotel, or a hospital. They will tell you what assistance is needed, and how they prefer things to be done, and you should always ask when meeting new people or involving yourself in new tasks. When this is not possible, you should ask those who know the person, possibly the informal carers who have given help until the point when you are going to take over; possibly other carers who know the person better than you do.

To slightly modify the advice given by the Winged Fellowship Trust to their volunteer holiday helpers: *'It may help to imagine yourself in the guest's situation, or to consider how you would feel if the guest was a close relative of yours.'*

Physical care

This may be your main concern before you start any placement with people with a physical disability, mainly because it is most probably a new experience, and will involve helping people with intimate and very personal needs.

All of us need to eat, drink, wash, dress, use the toilet and get in and out of bed every day of our lives. Some people, because of their disability, need help to carry out these basic daily needs. Obviously, helping with someone else's needs will be a new experience, and will demand much thought and consideration, but remember that these are *basic needs*. It is important that you help people without fuss, and without them feeling that these ordinary daily needs are a problem and an embarrassment.

When carrying out these tasks, here are some useful hints to consider:

- Always ask how individuals normally do things, and as far as possible, carry out their wishes.
- Skin care is very important for most disabled people, and can cause serious problems if not cared for properly. Always carry out washing and bathing carefully and thoroughly.
- Let people choose which clothes they wish to wear, and ensure clean clothing is available when needed.
- Be patient with people, particularly where communication may be difficult or time consuming.
- Don't take away independence for the sake of time and convenience to yourself.
- Consider the smaller personal needs such as cleaning teeth, shaving, combing hair, make-up, and even assisting with nose blowing. These can easily be forgotten as they are so often done without really thinking.
- At all times respect dignity and independence.

Lifting

Lifting is a task which will be commonplace in both placement and work situations. Advice will be given in college before you go and do it 'for real', and demonstrations should also be given in the workplace.

There are some basic ground rules to follow which should be a guide wherever you go:

1 Do not attempt to lift alone. This risks injury to both yourself and the person in your care.
2 Prepare for the lift; position yourself, your lifting partner and the person to be lifted in the most appropriate places. Make sure that furniture, beds or wheelchairs are secure, and that the brakes are on where appropriate, and all barriers are out of the way (bed tables, bed clothing, foot rests, etc.).
3 Tell the person to be lifted what is going on; this is common courtesy, and they may be able to help you.

4 Make sure you have a secure grip that is comfortable to both you and the person you are lifting.

5 Brace your stomach muscles prior to, and during, any lift. This will help protect your back from injury.

6 Take the strain using your leg muscles rather than your back.

7 Have the weight of the person you are lifting as close as possible to your body.

8 Make sure that the lift is co-ordinated with your partner (or partners, if more than two of you are required).

9 Wear sensible, flat shoes – not slip-ons which you can easily slip out of, and not high heels.

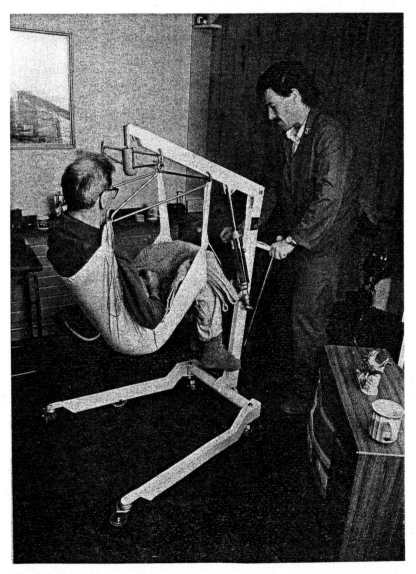

Fig 4.2 © John Birdsall Photography

10 Remove jewellery and watches which can catch on skin and cause injury during lifting.

There are also machines available to lift people, one of which is illustrated opposite.

Self care

Your own personal care is just as important as anybody else's. Take note of all the Health and Safety considerations of your workplace, and any rules and regulations which are brought to your notice.

Some general advice, again modified from the Winged Fellowship guidance to volunteers, is as follows:

1 Wear disposable gloves, particularly where skin contact with body fluids is likely.
2 Avoid risks by following the guidance on lifting.
3 Do not use any equipment until you have been shown how to do so properly (e.g. hoists, wheelchairs, specialist beds).
4 Wear appropriate clothing; i.e. comfortable, clean and tidy, no high heels, a minimum of jewellery, hair away from face. Use protective clothing such as plastic aprons, gloves, etc. where appropriate, e.g. when using bleach or other chemical cleaning agents.
5 Report any accidents or illness involving either yourself or those in your care.
6 Personal hygiene is important; physically hard work can make you sweat, and body odour needs to be kept in check.
7 Wash your hands regularly, especially after helping with the personal needs of people, and before handling food.

Routine tasks

The advice here is based upon advice given in the Dudley branch of Age Concern's booklet *A Guide for Carers*, and is used here with their kind permission.

Bathing

One of the things you will have to do on a regular basis, particularly if somebody is incontinent, is to bathe them. Remember that the bathroom is an accident black spot, and prevention is better than cure.

- Wet and slippy floors should be avoided, preferably by having a permanent non-slip surface, or by using proper floor coverings which will soak up any water, and not slip about.
- Make sure the floor is clean and dry before you bring in the person to be bathed.
- Make sure that all the equipment needed for that particular individual is there before you start; it is not a good idea to leave some disabled people alone in the bath while you run off to find something you have forgotten earlier.
- Avoid accidents caused by loose soap lying where it can cause accidents.

There should be specialised baths available where necessary, for example those in which you can sit up rather than lie down; those with sides which are hinged to allow easier access; moulded ones with seats and water controls modified for easier use. Other equipment may include bath boards, seats, mats, rails, and hoists. None of these things, even the apparently simple ones, should be used until you have been shown how they function, and you are confident about using them. If you are uncertain, then ask.

If you are going to run the bath, put the cold water in first; this can avoid scalding, and reduces the amount of steam in the room. If you wear spectacles, steaming up can be avoided by using a commercially available solution to wipe over the lenses before you become immersed in steam, or more cheaply by smearing soap on both the inside and outside and wiping it off with a handkerchief or cloth before going into the steam.

The person with the disability should be allowed to do as much as they can for themselves, and in their own time. Where full communication is possible, they can ask you for help when they want it. Maintain privacy and dignity as far as it is possible to do so safely, but at the same time do not be over-protective.

Washing is a daily task which you may need to assist with; again, allow as much independence as possible and maintain privacy and dignity. Help when requested, or when it is needed. Washing and combing hair; cleaning teeth (both natural and false), and shaving are other daily tasks. Shaving is better done with an electric razor, but some people may prefer a wet shave. Use a disposable safety razor for this if you know how, otherwise ask someone else to do it and learn from them.

There are many other tasks of a personal nature which some people require help with, or to be done for them. These are described in more detail in the competency statements of the NVQs of the Integrated Care Awards.

EXERCISES

[1] Write alternative captions to the cartoons opposite.

[2] Try writing some care instructions yourself.
   (a) Describe to a complete novice how to shave a man who is unable to do it for himself.
   (b) Describe how to put a shirt or blouse on for someone who is unable to use their arms.

See NVQ Competences to Level 2 in Appendix 1 on page 220.
See also GNVQ information in Appendix 1 on page 214.

DOs AND DON'Ts

(a)

SMOKING
Don't smoke
while helping

(b)

AWARENESS
Do be aware of
situations and
needs at all times

(c)

PRIVACY
Do knock before
you enter
someone's room

Fig 4.3 Cartoons drawn by Bill Tidy for the Winged Fellowship Trust, and reproduced here with their kind permission

DISABILITY AWARENESS

Exercises

While acknowledging that exercises such as those that follow are not ideal, and in some ways can be said to trivialise disability, they are still an important way for able-bodied people to develop some appreciation of the circumstances of people with disabilities. They can be both fun and threatening to take part in, but in either case are a valuable learning process.

GROUP EXERCISES

1 Ask all members of the group to put one hand behind their back, and then:

(a) try to write on a single sheet of paper on the desk top or other smooth surface;
(b) fasten and unfasten a button on some item of clothing;
(c) fasten laces on shoes or trainers.

This can then be repeated using the other hand. You could also try at home using only one hand to get dressed and undressed, butter the bread, do the washing and drying, and so on.

2 **Money recognition**

With a partner, get hold of a supply of money. Take it in turn to identify how much is there while keeping your eyes firmly closed, or wearing a blindfold. Try to do this using both touch and sound to help you, and then by touch only, using a different amount.

(a) How accurate were you?
(b) Was it easier with touch *and* sound, or with touch only?
(c) How do you think people with sensory disabilities cope when currency changes take place, such as when new size coins are introduced, or bank-notes changed?
(d) Are there any factors which helped you recognise coins or notes, such as design, texture, or weight?
(e) How is a pound coin different from a penny, or a 2p from a 10p?
(f) Can you make any suggestions which may further help with recognition? For example, would Braille markings in paper money be of any use?
(g) Do you foresee any additional problems if the money in question is 'foreign'? Consider holidays abroad and the problems of immigrant populations, and think of ways to reduce difficulties.
(h) What help could be given when currency changes occur in this country?

Paralysis

Equipment required: a chair, a wheelchair, a pair of rubber household gloves, and some elastic bands.

Disabled person's instructions

You are resident in a hostel, and paralysed from the waist down. You also have little use of your arms and hands. A member of the care staff is to take you for a trip around the grounds, and to the toilet before returning for dinner.

Decide which type of person you are going to be; quiet and compliant, or argumentative and disruptive. Do you want to go out or not? Do you want the toilet at all, and if so, now or later? Do not tell anybody beforehand what attitude you are going to adopt.

Put on the rubber gloves, and have somebody fasten your fingers together in pairs to restrict their movement. Sit in a chair and wait for the carer.

Carer's instructions

You are a care worker employed in a residential home for disabled people. A resident is paralysed from the waist down, and has little use in their hands or arms. You have to transfer him/her from a chair to a wheelchair, and take them for a trip around the grounds, and then to the toilet before returning him/her to their seat for dinner.

Collect the wheelchair, and push it to the correct position by the chair your resident is waiting in, and transfer him/her from one to the other. Observe all health and safety procedures while doing so.

Blindness

Equipment needed: chair, table, crockery and cutlery; sugar in a bowl, and food, and a blindfold, e.g. a scarf.

Carer's instructions

Terry is a middle-aged man who has recently become blind due to an accident. He is with you in a residential home awaiting a place on a rehabilitation course to teach him how to cope with being unable to see.

He always seems to be in a bad temper, and the staff do not enjoy their dealings with him. It is tea time, and you have to escort him from the sitting room to the dining room. Guide him to his seat, and leave him while you go and get the food (but do not tell him what you are doing); put it down in front of him, and tell him his tea is there, but nothing more. Serve a sandwich, cup of tea and a cream cake (you may have to change this to suit what is available in your college/school, but try to include something potentially messy). Include a bowl of sugar and a teaspoon.

After tea, Terry wants to go to the toilet and for a breath of fresh air. Lead him to the toilet (it doesn't have to be used, this is only a role play!), and out into the open air. If you are able, take him for a drive, leaving the blindfold in place.

Disabled person's instructions

Secure a scarf or similar material around your eyes so that you are unable to see.

You have recently become blind following an industrial accident, which you are still very bitter about. As a result of the blindness, you are always bumping into things and making other clumsy mistakes.

This makes you even more angry, and you tend to take it out on the people around you, snapping at them for the slightest thing, and blaming them when things go wrong. Nor will you ask them for advice about anything.

You are listening to the radio in the sitting room when a member of staff comes to tell you that it is tea time (you find it difficult to keep track of time at the moment), and takes you into the dining room. You grumble about wanting to listen to the radio programme, and about being led about like a dog going for a walk. The food is put in front of you without ceremony, and you have to tackle it alone. You are then taken to the toilet and for a walk in the garden. You may also go on a drive if possible.

De-briefing

After this exercise, try to describe to the other members of your group how it felt to be Terry, particularly with being left to get on with eating unseen and messy food, putting sugar in your tea; having to rely on somebody else to lead you around; and the experience of an unseen car journey – were you more aware of sounds and smells? Was it pleasurable or frightening?

The carers should also try to say what their feelings were to be responsible for somebody who is ungrateful:

- Can you understand why looking after Terry would not be a popular task?
- What may be the longer term effects on Terry?
- How would you try to modify his attitude?

CLASS EXERCISE

Find enough blindfolds to use on half the class. Divide into pairs; one person is blindfolded and the other is to act as guide and take that person on a tour of the school/college and grounds. Then swap over, and repeat the exercise.

Once again, discuss how it felt to be dependent upon another person, and what you felt as you were being led around. Also discuss how it felt to have the responsibility for someone else's safety.

As an alternative to using blindfolds, if you have access to a supply of distorting or 'simulation' glasses from a Visual Resource Centre, then these can be used instead of, or as well as, blindfolds.

Mobility

Equipment needed: splint, bandages or belts, a bed or substitute; a cardigan with buttons, shoes with laces; and a walking stick or frame.

Disabled person's instructions

You have had a stroke, so in order to emulate this, you should get someone to tie your dominant arm (your right arm if you are right-handed, left arm if you are left-handed) to your side with a belt or bandage, and to splint your leg on the same side so that it does not bend. You are lying on the bed, partly dressed, and wish to get up.

Try to move yourself to a sitting position, and then fasten the cardigan buttons using only the free hand, and also put on the shoes and fasten the laces.

When this is done, with or without help, go for a walk using the walking stick or frame. Tackle stairs and slopes, and going in and out of doors while still incapacitated, but make sure that two people are with you at all times.

Carers' instructions

Always be within catching distance, but do as little as is necessary for this person; leave them to do what they can for themselves, but do not let them come to any harm.

After the exercise, discuss how it felt to be the disabled person, and how it felt to be the carers, but having to watch while somebody struggles to manage what for most of us are relatively simple tasks.

General comments

These exercises can, of course, be recorded on video if required, and used for discussion purposes.

Other tasks can be added, such as food preparation; e.g. having to butter bread with one hand; make a cup of tea or coffee, and peeling potatoes. Personal hygiene tasks such as washing one's face, squeezing toothpaste from a tube, and using clothes fasteners can be practised.

Catalogues of aids available can be used to find the equipment which will best help with day to day tasks. Such catalogues can be obtained from Boots, Homecrafts, or the DSS Publications Unit.

When members of the group have taken part, the questions for discussion should centre on:

- how it feels to be dependent;
- how it feels to be responsible for another's daily needs;
- the advantages and disadvantages of residential care;
- alternative forms of care.

NINE COMMANDMENTS

For relatives, friends and those caring for hearing impaired people

1. **Remember!** Hard of hearing people need to see you clearly.

2. **Remember!** Face the light and the person at all times.

3. **Remember!** Include hard of hearing people in your conversation. Let them know what you are talking about.

4. **Remember!** Don't hide your mouth e.g. behind a newspaper.

5. **Remember!** Talk directly to hard of hearing people.

6. **Remember!** Speak clearly, not too fast and repeat if necessary.

7. **Remember!** Don't shout into the ear or hearing aid.

8. **Remember!** Tell hard of hearing people what you are laughing about.

9. **Remember!** Avoid unnecessary noise. Get the person's attention before speaking

Reproduced from the Brierley Hill and Kingswinford branch of Age Concern's *Guide to Carers*, and reproduced with their kind permission

Communication

See the illustration opposite on points to remember when communicating with hearing impaired people.

Charades

Organise a game of charades, i.e. act out or mime a word or phrase without using speech or writing.

This should demonstrate the difficulty and frustration of passing on information without speaking, and do so in an entertaining way.

Lipreading

In pairs, talk to one another soundlessly, i.e. make the lip movements only. Write down what you think the other person is saying, and compare notes afterwards. Bear in mind the additional difficulties for non-English speakers.

Phrases to use can include:

– *You owe me eighteen pence.*
– *Paul has a new ball.*
– *Billie's on the Pill.*
– *Buy me some chops at the shops.*
– *Could you match this patch?*
– *Are you expecting any visitors?*
– *The doctor is coming to see you today.*
– *Do you want to go for a walk?*
– *What do you want for dinner?*
– *Do you think Joyce has made a good choice?*

Sign language

Look at the sign language shown on page 38 and spell out your name and address to a partner. How easy is it to communicate in this manner?

More communication

This is to take place in a residential home, and involves care staff and residents.

Equipment required: a chair, a pillow, a blanket for lifting, and a wheelchair.

Carer's instructions

One of your residents has come to tell you that one of the other residents, who is frail, elderly, and deaf, has fallen over in the day room. In addition, her command of English

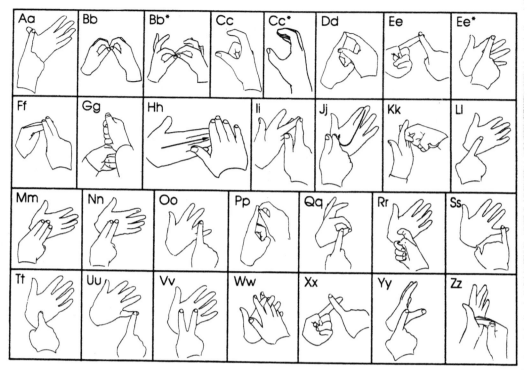

British Two-Handed Fingerspelling
Reproduced by kind permission of the British Deaf Association

is poor. You go to see what is going on, and find Sucheta, a lady who is very difficult to communicate with, lying on the floor. She is obviously distressed, and is unable to get up, but is also unable to tell you if anything is damaged.

Joan is trying to help her, but you are worried that she may fall over next.

Resident's instructions

You are deaf and unable to lip read; while getting from your chair in the day room to pick up a magazine, you have somehow managed to fall over on to the carpet.

It is the first time that this has happened; nothing seems to have been broken, but you are breathless and do not seem to be able to pick yourself up and you are starting to panic. Another resident is trying to help you, but even between you, you cannot manage.

Decide who is going to play the parts of residents and staff, and deal with the situation as you think best. Do not share the above information; the 'residents' ears can be covered or blocked with cottonwool or ear-plugs.

The carer must first decide how they are going to communicate. *See also* Assignment 1 on page 194.

THE WHEELS COMMUNITY

The Wheels Community is a purpose-built residential estate which is geographically isolated, and inhabited only by people in wheelchairs.

All the buildings are single storey, with ramped entrances and low, wide doorways. Ceilings are set at five feet high, as nobody living here needs more than that. All switches, handles and other controls are at a sensible height for the users. The same is true of counters, tables, work surfaces and so on. None of the cafes and restaurants has chairs, as all their customers provide their own. The same is true of the cinema and Concert Hall.

Many other facilities are drive-in, such as banks, supermarkets, fast food outlets, etc., in order to cater for the large number of vehicles specially adapted for the townspeople. Most of these vehicles are not equipped with seats, but with clamps to anchor the wheelchairs into position.

The system works well, and the first generation of residents continued to refine their environment to suit their needs. The community developed, and, as is the nature of things, romances developed and marriages took place in the church without pews and the drive-in Registry Office.

Being moral and upstanding citizens, it was only after these marriages that children began to appear on the scene. It was not at first apparent, but as the children grew, the parents began to notice that things were not as they should be. These children only needed wheelchairs for the first year or two of life. While this new generation remained small, their problems could be managed at home and within the community. As they grew up, however, they suffered frequent bruising to the head as they tried to walk through the low doorways, or to stand up in the low-ceilinged rooms. There was also an increasing amount of toe damage as they would get their feet underneath some of the thousands of wheels about the town. Many also complained of back problems from having to bend down all the time.

Communication became difficult, as eye contact was lost with the children's increasing height and distance from the speaker. They began to be marginalised as they could not use the facilities at the Youth Club or join the basketball teams, or even sit in the coffee bar with their wheelie friends.

It became increasingly obvious that special provision would need to be made for them. Residential hostels were built, and social workers employed to counsel both them and their parents about their obvious differences from the mainstream of society. Areas were set aside especially to cater for them, with chairs available in cafes and cinema, and separate entrances to allow for their greater height were built where possible.

Some parents even went as far as providing protective headgear for their children; charities were set up to help these poor able-bodied people who needed help. Money was raised to send them off to special schools where their problems could be catered for. Many suffered psychological problems, however, and there was an element in the community who shunned them and insisted that they should live a separate life. These people would give to the charities, but not let their daughter marry one (not their wheelie daughter anyway). An extremist group even went as far as raising money to be used for the amputation of the lower limbs of the able-bodied, but this was always a minority view.

Some of the 'able-bodied handicapped' reacted to this attitude and set up their own pressure group, organising marches demanding equal rights, adapted building suitable for their needs as well as everybody else's, and a guaranteed 'able-bodied' allowance from the Town Council.

They came to be seen as troublemakers, and the wheelie townspeople did not know how to deal with them. They came to feel uneasy in their presence, and then to avoid them if they saw them about, sometimes even crossing the street so that they did not meet.

QUESTIONS

(a) Who are the handicapped population in the Wheels Community? Why would you describe them as handicapped?

(b) How could the problems of the able-bodied people be solved?

(c) Why did the able-bodied come to be seen as troublemakers to the point where people went out of their way to avoid them?

(d) Do you think it would be a good idea or a bad idea to create such a community? Give your reasons for the conclusion you have reached.

(e) What problems would the residents face if they went away on holiday?

(f) Write your own short story about life in this town.

DISABILITY AWARENESS QUIZ *see* **page 228 for answers**

1 Approximately how many disabled people are there in the UK?
   (a) 6 million   (b) 1 million   (c) 10 million

2 How many disabled people are of working age?
   (a) 1.1 million   (b) 2.4 million   (c) 3.9 million

3 What percentage of disabled people are wheelchair users?
   (a) 10%   (b) 5%   (c) 15%

4 All disabled people have learning difficulties.
   True ☐   False ☐

5 If a company employs more than 20 people, what percentage of them should be registered as disabled?
   (a) 3%   (b) 5%   (c) 8%

6 A Disablement Resettlement Officer helps disabled people find somewhere to live.
   True ☐   False ☐

7 Which of the following is a 'hidden' disability?
   (a) Cerebral Palsy   (b) Epilepsy   (c) Spina Bifida   (d) Amputation

8 Quadriplegia means paralysis of the quadriceps.
   True ☐   False ☐

9 What do the following initials stand for?
   SSD   DSS   OT   MS   HCA

10 You see somebody in the street carrying a red and white striped walking stick; what does it tell you about them?

11 A ferrule is:
   (a) a type of metal crutch
   (b) the rubber protection on the end of a walking stick
   (c) the small wheel on the front of a wheelchair
   (d) the handle of a cooking pot

12 What does an 'Orange Badge' on a car allow the driver to do?

13 Why do Pelican Crossings have a bleeping sound as well as pictures of a green and red man?

14 How many people with disabilities live in some kind of communal establishment?
   (a) 100 000   (b) 250 000   (c) 400 000

15 What percentage of adults living in private households have at least one disability?
   (a) 5%   (b) 9%   (c) 14%   (d) 19%

16 There are more disabled women than men.
   True ☐   False ☐

17 What percentage of disabled people are in employment?
   (a) 21%   (b) 31%   (c) 41%   (d) 51%

18 What was the first disability to be defined by law in the UK?
   (a) Deafness   (b) Blindness   (c) Paralysis   (d) Epilepsy

19 What is:
   (a) Spastic paralysis?   (b) Flaccid paralysis?

20 Occupational therapists help disabled people to find a job.
   True ☐   False ☐

Part Two

CAUSES AND EFFECTS OF DISABILITY

Chapter 5

DEFINITIONS OF DISABILITY

Arrange the class into groups of four, and ask each group to decide upon a definition of disability, handicap and impairment. Everyone in the class must have heard of disability and handicap, and have a picture in their mind's eye of a 'handicapped person'. A useful starting exercise is to compare these individual ideas, and for the group to create a pen picture of the 'handicapped person' we carry around in our head.

After this exercise, it is hoped that you will speak of people with disabilities, or disabled people, in preference to any other terminology. The reason for this is to remind us that we are not talking about objects or things, but people. Terms such as 'The Disabled' and 'The Handicapped' deny the personalities and individuality of the real people about whom we are concerned here.

Reasons for definitions

There are a great many definitions of handicap, some more confusing than others. What should be remembered is that each definition was created for a specific purpose, and more often than not, this purpose was to enable people to get help of various kinds.

There is no chance of getting a Disability Allowance, for instance if you are not disabled. But who decides whether you are disabled, and how, and to what degree? Those responsible for administering the funds have to go to their rules and regulations, and compare the individual with the description in the rule book.

The Disabled Persons (Employment) Acts of 1944 and 1958 state the definition as 'a person who on account of injury, disease or congenital deformity, is substantially handicapped in obtaining or keeping employment, or in undertaking work on his own account, of a kind which apart from his injury, disease or deformity, would be suited to his age, experience, and qualifications.' If you can work this out, and get a person to fit the description, he or she can be given help.

Another definition comes from the Disabled Persons (Services, Consultation and Representation) Act 1986; this simply states that 'For the purposes of this Act, a "disabled person" is defined as a person with a mental, physical or sensory disability or a mental illness.'

The 1989 Children Act defines disabled children under section 17(11) as follows: A child is said to have a disability if the child is any of the following:

- blind;
- deaf;
- dumb;
- suffering from any kind of mental disorder;
- substantially or permanently handicapped by illness, injury, congenital deformity, or any other prescribed disability.

This is a legal definition for Local Authority guidance when deciding upon who they should be providing services for.

'Handicap' is not a word specific to the caring professions. It is heard in betting shops and on golf courses as often as it is in social services offices or hospitals. So what does it mean?

Check in an ordinary, everyday English dictionary and see what it says before reading on. Now look in a medical dictionary and compare the definitions. The first one will say something like this:

(1) Race or competition in which chances of competitors are made more nearly equal by conceding start, difference in weight to be carried (as in a horse race) or other condition or advantage to be conferred; number of strokes by which golfer normally exceeds par for course.

(2) Hindrance; thing that prevents one from doing something.

(3) Suffering from mental or physical disability. (From 'Hand i' th' Cap', or begging.)

The first description seems to have little to do with the caring professions – other than that there is no reason why handicapped people, or indeed care workers, cannot have an interest in horse-racing or golf.

The second seems very apt; and the third puts us back where we started. What is meant by disability? Go back to your dictionaries and look at the definitions of 'disability'.

Words have different meanings in different contexts and in our own heads. This exercise can be used to highlight that fact. The first stage is for students to write down their own understanding of the words 'handicap' and 'disability'; then find the definitions of these words in a standard dictionary (or use the ones reproduced here), and finally to look for the same words in a medical dictionary. The findings then become the focus of a discussion to reach a consensus definition to use for the remainder of the course.

In 1980, the World Health Organisation (WHO) produced what have become the standard international definitions for the following terms:

1 Impairment. Any loss or abnormality of psychological, physiological or anatomical structure or function, i.e. A part of the body does not work properly, or is missing.

2 Disability. Any restriction or lack (resulting from an impairment) or ability to perform an activity in the manner or within the range considered normal for a human being, i.e. You check what people *cannot* do when compared with the majority of other people.

3 Handicap. A disadvantage for a given individual, resulting from an impairment or disability that limits or prevents the fulfilment of a role, depending on age, sex, and social and cultural factors, for that individual.

This looks at what an individual can and cannot do in a particular environment or situation, and in relationships with other people.

These definitions become easier to understand when they can be related to real people. How did the definition arrived at in the exercise on page 44 compare with these?

Some examples of impairment are the early effects of arthritis, where there is some loss of movement in a joint, but there is no effect on the quality of life, and no steps have to be taken to remedy the loss. The loss of some teeth could impair the chewing of food, but is unlikely to be classed as a disability, much less a handicap. The loss of part of a finger (from the upper joint, say) may be painful at the time, and be handicapping in the short term. In the long term, however, the person will probably be able to do everything they did before the finger was damaged.

When it comes to more severe disabilities, they may not be handicapping for some individuals, but greatly so for others. Colour blindness, for instance, may not be anything more than a minor irritation for the majority of the affected population. The problem occurs when certain careers are being considered, for instance, such as electronics engineering, where colour coding is used for wiring systems; art, interior design, and perhaps computer operating.

The fact is that a disability is a disability, but whether it is handicapping or not is socially determined. What this means is that the degree of handicap that goes with any given disability depends on where you live, how you live, social class, income, (if you have sufficient income, it is much easier to buy the equipment to make life more manageable); the job you do or would like to do, and the attitudes of both yourself and those around you.

The Office of Population Censuses and Surveys (OPCS) figures, using the WHO classifications above put the number of disabled people in the United Kingdom at 6.2 million, of which 2.4 million are of working age, and 31% are actually working. Fewer than 5% of disabled people are wheelchair users, and only 400 000 in some kind of communal establishment.

It should be remembered, however, that where facilities are available for wheelchair access, then many other individual requirements can be catered for, whether concerned with disabled people, or mothers with prams and pushchairs. Therefore to aim for wheelchair access is a useful benchmark to allow for use by many other groups of people.

EXERCISE

Make a list of any physical disabilities you know. Divide a piece of paper into two columns, headed 'Temporary' and 'Permanent'.

- If anyone in the group has broken an arm or a leg, ask them if this was an impairment, a disability or a handicap.
- Are there any members of your group disabled in any way?
- How many disabled students and staff are there in your college or school?

Perhaps you/they would welcome an opportunity to speak to the group, or answer a questionnaire, or write something for you to discuss, if invited to do so? (*See* 'Inviting a Guest Speaker' on page 202 in the assignments section for guidance on this.)

When this has been done, change the column headings to 'Apparent' and 'Hidden', and see how many disabilities in these two categories you can identify.

There are a great many definitions of disability and handicap, both general and specific, and all there for a particular purpose.

Which one you use, and when, must be determined by the purpose for which it is being used. If you are helping somebody to claim Disability Living Allowance, then you must use the description in the claim forms; if applying for a job, the definitions used in the Employment Acts, and so on.

For day to day use, you can use any definition which you feel most at home with.

4 Illness. There is no doubt that illness is disabling to a greater or lesser degree. It may only be a transient state of affairs which lasts only as long as the disease process.

There are some diseases, however, which leave a permanent legacy, and lead to unequivocal disablement, for example untreated leprosy, poliomyelitis and even measles. Other types, such as osteo-arthritis, some types of cancer, and AIDS can lead to impairment and disability even if treated. It is important to differentiate between the medical treatment aspects of the disease and the socially determined handicaps which result.

Chapter 6

SENSORY IMPAIRMENT

This is the general name given to the group of disabilities which involve disorders of the senses; i.e. sight, hearing, touch, taste or smell. The most common are disorders of sight and hearing, but there are some less common types which are very subjective in nature, and come into the category of hidden disabilities:

Anosmia (loss of the sense of smell)

Taste and smell are closely inter-linked, and loss of one means loss of both. This not only makes life much less interesting, but on occasion could be life-threatening due to the inability to smell or taste dangerous substances. The cause is usually head injury or disease causing nerve degeneration; rarely it is a congenital abnormality.

The results of **agnosia** (faulty functioning of nerves) are similar, but it is not the senses which are faulty, but the interpreting centres in the brain (this problem can affect all the senses).

In general a disorder of this type would be classified as an impairment only.

Anaesthesia

Although this term is almost always heard in the context of hospitals and having operations, it does not necessarily mean being put to sleep. It is also the general term for a loss of the sense of touch in all or part of the body. Often found in association with paralysis, it can also accompany damage or disease to nerves, such as is found in leprosy, alcoholism, and vitamin B deficiencies.

Blindness and partial sight

The inability to see any light whatsoever is total blindness; only about four per cent of people registered as blind in the UK are affected to this degree. There are varying degrees of visual impairment much less severe than this which can still be classed as blindness for registration purposes. A rule of thumb is that if a person is unable to read a car number plate from a distance of three metres, then he or she is technically a blind person.

The Blind Register itself is maintained by the Social Services Department, but is based on medical evidence supplied by a Consultant Ophthalmologist (eye specialist). There

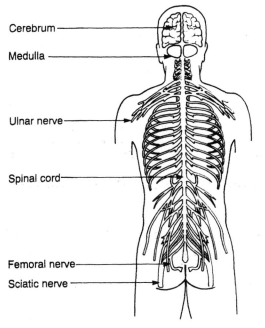

Cerebrum

Medulla

Ulnar nerve

Spinal cord

Femoral nerve

Sciatic nerve

Fig 6.1 The human nervous system

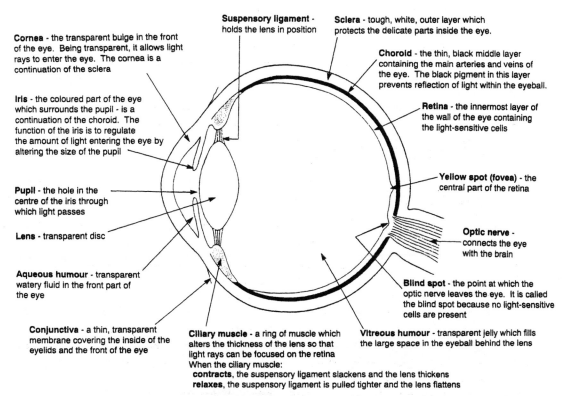

Suspensory ligament - holds the lens in position

Sclera - tough, white, outer layer which protects the delicate parts inside the eye.

Cornea - the transparent bulge in the front of the eye. Being transparent, it allows light rays to enter the eye. The cornea is a continuation of the sclera

Choroid - the thin, black middle layer containing the main arteries and veins of the eye. The black pigment in this layer prevents reflection of light within the eyeball.

Iris - the coloured part of the eye which surrounds the pupil - is a continuation of the choroid. The function of the iris is to regulate the amount of light entering the eye by altering the size of the pupil

Retina - the innermost layer of the wall of the eye containing the light-sensitive cells

Pupil - the hole in the centre of the iris through which light passes

Yellow spot (fovea) - the central part of the retina

Lens - transparent disc

Optic nerve - connects the eye with the brain

Aqueous humour - transparent watery fluid in the front part of the eye

Blind spot - the point at which the optic nerve leaves the eye. It is called the blind spot because no light-sensitive cells are present

Conjunctiva - a thin, transparent membrane covering the inside of the eyelids and the front of the eye

Ciliary muscle - a ring of muscle which alters the thickness of the lens so that light rays can be focused on the retina
When the ciliary muscle:
  contracts, the suspensory ligament slackens and the lens thickens
  relaxes, the suspensory ligament is pulled tighter and the lens flattens

Vitreous humour - transparent jelly which fills the large space in the eyeball behind the lens

Fig 6.2 Diagram of a horizontal section through a right eye as seen from above (a right eye because of the direction for the optic nerve)

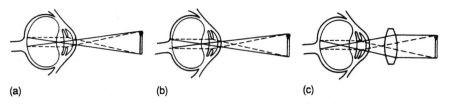

(a)   (b)   (c)

Fig 6.3
(a) Normal eyesight. The eye focuses on the matchstick and the image is projected upside down and back to front on the retina. The brain puts the image the right way up.
(b) Longsight (presbyopia). The lens is less able to change shape so that image falls behind the retina.
(c) Corrective glasses. Opticians prescribe glasses with lenses that curve outwards making the image fall on to the retina.

are two parts to the register, one for blindness and one for partial sightedness. Inclusion enables access to further help and benefits in cash or kind from both statutory and voluntary bodies.

Blindness was, in fact, the first disability to be legally defined in the UK, under the Blind Persons Act, 1920.

QUESTIONS

(a) What is the loss of the sense of smell called?
(b) Why may it be life threatening?
(c) Explain how anosmia differs from agnosia.
(d) Give two meanings for 'anaesthesia'.
(e) What percentage of people registered as blind are unable to see any light whatsoever?
(f) What test is used to determine if a person if technically blind?
(g) Which statutory body maintains the register of Blind and Partially Sighted People?
(h) Who provides the evidence for inclusion on this Register?
(i) When was blindness first legally determined?

QUESTIONS

Carry out your own research, read through the statutory form BD8 reproduced in Fig 6.4 and answer the following questions:

(a) Under which Act of Parliament can an individual be certified as blind?
(b) What is the statutory definition of blindness?
(c) How many groups can they be classified into?
(d) Can you find out what 'Snellen' is?
(e) What is the legal definition of partial sight?
(f) What are the criteria an individual must meet to be classed as partially sighted?
(g) What is 'binocular corrected vision'?
(h) Who should sign part 2 of the form BD8?
(i) Where are the four copies of this form distributed to?
(j) What is part 5 of the form used for?

In confidence

Record of examination
to certify a person as blind or partially sighted

BD8(1990)

Parts 1 to 4

Part 1   About the patient

Surname	Address
Other names	
Title	Mr/Mrs/Miss/Ms
	Postcode
Date of birth	Daytime phone number

Details of General Practitioner

Name
Address

Postcode

Details of patient's local Social Services department

Name
Address
Please refer to the
*Social Services Year
Book* for correct
details

Part 2   Consent form - for disclosure of information

I am
- [ ] the patient
- [ ] a parent of the patient
- [ ] the patient's guardian
- [ ] a representative authorised to sign for the patient

The patient understands
- [ ] what this form is for and how it will be used

The patient agrees
- [ ] to a copy of Parts 1, 2, 3 and 4 being sent to the local Director of Social Services named in Part 1, or their agent
- [ ] to a copy of Part 5 being sent to the Office of Population Censuses and Surveys
- [ ] to a copy of all parts being sent to the General Practitioner named in Part 1.

I confirm that the statements that I have ticked opposite are true.

Signature

Date

Signature of witness normally the examining ophthalmologist

Date

Part 3   Aspects of visual function

Visual acuity
Snellen or functional assessment,
for example hand movement or finger counting

	Right eye	Left eye
Unaided		
With spectacle correction		
Best with both eyes open		

Field of vision
Please tick
if abnormal
- [ ] Total loss of visual field
- [ ] Extensive loss of visual field including hemianopia
- [ ] Primarily loss of peripheral field
- [ ] Primarily loss of central field

Duration of sight loss
- [ ] Less than one month
- [ ] Less than one year
- [ ] More than one year

Low vision aids
- [ ] Prescribed
- [ ] To be assessed
- [ ] Not appropriate

General information
- [ ] Sight loss only
- [ ] Also poor mobility
- [ ] Also significant hearing impairment

Other relevant information
For example
patient lives alone

Part 4   Certificate of blindness or partial sight

I consider
- [ ] that this person is blind. They cannot do any work for which eyesight is essential.
- [ ] that this person is partially sighted. They are substantially and permanently handicapped by defective vision caused by congenital defect or illness or injury.

Consultant's name

Address

Signature

Date

To the patient's local Social Services department
as soon as possible after examination

Fig 6.4(a) Statutory form BD8 Parts 1 to 4:
Part 1: to the patient's local Social Services Department; Part 2: to the patient's General Practitioner;
Part 3: to the patient; Part 4: to be kept by the Consultant Ophthalmologist

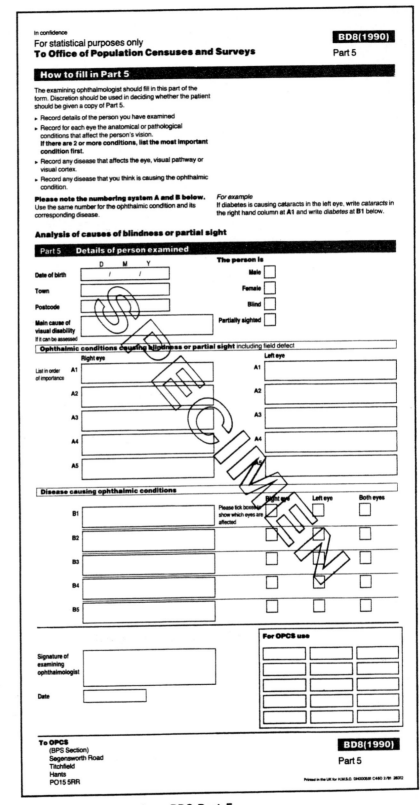

Fig 6.4(b) Statutory form BD8 Part 5

52

Deafness and partial hearing

This is the total or partial loss of hearing in one or both ears. There are a variety of causes, and an estimated ten million people affected in the UK; no formal register is kept, however, and there is no legal definition.

The most common reason for faulty hearing is the ageing process.

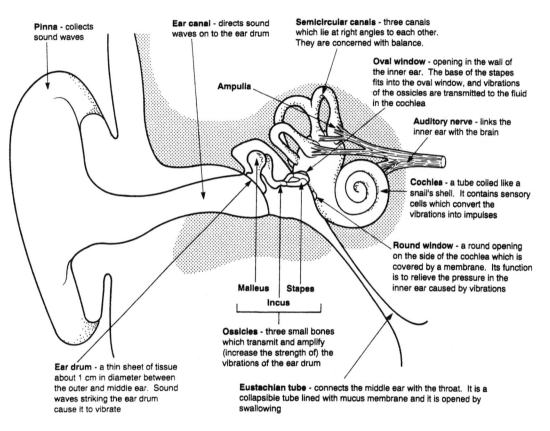

Pinna - collects sound waves

Ear canal - directs sound waves on to the ear drum

Semicircular canals - three canals which lie at right angles to each other. They are concerned with balance.

Ampulla

Oval window - opening in the wall of the inner ear. The base of the stapes fits into the oval window, and vibrations of the ossicles are transmitted to the fluid in the cochlea

Auditory nerve - links the inner ear with the brain

Cochlea - a tube coiled like a snail's shell. It contains sensory cells which convert the vibrations into impulses

Round window - a round opening on the side of the cochlea which is covered by a membrane. Its function is to relieve the pressure in the inner ear caused by vibrations

Malleus   Stapes
        Incus

Ear drum - a thin sheet of tissue about 1 cm in diameter between the outer and middle ear. Sound waves striking the ear drum cause it to vibrate

Ossicles - three small bones which transmit and amplify (increase the strength of) the vibrations of the ear drum

Eustachian tube - connects the middle ear with the throat. It is a collapsible tube lined with mucus membrane and it is opened by swallowing

Fig 6.5 Structure of the ear

EXERCISE

(a) Find out what you can about Tinnitus.
(b) What is Ménière's Disease?

Try the awareness exercises on pages 32–8.

Chapter 7

CAUSES OF DISABILITY

There are three main ways in which an individual can become disabled. In a nutshell, they can be summarised as 'before', 'during' and 'after' birth.

Congenital reasons (before)

Before birth, the developing baby is constructed according to instructions from the mother and father through the mixture of their genes at the time of conception.

A gene is the basic unit for heredity, carrying a code to tell the developing baby (foetus) how and what to grow. They decide such things as which sex the child will be, colour of hair and eyes, height, and other physical characteristics. Unfortunately, they can also carry faulty codes, or pieces of the code can be missing. When this happens, congenital deformities occur such as muscular dystrophy, spina bifida, or cystic fibrosis.

Some of these problems can be corrected after the child has been born (hole in the heart, cleft palate, polydactyly) and thus are prevented from becoming disabling.

Others are permanent, and so *are* disabling. Examples are Spina Bifida, Cystic Fibrosis and Huntington's Chorea. Medical tests can now determine the presence of many of these disorders in the womb, and parents given time to decide upon a course of action.

EXERCISE

Read the pamphlet on ante-natal screening reproduced on pages 55–6 with the kind permission of ASBAH. It is an outline description of what is available, and can be used as a starting point for further research.

Answer the following questions based on the piece:

(a) Why are regular medical checks carried out during pregnancy?
(b) Who carries out these checks?
(c) What does AFP mean?
(d) What does a high level indicate?
(e) What does a low level indicate?
(f) What further tests are needed to confirm these indications?
(g) What risks are associated with the AFP test?
(h) How does ultrasound scanning work?
(i) At what stage of pregnancy is an ultrasound scan best used to detect serious abnormalities?

ANTE-NATAL SCREENING

Introduction

Throughout pregnancy, woman are given routine checks by doctors and midwives at ante-natal clinics, surgeries and health centres. These tests are carried out to ensure that both mother and baby are in good health. This information sheet outlines the main tests available which enable a more accurate diagnosis to be made.

The AFP Blood Test - Maternal Serum Alpha feto protein

This is a simple blood test carried out between the 16th and 18th weeks of pregnancy. A small amount of blood is taken from the arm and tested to find out the level of alpha feto protein. A high level indicates the possible presence of a neural tube defect, e.g. spina bifida. A low level indicates the possible presence of Down's Syndrome.

However, there may be several other reasons for these results. It is important to stress that, when a high or low AFP level is detected, it does not necessarily mean that there is something wrong with the baby. The AFP blood test is a screening procedure and other tests are required to confirm the presence of a neural tube defect. These tests are a detailed ultrasound scan and/or amniocentesis.

The AFP blood test is not performed routinely at all ante-natal clinics. Where it is the policy of the hospital to screen for AFP levels, all mothers are tested unless they specifically request not to be included in the programme. When the test is not routine, parents can request that it is carried out.

The AFP blood test carries no risk to either mother or baby. The results are normally available within a few days to a week.

Ultrasound

Ultrasound scanning uses sound waves to form a picture of the baby in the uterus. It is a completely painless procedure that can be carried out at any stage of pregnancy. It is usually requested that the mother has a full bladder at the time of the procedure.

Ultrasound is often used between the 12th and 16th week of pregnancy to confirm the age of the baby and to determine the presence of twins. However, for accurate results, ultrasound scans to detect serious abnormalities need to be performed at approximately 18-20 weeks.

These more lengthy and detailed scans are performed when there is thought to be an increased risk of developmental abnormalities, i.e. spina bifida or hydrocephalus.

An ultrasound scan is a non-invasive technique and there is no known risk to the health of either mother or baby.

Amniocentesis

This test is normally performed only when there is considered to be an increased risk that the baby has a congenital abnormality or other serious condition.

Amniocentesis is usually carried out between the 16th and 20th weeks of pregnancy. Ultrasound examination is often used at the same time to ascertain the position of the baby and the placenta.

A local anaesthetic is usually given to numb the abdominal area. A fine needle is then inserted into the mother's abdomen and a small amount of the amniotic fluid surrounding the baby is withdrawn. The fluid is then sent to the laboratory for testing.

Amniocentesis does not usually require admission to

▶

Fig 7.1 The information sheet on ante-natal screening published by ASBAH
Reproduced with their kind permission

hospital. Some women may experience soreness or a tightening feeling in the abdomen for a short time after the procedure. Mothers are recommended to rest for a while before leaving the hospital and then to take things easy for a couple of days, particularly avoiding any heavy lifting or strenuous exercise during this time.

The results for detection of neural tube defects and other structural abnormalities are normally available within a week.

Other conditions which an amniocentesis test can detect include:

▲ Down's Syndrome

▲ Turner's Syndrome

▲ Inherited metabolic disorders (e.g. Tay-sachs disease)

▲ Certain sex-linked conditions

The results of screening for these conditions take about three to four weeks as these tests involve growing the cells from the fluid in the laboratory.

The sex of the baby can also be determined following amniocentesis.

Unfortunately, there is a slight chance that a miscarriage may occur following amniocentesis. This risk is now less than one in a hundred pregnancies. It is for this reason that the test is not performed routinely but when the baby is considered to be at greater risk.

Chorionic Villus Sampling - CVS (sometimes called ▲▲ Chorion Biopsy)

Chorionic Villus Sampling is a relatively new technique being used to diagnose conditions which previously have not been detectable until about 16 weeks of pregnancy by amniocentesis. CVS CANNOT DETECT THE PRESENCE OF SPINA BIFIDA OR OTHER NEURAL TUBE DEFECTS.

The CVS test is only advisable for women who are considered to have a greater risk of carrying a baby with an abnormality and is carried out by specialist centres. Most centres offering CVS are taking part in the Medical Research Council's trial. Women who wish to take part in the trial are randomly allocated to one of two groups, either to take amniocentesis or to have the CVS. They are not free to choose the group to which they are allocated. However, most of these centres offer the CVS test to women who have previously had a baby with an abnormality and these would not be included in the MRC trial.

The CVS test is usually carried out between the 8th and 11th weeks of pregnancy, although some centres prefer to test slightly later. An ultrasound scan is used to show the position of the developing pregnancy (part of which is the chorionic tissue) in the uterus. A tiny fragment from the edge of the chorionic tissue is removed for tests.

Most women do not find this test painful, although it can be a little uncomfortable. A general anaesthetic is not necessary. Mothers are recommended to rest for a while before leaving the hospital and then take things easy for a couple of days, particularly avoiding any heavy lifting or strenuous exercise during this time. Results are usually available in about 4-12 days depending on what the test is screening for.

One of the greatest advantages of the CVS test is the ability to diagnose some congenital abnormalities in the early part of the pregnancy. Results are available much earlier and more quickly than with amniocentesis.

An important aspect is the miscarriage rate after this test. The natural miscarriage rate is higher in early pregnancy, around the time when the CVS test is performed. It is therefore more difficult to know exactly what the miscarriage rate is for the CVS test, although it is felt to be higher than for amniocentesis.

▲▲ How to find out more

It is very important that, when considering CVS, the matter is discussed with the doctor and/or genetic counsellor before pregnancy begins.

It is hoped that this outline of the screening procedures available is helpful to you. You can obtain further detailed information and advice from your Midwife, Obstetrician or General Practitioner.

You may feel that there is insufficient time to discuss these matters during an Ante-Natal Clinic appointment. If so, talk to your midwife and arrange a further appointment. It is much better to have a clear understanding of what a particular test involves before it is carried out. In most cases, these tests are quite routine to hospital staff but a new experience for expectant parents. As a result, you may feel unsure when or what to ask for for fear of wasting staff time. Doctors and midwives will explain things in greater detail but do not always realise what areas cause uncertainty. So it is up to you to ask.

As already stated, not all hospitals routinely provide some of the screening tests available. If they are not available locally, you can be referred to another centre where they are performed. Ask if you want to know about the tests your hospital can provide.

Fig 7.1 continued

(j) What is amniocentesis?

(k) At what stage of pregnancy is it usually used?

(l) How long do the results of amniocentesis testing for neural tube defects take to be reported?

(m) Why is amniocentesis not carried out routinely?

(n) What cannot be detected by CVS testing?

(o) What is the main advantage of CVS testing over amniocentesis?

Increasingly the risks of having a baby with congenital disorders can be determined by family history and genetic testing of the parents, and counselling offered before conception. Some parents decide not to have children at all as the risks are higher than they wish to take. Others may reach the decision after genetic counselling that they would prefer to have an abortion, and either give up the idea of ever starting a family, or try again and hope that this next child will have no abnormalities.

EXERCISE

Read the guidelines for a debate in Assignment 6 on page 205, and organise one on the issues surrounding abortion as outlined there.

Alternatively choose another area such as genetic counselling – for example, you could choose to debate on whether *'People should accept their destiny, and not meddle with nature'*.

CASE STUDY

HAEMOPHILIA

INHERITANCE

Haemophilia is an inherited condition. However, it is possible for the condition to appear in any family – it is thought that 30% of people with haemophilia have no family history of a bleeding disorder. It is difficult to be exact about this because of the way in which haemophilia is inherited. Technically, it has a 'sex-linked recessive' inheritance pattern. This means that while only males suffer from the condition, it is passed through the female members of the family.

The sex of a newly conceived baby is determined by the type of chromosomes it receives – one from each parent. A boy inherits his mother's 'X' and his father's 'Y' chromosome, and a girl has two 'X' chromosomes, one from each parent. (*See* Fig 7.2(a).) The defect that causes haemophilia rests in the 'X' chromosome therefore the daughter of a man with haemophilia will inherit his 'X' chromosome and be

a 'carrier' of haemophilia. (*See* Fig 7.2(b).) She will not suffer from the condition herself because the normal 'X' chromosome she inherits from her mother will over-ride the defective one from her

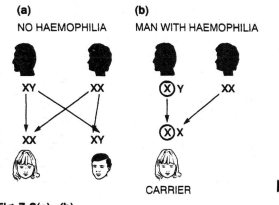

Fig 7.2(a)–(b)

Reproduced by kind permission of the Haemophilia Society

57

father. All the daughters of a man with haemophilia will be carriers. Since the son of a haemophilic father must inherit his father's 'Y' chromosome, he will not be affected by haemophilia, nor will he be a carrier. (*See* Fig 7.2(c).)

A carrier female has one normal and one defective 'X' chromosome. If she has a son, the son has a 50–50 chance of receiving his mother's defective 'X' chromosome (and equally a 50–50 chance of being normal). (*See* Fig 7.2(d).) The daughter of a carrier female also has a 50–50 chance of being a carrier herself. (*See* Fig 7.2(e).) It is because of this ability

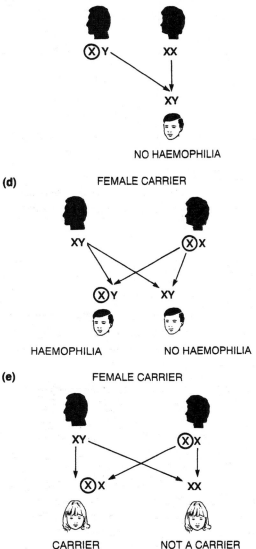

Fig 7.2(c)–(e)

for the defective gene to remain hidden through several generations of carrier daughters that makes it so difficult to know whether there really is no family history, or whether the problem has just been dormant for several generations.

The inheritance pattern is a difficult one to understand at first. It is very important to understand it properly so that families who know that there is haemophilia present can get accurate advice about their situation. It is possible for the Haemophilia Reference Centre to arrange tests to detect whether a female is a carrier. Unfortunately these tests do not provide an answer in all cases, but they do enable doctors and genetic counsellors to provide families with some of the factual information they need.

Genetic counselling is an important factor in the management of haemophilia. All Haemophilia Reference Centres provide full genetic counselling. Patients can be referred by their GP, or the consultant, to a geneticist for counselling.

This service offers clarification of the inheritance pattern and an opportunity to discuss anxieties concerning family planning and alternatives. With the geneticist's support, the Centre staff and GP can often help parents to make more informed decisions.

Some parents find it difficult to discuss with their daughters the possibility that they may be carriers and all that could be involved. A professional counsellor can be especially helpful in this situation. Provision of information and explanation to possible or confirmed carriers is particularly important to help them to come to terms with their own feelings about having a son with haemophilia or a daughter who may be a carrier. Teenage girls in particular need the opportunity to discuss their fears and expectations away from the family and also to have the opportunity to bring boyfriends or fiancés for a frank discussion.

ANTE-NATAL DIAGNOSIS

When a woman, either definitely, or highly probably, is a carrier, the risk of having a haemophilic son is so high (50–50 for each male) that formerly many women elected termination of all male foetuses, or decided not to have children at all.

Now, however, it is possible to take a blood sample from a male foetus at 18–20 weeks into pregnancy and directly determine if it is haemophilic or not. This means that the carrier can make an informed decision as to whether or not to carry on with the pregnancy. With the advent of DNA technology, and the development of a technique called chorionic villus sampling (CVS), it is now possible to test for markers of haemophilia at 9–11 weeks of pregnancy. CVS is a specialised technique which is not yet available in all hospitals.

Sadly, since the HIV crisis began in 1983, it is essential that men with haemophilia who are HIV antibody positive discuss family planning with their partner carefully following medical advice. There is both the danger that their sexual partner will become infected and if their partner is already infected with HIV, it is possible that the child will also be HIV antibody positive and the lives of both mother and child will be at risk.

Other problems in the 'before' category relate to the mother's habits and living conditions. Smoking, drug addiction and dietary matters (including alcohol intake) have a profound effect on any child conceived.

Occupational hazards (such as exposure to radiation and certain chemicals) and environmental influences (such as living close to a large chemical factory with poor pollution control, exposure to radiation or gas from natural or unnatural sources), and water pollution can sow the seeds of *in utero* problems.

EXERCISES

1 The principles of a healthy diet are based upon knowing a person's needs, and then organising meals to meet them.

Prepare a booklet for women wanting to start a family advising them of the importance of a healthy diet and lifestyle. Include sections on what to eat, and its preparation; the hazards of smoking, alcohol and other drug abuse; and any other alterations to lifestyle which you may feel are required.

BTEC Common Skills: 1, 2, 8, 9, 10, 12, 15, 18.
GNVQ Level 2: 2.1, 3.1, 3.2, 3.3, 6.1, 6.3.
GNVO Level 3: 3.1, 3.2, 3.3, 4.1, 4.2, 5.1, 5.2.

There are many publications which can be used to research these matters, from e.g. the Health Education Authority, voluntary organisations, magazine and newspaper articles, and from the library. Remember also the useful leaflets available from the major supermarkets.

You may also want to invite guest speakers in to help you, e.g. health visitor, dietician, midwife or doctor.

2 Read the following extract and fill in the missing words as you think appropriate:

Diagnosis
When haemophilia is known to be present in a family and a woman is identified as a carrier, prenatal _____ from a foetal blood sample is possible. Alternatively a _____ sample from the new-born baby can be used to make a diagnosis. This applies to mild, _____ and severe cases. In some _____ of cases of haemophilia there is no known _____ history and the occurrence of _____ is presumed to be the result of a spontaneous genetic mutation. Cases of severe

haemophilia may become apparent and be diagnosed at an early age as a result of _____ or injury. For example, prolonged bleeding may follow circumcision or routine blood sampling. More often the first _____ of a bleeding tendency is in the form of extensive bruising as the child learns to crawl or _____. Unfortunately this is sometimes suspected to be a result of non-accidental _____, but increasingly in such cases it is automatic that coagulation tests are used to _____ the possibility of the child having a blood disorder. Cutting teeth is another stage at which the _____ may become apparent.

Moderate and mild haemophilia may not be diagnosed until later in _____ or in some cases even adulthood. Because there is some _____ factor available more minor injuries will heal normally and it may not be until a major injury occurs that the deficiency is _____. The process of diagnosis involves many _____ laboratory tests on blood samples and takes several days to _____.

Words to be inserted:

injury	childhood	diagnosis	complex	blood
walk	complete	30%	clotting	surgery
haemophilia	revealed	condition	family	
moderate	investigate	symptom		

(*See* page 228 for answers.)

(This passage has been reproduced from the Haemophilia Society publication *Introduction to Haemophilia*, with their kind permission. Copies can be obtained from their address in the Useful Addresses section at the end of this book on page 224.)

Developmental reasons (during)

These include those matters covered in your advice booklet if the advice is not heeded during pregnancy.

Pregnant women are always advised to stop smoking, drastically reduce alcohol intake and improve their diet when pregnant. Leaving work, at least temporarily, is inevitable, but may have to be sooner rather than later. Moving house in order to avoid inherent environmental hazards may not be so easy.

Some parts of the UK have a higher incidence of some disorders than others, as can be seen from the maps shown in Fig 7.3(a)–(d).

The first three months (or trimester) of a pregnancy are when the foetus is particularly sensitive. Medication of any sort should be strictly controlled (in addition to the smoking and alcohol mentioned already). The Office of Population Censuses and Surveys (OPCS) received 8202 notifications of significant congenital malformations from England and Wales in 1990; and this only concerned babies which survived.

EXERCISES

1 During the 1960s, a drug called Thalidomide was in widespread use to stop pregnant women suffering from the effects of morning sickness. Unfortunately, it had some quite dramatic side effects.

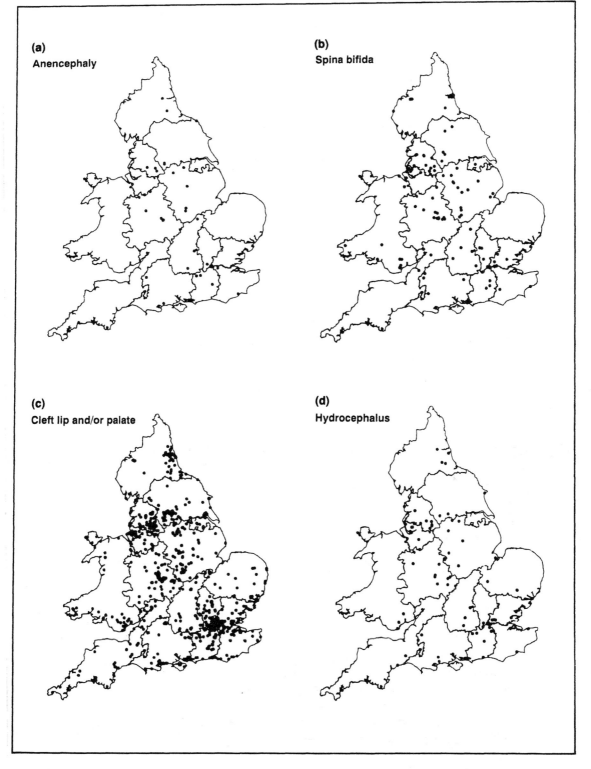

Fig 7.3(a)–(d) Maps showing notifications of selected malformations by place of usual residence, England and Wales, 1990

Reproduced by kind permission of the Office of Population Censuses and Surveys (OPCS)

Find out all you can about the drug Thalidomide, and relate your findings to disability.

2 All girls should be immunised against Rubella (German Measles) during their teens. Find out why this is so, and again, relate your findings to disability.

Trauma, or accidents, can also affect the baby in the womb. Dangerous sports such as hang-gliding, mountain climbing, abseiling and horse riding should be avoided during pregnancy. Even driving should be reduced, especially during the third trimester.

The final hazard in the 'during' category is the birth itself. When difficulties occur, more often than not it is the fragile baby which suffers.

EXERCISE

Find out all you can about:

(a) ectopic pregnancies;
(b) multiple births;
(c) breach births;
(d) caesarian sections;
(e) lack of oxygen to a baby;
(f) forceps delivery;
(g) premature birth.

Investigate particularly the problems which can occur and lead to a permanent disability, but remember to keep the information in context with the overall number of births in any given time period.

The hazards of living (after)

The 'after' category brings in anything which can happen after birth. This can be in excess of 100 years for some people, but around the three score years and ten for the majority of us.

Illness and accident are the main causes of disability occurring in those born with no problems. Poliomyelitis is one of the best known: this is an infectious disease affecting the central nervous system, and the after-effects can include permanent paralysis of one or more limbs. In some parts of the world dietary deficiencies are also a cause; rickets, for example. And what in the western world are minor childhood diseases such as measles can be fatal to Third World children.

Motoring accidents, industrial injuries, and mishaps in the home leave many people disfigured, without limbs, losing a sense such as sight or hearing, immobile or with head injuries. Figures from RoSPA, the Royal Society for the Prevention of Accidents, indicate that there are three million accidents in the home which require hospital or other medical treatment each year; plus 320 000 accidents on the roads, and some 300 000 industrial injuries are reported. About 113 000 of these lead to serious injury and/or disablement each year.

EXERCISES

1. Prepare a magazine article about the hazards of accidents in the home.

   Find out who are the most vulnerable age groups and interpret the statistics, and decide upon your 'target audience'; which magazine will you write the piece for? Why have you chosen the one you have? Include photographs and/or drawings to illustrate the points you are trying to get across.

   This can be done either as an individual exercise, in pairs, or in small groups.

   BTEC Common Skills: 1, 2, 4, 8, 9, 10, 12, 13, 14, 15, 17, 18;
   **   6, 7, 11 (if groupwork); 16 if word-processed.**
   GNVQ Level 2: 2.1, 2.3, 3.1, 3.2, 4.1, 4.3, 6.3.
   GNVQ Level 3: 1.1, 3.1, 3.2, 4.1, 5.1, 5.2, 5.3, 5.4, 8.2.

2. **To be prepared by the teacher/lecturer**
   Write a sufficient number of the following (enough for one for each member of the group) on to a small piece of paper.

AMPUTATION AND PROSTHESES	DWARFISM	MULTIPLE SCLEROSIS
APHASIA	EPILEPSY	MUSCULAR DYSTROPHY
ARTHRITIS	FRIEDREICH'S ATAXIA	MYASTHENIA GRAVIS
ASTHMA	FRAGILITAS OSSIUM	PARALYSIS (PARAPLEGIA,
BLINDNESS AND PARTIAL	HAEMOPHILIA	QUADRIPLEGIA, ETC)
SIGHTEDNESS	HEMIPLEGIA	PARKINSON'S DISEASE
CEREBRAL PALSY	HUNTINGTON'S CHOREA	POLIOMYELITIS
CYSTIC FIBROSIS	HYDROCEPHALUS AND	RICKETS
DIABETES	SPINA BIFIDA	SCOLIOSIS AND KYPHOSIS
DEAFNESS AND PARTIAL	INCONTINENCE	STROKE (CEREBRO-VASCULAR
HEARING	MOTOR NEURONE DISEASE	ACCIDENT)

(If any more are required, consult a Medical Dictionary.)

Place them into a container, and then go round the group for students to choose one each.

Students should then research their subject, and prepare a class presentation of five to ten minutes (one week in advance should be enough time to prepare for this). They should use the following headings to help them structure their talk:
- what it is
- causes
- effects
- care needs.

A 'running order' may be of help, so that people know when their turn is to be. This can be decided randomly, alphabetically, by drawing lots, or by instruction. The exercise may be recorded on video, and the written work can be collected in and marked as a written assignment in addition to the verbal presentation.

A class resource can be established, using the pieces prepared as a reference library.

Spina Bifida and Hydrocephalus Explained

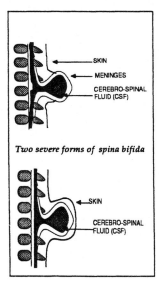

Two severe forms of spina bifida

An example of a shunt in place

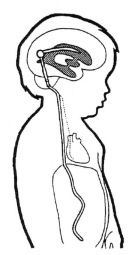

Spina Bifida remains one of the most common congenital defects occurring very early in pregnancy - within the first 25 days. It is a fault in the development of the spine and spinal cord, which is the body's central nervous system.

One or more of the spinal vertebrae fail to close properly, leaving a gap. This frequently results in babies being born with a hole in the back, through which protrudes a sac containing cerebro-spinal fluid (CSF). In the more severe cases, which unfortunately are also the most common, the sac also contains part of the spinal cord. The spinal cord can become irreparably damaged, resulting in paralysis below the level of the fault.

Walking may be impaired or impossible. Very often, there is also the problem of incontinence. Problems with spinal curvature and twisting often develop later in life.

One cause of spina bifida is a deficiency of folic acid (vitamin B9) in the mother's diet at the time of conception. Folic acid supplementation must take place from before conception until the 12th week, when the pregnancy is well-established.

Babies will still be born without the benefit of folic acid supplementation, some women may be unable to absorb folic acid and there is no proof that folic acid-deficiency is the only cause of spina bifida.

More than 85% of people with spina bifida also have, or develop, hydrocephalus. It may also occur independently, with a growing group of people having hydrocephalus without spina bifida.

With hydrocephalus there is an excess of cerebro-spinal fluid in the brain and raised intracranial pressure due to blockage of ventricles (cavities) in the brain. The main outward sign of hydrocephalus is an accelerated growth of the head; if pressure is not speedily relieved, brain damage or even death can result.

Relieving the pressure is usually done by the surgical insertion of a valve (shunt) which drains the excess fluid into the abdominal or heart cavities. Valves, unfortunately, can cause problems. They are liable to infection or blockage which can be life-threatening, and ASBAH is funding research aimed at mitigating these complications.

Hydrocephalus can cause a variety of 'hidden disabilities' - such as difficulties with learning, lack of spatial awareness, inability to concentrate for any length of time, loss of short-term memory. Very often, the outward signs are misinterpreted as laziness or clumsiness and, without appropriate support, the underlying problems can hinder a young person's progress at school, at work and the ability to live independently.

Some low-weight premature babies now surviving in special baby care units are developing hydrocephalus. There is also evidence of hydrocephalus occurring in pre-term multiple births after treatment for infertility.

Improvements in medical care mean that the statutory services must deliver a wider range of services to young people and adults than ever before. When they fail to do so, ASBAH with its unique expertise in the fields of spina bifida and hydrocephalus will vigorously remind them of their responsibilities.

Fig 7.4 Taken from ASBAH Annual Report 1991 and reproduced with their kind permission

The piece on Hydrocephalus and Spina Bifida reproduced opposite from ASBAH (the Association for Spina Bifida and Hydrocephalus) is a good example of how to encapsulate information, and keep it brief and to the point.

Chapter 8

THE EFFECTS OF DISABILITY

Hidden disabilities

People with an obvious disability are noticed very quickly by those around them. The response to them may be of repugnance, sympathy, fear, embarrassment, or ridicule. Nevertheless there will undoubtedly be a response.

But what of people with no visible sign of a disability, which could still be profound and debilitating? You must have heard the jokes about deaf or hard of hearing people, and about people with speech defects, such as stammering. Those disabilities come to light quite quickly when you speak to someone affected in this way. Other disorders are far less easy to discern. Circulatory and respiratory problems may take some time to be noticed in strangers; and how would you know if somebody had diabetes or epilepsy in your normal day-to-day contact with them?

When a disability is obvious, allowances are made for that person, even if it is only moving to the side to allow room for elbow crutches. If an individual standing in front of you on the crowded bus declines to respond to your requests to let you through at your stop, you assume ignorance and end up pushing your way through, perhaps a little more roughly than is necessary; but was that passenger perhaps hearing impaired?

The car with the Orange Badge and parked on the yellow line seemed to hold a perfectly fit driver who went into the paper shop. Perhaps, however, he should carry a sign saying 'heart disease; only able to walk 100 yards at a time'. (To find out more about the Orange Badge Scheme the Department of Transport publishes a leaflet explaining how the Scheme works.)

There is a scheme which does, in fact, do something similar to this, although not quite as ostentatiously. It is the Medic-Alert scheme, which provides subscribers with a bracelet or pendant containing folded card upon which can be written vital information about the disorder and what to do in an emergency. People with diabetes and epilepsy use them, but they are also available for any other disorder, noticeable or not. As a back-up, there is also a 24-hour phone line from which more detailed information can be obtained (*see* page 225 for their address and telephone number).

How Does Medic Alert Work?

Your Medic Alert emblem bears the internationally recognised medical symbol.

Your emblem is engraved with your medical condition, personal identification number and Medic Alert's 24 hour emergency number.

When needed, Doctors or other medical professionals can immediately get vital information by a telephone call, from anywhere in the world.

Your vital medical records help medical personnel provide proper diagnosis and could save your life.

Your Medic Alert membership also provides you with an updated record whenever you inform us of changes to be made to your computer file.

Remember ... Medic Alert is the only internationally recognised medical identification system that has to be endorsed by doctors and has further information stored on computer. It communicates ALL of your special medical needs quickly and accurately when and where it counts.

Medic Alert is a non-profit making registered charity. All of the revenue is used to benefit the members.

Complete this membership form and return it to:

12 Bridge Wharf, 156 Caledonian Road, London N1 9UU
Tel: 071 833 3034

Sponsored in the British Isles and Ireland by Lions Clubs

Registered Charity No: 233705 VAT Registration No: 239 2013 84

Fig 8.1 Part of the leaflet produced by Medic Alert
Reproduced by kind permission of Medic Alert

Stereotyping

You should already have done an exercise on stereotyping (*see* page 44); if you did not, then you should do it now and use this as your starting point. Did you draw a word picture of the typical 'handicapped person' as an exercise when beginning the subject of disability? Look back to page 44 for instructions.

You may have come across the term before, possibly when studying children, and the stereotyping of male and female roles.

Stereotyping is something that you are probably doing every day. Check that out by going round the group and getting group members to contribute a descriptive word or phrase appropriate to the following groups of people – not just the physical characteristics, but what their attitudes and personalities are perceived as being. Somebody should be nominated to record the words and phrases chosen; choose the first words which come to mind. It does not matter if this leads to repetition.

- a police officer
- a nurse
- a social worker
- a German
- an Italian
- a football supporter
- a film star
- a businessman
- a pop star

or any others you might like to use or add.

Finish with a stereotype for a student, and compare this with the reality, i.e. yourself.

A stereotype is the term used when certain characteristics of any given group are applied to all the individuals within that group. Look at the stereotype of a student, which includes yourself, and think of how the general description fits. How does it fit all the other people in the class? Is it not the case that you are all individuals with characteristics and personalities of your own, yet you are all, nevertheless, students? How accurate, then, is the stereotype of the other groups of people in the list?

How your stereotype is perceived by others influences the way in which you are treated by them. Would somebody in jeans, tee-shirt, anorak, and football club scarf and hat be greeted in a shop with the same attitude as a man in a pinstripe suit and a bowler hat? Yet some robberies are carried out by men in pinstripe suits and bowler hats, and some good samaritans are football supporters, too.

Transfer this to people with disabilities. Does your stereotype have this person in a wheelchair, perhaps? It does more often than not in the collective mind. Can you remember what the logo denoting access for disabled people is like? There are some six million people with disabilities in the United Kingdom, of which less than five per cent are wheelchair users.

Stereotyping is not all bad; it is a psychological phenomenon which helps us to understand things more easily. As such, it is a starting point, and insofar as it is recognised for what it is, can serve a useful purpose. Once a person has been labelled as 'handicapped', however, they first have to live down the stereotype and establish individuality. Just as you have to as a 'student'; your needs are not exactly the same as all your fellow students, are they?

Labelling

Labelling is linked to stereotyping, in that one leads to the other. When you assign someone to a category, or classify them by using a label, you then ascribe to them the perceived qualities, faults, or other characteristics of all members of that group. Labels can be as general as boy, girl, soldier, or 'foreign', or more personal such as 'troublemaker', 'dunce' or 'cripple'.

Not only is there a tendency for other people to treat the labelled individual in a way that is in keeping with that label, but also the possibility that the individual could take on the characteristics assigned to that group by society. The dangers of labelling within a family are that the disabled individual will take on the 'sick role', and increase their dependence when this is not really necessary. The role may also suit other members of the family, who can then increase their esteem in their own and others' eyes by being the provider, and described as 'a saint', 'a martyr', etc. as may be the case with Mrs Church (*see* page 183).

'Cripple' has become a derogatory term for the disabled person in general (it used to mean somebody who was lame, i.e. had difficulty with walking). If somebody is labelled as disabled, they may decide that they cannot cope without the help of others, and give up trying to manage. They live up to the label they have been given, and let others cater for their every need. This can have a devastating effect on families, and on the social services in general.

Read the case study on Betty Church on pages 183–4, and complete the exercises associated with it.

The following extract is taken from the Haemophilia Society magazine and illustrates how people with haemophilia are labelled.

What's in a name

In today's 'let's give it a label' society a great deal rests within a name and it's for that very reason that the Society is at the forefront of ensuring people with haemophilia are able to maintain their individual identity.

The tag 'haemophiliac' has been perpetuated both among the press, general public and even among health professionals but it is not a term which the Society feels adequately reflects the true situation.

'Quite simply people with haemophilia are just that, people with a certain condition,' explains David Watters, General Secretary. 'When the other term is used it merely describes a condition and puts the person into an abstract.

'We are about caring and compassion not about putting people in pigeon holes, so let's be clear it's people with haemophilia clear and simple.'

(Reproduced with kind permission of the Haemophilia Society)

Being given a label may have an opposite effect, of course. There are some very active sports people with a disability. The fact that somebody is given the label of disabled, and the connotations that go with it, can bring about a reaction to prove 'the experts' wrong. The one-legged man then goes on to play football or undertake marathon walking, or the blind person to climb mountains. (*See* Chapter 15 Sport and Leisure.)

Stigma

Linked with labelling and stereotyping is the concept of 'stigma'; this used to relate to the mark branded on people such as criminals and slaves. It marks them out as being different, but being different in a negative way.

If somebody is 'stigmatised', they are seen as different by those around them; this can be a social stigma such as 'she's been in prison', 'he smells', or 'he's a drug addict', but can just as easily be 'they are handicapped/deaf/blind/disabled'. There are also examples of the help-giving agencies also conferring stigma on to their users, for example 'she's been in a mental hospital'. The difficulty can then be in getting people to accept help, in this case in a psychiatric unit, the present discomfort being seen as preferable to the stigma of being or having been 'a mental patient'.

Being seen as different can lead to discrimination, and in turn to prejudice.

EXERCISES

1 (a) Can you think of examples of people who are currently stigmatised?
  (b) Have you personally, or anyone in your student group ever suffered from the effects of stigma? If so, what were the effects of this?
  (c) How do you think being seen as different from other people might affect behaviour?
  (d) What does stigma have to do with disability?
  (e) Can you explain the term 'prejudice'?
  (f) Discrimination is another term mentioned above: find out about positive and negative discrimination, and say how you think both of these might affect people with a disability who are looking for a job.
  (g) Consider the additional problems of disabled people from ethnic minorities; how could they be eased?

2 **An exercise in empathy**
  You go to a disco on Saturday night, have a great time, but then find you can't get home. It is late, so you accept the offer of a lift from some friends. The car is a Mini, and you have to squeeze in.

  There is a lot of joking and laughing going on, as you have all had a bit to drink. The next thing you know is when you wake up in hospital. The nurse tells you it is ten days since your accident, and when you try to talk, you find it very difficult, as your mouth refuses to do what you tell it. You can hear with no trouble, though, and you learn that you have received a severe head injury. Your left side is paralysed as well as your speech being difficult.

  (a) What are your thoughts as you lie in bed on the day you wake up and hear what has happened to you for the first time?

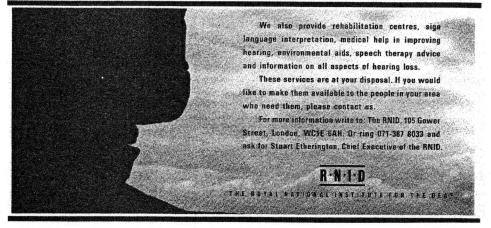

Fig 8.2 The advertisement produced by The Royal National Institute for Deaf People
Reproduced with their kind permission

(b) What do you think your parents have been feeling and saying, both to each other and to you?

(c) What effect is your accident going to have on their lives?

(d) Which other people will have been affected by your accident?

(e) What changes will you need to make in your life to accommodate the new circumstances?

(f) What are the stages of 'loss' that you are likely to go through?

(g) What medical and paramedical help will be available to you?

(h) What care will be available when you return home, and who will provide it?

(i) What benefits will you be able to claim if the disability turns out to be permanent?

(j) Devise posters and leaflets to deter teenagers in particular from drinking and driving.

(k) Identify the reasons why you have chosen the designs/approaches that you have.

(l) What are the current statistics for drinking and driving accidents? (RoSPA will be able to provide national figures; and the local Town Hall, County Hall or Police Headquarters should have the local figures. Local newspapers may be another useful source.)

How do they relate to different age groups? Illustrate your findings with graphs or pie charts.

(m) Would you be able to claim any damages for your injuries? If so, from whom?

GNVQ Level 2: 2.1, 2.3, 3.1, 5.1, 5.2, 5.3, 6.3.
    Level 3: 2.1, 2.2, 3.2, 5.2, 5.3, 6.1, 6.2, 6.3, 7.3.
BTEC Common Skills: 1, 2, 8, 10, 12, 15, 17, 18.

3 Experiential poems

Both of these poems were written by Brian Reck, who retired from legal practice due to the effects of multiple sclerosis. They are reproduced here with his kind permission.

ADVANTAGES AND DISADVANTAGES

So having this complaint acts like
A shield
Which means to some attacks I
Need not yield
Though I wouldn't choose to have
This burden sent
It means from some chores I
Am exempt
(I can't,) and need not dance or
Drive or run
Not working probably means a stroke
Won't come!
So if I draw a mental balance
Sheet
I've enough in hand for potential
Debts to meet.

BATTLING AGAINST THE ODDS

I write some ill-penned verses
And she praises them and me
But I've exercised nothing
Except my brain and hand
And my moaning tongue.

She organises house alterations
Tradesmen of every description
Materials colours shapes and designs
Bargains for reductions and discounts.
She pays and disputes accounts
Writes letters and makes calls
In between shopping and car driving,
Arranging for the doctor
And physio and nurses to call.

Her holidays and free times are few
And she worries about care provision
For me whilst she's away.
In return she asks for nothing
Except that I be cheerful.

(a) What is Brian saying to the reader in the first poem?
(b) Why is the complaint like a shield?
(c) What are the possible advantages of a disability?
(d) Who is being written about in the second poem?
(e) What does she do for Brian?
(f) What does she expect in return?
(g) Why should she need to organise house alterations?
(h) Could you write a verse of your own to describe the effects of a disability?

4 Look at the publicity material in Fig 8.4 on page 74 issued by the Friedreich's Ataxia Group, and read the comments from each member of the family.

(a) What message are they trying to get across?
(b) Does it give a positive or a negative image of disability?
(c) From the comments of each family member, can you appreciate what thoughts must have gone through their heads when the news was first given to them? Write down what you think these thoughts may have been.
(d) In small groups, design publicity material to get the same message across in a different way. Use any format you like: posters, leaflets, video, newspaper/ magazine article, audiotape piece for local radio, or any other method you consider appropriate.

BTEC Common Skills 1, 2, 4, 5, 6, 7, 8, 9, 10, 11, 16, 17, 18.

HER FATHER.

Your doctor tells you your child is going to become a cripple. You can forget most of the things you'd planned to do together.

Instead you'll have to watch her grow more and more helpless. Then you notice your wife begin to change. She's the one who has to live with it, every day.

And when you come home, you have to put your own feelings aside and give her all your support. Because you know that if you don't, your marriage may not take the strain.

THE SUFFERER.

When Sarah was eight, she was told she had a strange disease which was never going to go away.

What she wasn't told was this: it's a progressively crippling disease of the nervous system. And it usually reveals itself in apparently healthy children between the ages of eight and fifteen.

The first characteristics are unsteadiness and the inability to co-ordinate movements.

Then come the speech difficulties. The tremors of the hands, head and eyes.

The deformity of the feet.

And finally curvature of the spine sets in.

The brain stays perfectly healthy.

But it's trapped in a crippled body.

Sarah has been in a wheel-chair since she was eleven. But cruellest of all, the disease is genetic. So if one child develops it, there's a chance it will affect the younger one too.

Friedreich's ataxia.

As yet, there's no known cure.

HER MOTHER.

First there's the shock of finding out your daughter has a terrible disease.

Knowing that her body will slowly waste away in front of your eyes.

And that eventually she'll be incapable of washing, dressing or going to the toilet without you.

Then comes the second blow. The younger one may get it too.

You watch her like a hawk. If she stumbles, you panic.

Was it an accident? Or was it the first sign?

Night after night you lie awake worrying. Waiting for the worst to happen. Knowing that it could tomorrow.

HER SISTER.

One day you're told there's something very very wrong with your sister. You don't understand.

All you know is that she'll never be able to join in your games any more.

And suddenly you're frightened. Because you find out it might happen to you, too.

Fig 8.3 The publicity material produced by the Friedreich's Ataxia Group

Reproduced with their kind permission

The following is an extract from an article written by Karin Weatherup for the Muscular Dystrophy Group magazine of Summer 1991, and is reproduced here with the Group's kind permission:

THE ROSAM FAMILY

One person who does not underestimate the impact of having a brother or sister with a neuromuscular condition is Linda Rosam whose son, Simon, aged seven, has Duchenne dystrophy. Linda has also been on the other side of the fence: her elder son, Darren, aged ten, does not experience the same bewilderment she felt in the face of her brother's progressive disability.

'I was seven when Mum told us that Stephen had Duchenne. We were just told the name of the condition, nothing about the future. Mum wouldn't talk about it. I think she blamed herself. My Dad never talked about it, he doesn't now. It was a very confusing situation. I couldn't understand why Stephen's legs wouldn't work, why he couldn't come to my school, why he kept going into hospital, why he died.'

'I grew up with a guilt complex about my brother, because he was ill and I wasn't. I thought it was maybe something I had done. A child's way of thinking. And it upsets me how people used to stare at Stephen when we went out. If we were sitting in the recreation ground, the other kids would run off. They wouldn't want to know. That would make me angry. Stephen didn't bite! It's different now, though. Simon goes to the same school as Darren and they have the same friends. There's a boy with cerebral palsy and a girl with congenital dystrophy there too, so the other kids just accept it. The whole situation is certainly very different from twenty years ago. Now you've got the support.'

'Darren went through a phase at school when he got upset because other children were calling his brother names and he got into quite a few fights because children laughed at the way Simon gets up, and he went and belted them one.'

'Then Darren kept on getting all worked up with his brother and didn't want to touch him, and he found it hard to talk to me. I didn't want him to hide away in himself like I did, so I called the MD Group's Family Care Officer and explained how Darren was having problems with the situation. She came to talk to him up in his bedroom to find out what was wrong. It turned out that he was worried that he would get what Simon's got. And he'd heard someone say that his brother was going to go into a wheelchair permanently, and Darren thought that meant Simon was going to die. When I asked him why he hadn't wanted to tell me what was wrong, he said "Because I didn't want to upset you". But ever since, he's talked to me about how he feels.'

Linda and her husband, Alan, make a point of explaining everything to both Simon and Darren together, whether it's about callipers, the advent of an electric wheelchair or how best to plan the adaptations to their home. 'You've got to tell the children everything – they must learn it from you. We've tried to explain the genetics to Darren in a way that he can understand, so that he can see why he isn't going to get Duchenne.' (Linda is a carrier, although she and her two sisters were assured that they couldn't pass it on.)

'Darren and Simon play together, they have the same friends. They quarrel sometimes, but what brothers don't! Darren wants to help Simon now, and to do things with him – without Mum. Sometimes when I ask him to get something from upstairs, he does ask why Simon can't do it and I explain that Simon might hurt himself and that he does things downstairs. I'm probably a bit over-protective with Darren. I tend not to want him to do things away from us, but he has to. He's got to have his independence, just like Simon has to have his. You've just got to set aside time for each child, individually.'

A shared experience can be a problem halved, but what of now being in the new position of a parent with responsibility for balancing the needs of both her sons?

'The hardest thing is to put yourself in a neutral position between two children. I know how one feels and I know what the other one is going through, and I'm sort of stuck in the middle. The main thing is communication, and that includes between the parents because if they don't talk to each other about their feelings, the children will sense it and won't ask questions. Both the children must feel confident that they can talk to you – they need to ask questions. You need to help them to do that.'

QUESTIONS

(a) Which of Linda's relatives are affected by muscular dystrophy?

(b) How old was she when her Mum told her about Stephen?

(c) What questions did she ask herself?

(d) Why did she have a guilt complex?

(e) How did the other kids make Linda angry?

(f) Why didn't Darren want to touch his brother?

(g) How did the family tackle this problem?

(h) How would you explain the genetics to Darren?

(i) Why do you think Linda is over-protective toward Simon?

(j) Why is communication within the family important?

The article shown opposite, which was written by Trevor Whitehead and published in *FAX* magazine, underlines in a lighthearted way how those with disabilities can be patronised.

HOW OTHERS SEE US
A Manual for the Successful (?) Disabled Person
(or How to Conform)
by Trevor Whitehead

The following points were written with my tongue firmly wedged in my cheek — it is not my intention to upset or offend anybody . . .

(1) Welcome every opportunity to fill your time, however boring the activity; inactivity is unacceptable. Everyone knows that if one is disabled it is certain that one's brain will not function. So you can't claim to be thinking, or planning anything you have always wanted to do.

(2) Always smile, it is absolutely forbidden to be angry or cry.

(3) Don't expect to be asked your views on anything — your opinions make other people uncomfortable.

(4) Be eternally happy to wear a label:—
Handicapped!! spastic!! or perhaps *cripple!!*
You may prefer *people with special needs!! the mentally handicapped!!* or what about *disabled . . . . . . !!*
There are plenty to choose from. They are all excellent for demoralizing and diminishing us.

(5) Really look forward to ending your days in an institution — so much tidier for everyone.

(6) Don't expect any privacy, after all our bowels and bladders are public property. Our dignity is of no importance.

(7) Be good girls and boys. Go to bed early, don't expect helpers to turn out late at night just because *"you"* enjoyed an evening out.

(8) Don't expect to live in a *"normal"* house in a *"normal"* street. The world says we are different, so we must be.

(9) Always be brave; it is expected.

THANK YOU KIND SIRS FOR DEIGNING TO NOTICE THIS UNWORTHY AND HUMBLE PERSON!

(10) *never* make spontaneous decisions to do anything. You must leave time to plan. Can you use the transport? Can you get into the building? Can you get into the loo? Is the information correct? If you are deaf, will there be a loop system? or will someone sign for you? If you cannot see very well, will there be tactile maps and signs? If you are in a wheelchair, is there a lift (in working order of course)? On second thoughts, why do you want to go anyway. Disabled people are best at home with their computers!!!!

(11) Enjoy the stares, and *"never"* speak for yourself.

(12) Give in to *"everything"* willingly, never make a fuss. *"They"* know best (or do *"they?"*)

(13) Remember to be grateful for everything and to grovel whenever possible.

(14) Rattle your collecting box in the street whenever you can, it makes people happy to give you money, and your begging helps society to ease its conscience by giving to the poor and pathetic, whom it disregards in all other ways.

(15) Positively enjoy waiting about for transport, like a parcel in Lost Property. After all, the two hour round trip delivering everyone else home first will give you a change of scene!!!

(16) Never expect to be accepted as people. After all, we are all aliens in this world — not *"normal"* (whatever that is)

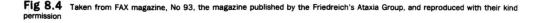

Fig 8.4 Taken from FAX magazine, No 93, the magazine published by the Friedreich's Ataxia Group, and reproduced with their kind permission

Part Three

THE CARING ENVIRONMENT

Chapter 9

COMMUNICATIONS

The most obvious form of communication is speech; when this is absent, the individual is automatically handicapped until an alternative method of communication can be found.

NB: It is important not to assume that because an individual is unable to communicate, they are unable to understand. Even when a person is apparently unconscious, the last facility to fade is hearing. Never talk *about* people in their presence, talk *to* them, or include them in the conversation by looks and gestures.

If you are with someone who is deaf, then speech may be enhanced with a hearing aid, or understanding increased by lipreading. Where this is impracticable, or there are

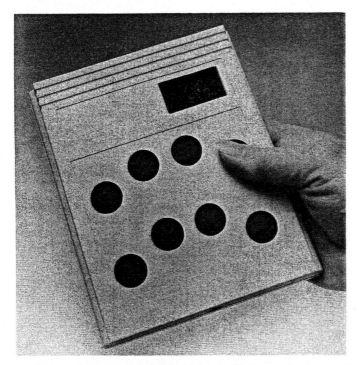

Fig 9.1 A phraser: a portable high quality, speech communicator system, designed for use by the non-vocal. The phraser contains eight separate phrases each up to six seconds in length. A pull cord activates an alarm to attract attention. The phraser is particularly useful when used over the telephone to indicate messages to one's helper

Reproduced by kind permission of Possum Controls Limited

other disorders which prevent you understanding them rather than them not understanding you, then written communication may be the answer. Where this is the case, you should ensure that paper and pencil is always within reach. You may also be with people where writing is a problem either mechanically or because it is in a foreign language. There are commercially available pointer-boards available, or you could make one from a piece of cardboard. If you mark out the alphabet on a card and a pointer is used to spell out words, this is one way, but may be rather time-consuming.

There are electronic variations of this on the market, as are computers with voice synthesisers; the instructions still have to be keyed in, however.

Another form of writing is braille; most libraries have some books in braille.

A modification of the alphabet card is to have one with basic requirements such as 'Hungry', 'Thirsty', 'Toilet', and so on printed on it, so that messages can be relayed more quickly. Where language is a problem, however, this may not be the answer. Pictorial representations may be much more relevant.

EXERCISE

Make a pointer board for a person with communication difficulties who does not speak English. Decide what the basic messages will be that need to be included, and design a pictorial representation of that message. Try it out on other people to see if it is readily understandable, and modify as necessary.

BTEC Common Skills: 1, 2, 4, 6, 8, 9, 11, 12, 13, 14, 17, 18
GNVQ Level 2: 1.2, 1.3, 2.1
GNVQ Level 3: 1.1, 2.1, 2.2, 3.2, 4.1, 7.2

Telephones

Under the provisions of the Chronically Sick and Disabled Persons Act 1970, Social Services Departments have the power to provide telephones to disabled people. Whether they are available or not depends partly on whether the authority has any money in its budget to pay for them, and secondly on the strict criteria laid down for eligibility.

In order to qualify for such assistance, an individual must meet all the following criteria. They must:

- be suffering from a severe medical condition.
- live alone, or be regularly left alone during the day or night; or live with a person who cannot deal with an emergency or maintain outside contacts.
- need to call urgent medical attention on a regular basis.
- be unable to leave the house in normal weather.
- be physically capable of using a telephone (modified, if necessary).
- have neighbours, friends or relatives who would be willing and able to help if contacted by telephone.
- be isolated by having no daily contact with family, friends, neighbours or domiciliary services.

81

This seems to be quite an obstacle course to overcome, and the last two requirements seem to cancel each other out.

Nevertheless, there are a large number of people with phones supplied to them by SSDs. An even greater number rent or buy them from private suppliers, the major one being British Telecom.

BT's facilities for people with disabilities

BT have a number of facilities specifically targeted to people with disabilities (*see* Fig 9.2 and Fig 9.3 later). The following text has been taken from *The BT Guide for people who are disabled or elderly 1992*, with the kind permission of BT.

Hearing the phone ring (partial hearing loss)

Adjustable ringing
Many telephones have a volume control which lets you adjust the loudness of the ringing tone. On some phones you can also vary the pitch to see if it can be heard more easily. A louder ring may be obtained if your telephone is placed on a hard surface.

Extension sockets
Adding extra sockets to other rooms in the house enables you to move the phone round with you. Or you might consider a cordless phone.

Extension bells
Two types are available. The bell 50E comes with a 3 metre cord and a plug and is suitable for indoor use. The 80D is a loud 6″ diameter bell which can be sited permanently indoors or outdoors. Both types can be supplied free of charge for residential customers with impaired hearing.

Extension tonecaller
This device produces four different warbling sounds. It also has a volume control and comes with a 3 metre cord and plug. It can be supplied free of charge for residential customers with impaired hearing.

Doubler
This double socket plug enables you to use two devices from one socket. For example a telephone and an extension bell or tone caller. It can be supplied for this purpose free of charge to residential customers with impaired hearing.

Extension cord
With an extension cord your telephone does not have to be situated close to the phone socket. There is no need to rush to the phone as the extra length means you can place the telephone next to where you sit (take care though of any trailing wire). There are 2 types of cord in the BT range. A 3 metre (10ft) and a 5 metre (16ft).

More information
Call us free on
0800 800 150
0800 243 123 (textphone)

New booths
The old red kiosks are also being replaced by new booths in which the payphone is set at a lower, more convenient height. The lighting inside these booths is also much brighter to assist people with poor eyesight and to deter vandals.

This new range of booths features an 'open' design to provide barrier free access to disabled and wheelchair users. For sites where excessive noise or protection from the weather is needed, there is a total enclosed model which has a door which is easier to open than the door of the red kiosk. It also has a red or green panel on the door to identify the type of service provided (red for cashphone, green for Phonecard Phone) and to make it immediately recognisable to people with poor eyesight.

Blind and disabled customers
We also provide a free Directory Enquiry Service if you are unable to hold, handle or read a printed Phone Book because of a disability or medical condition.

Application form
The application form is to be completed by or on behalf of the customer. There is a section in which the customer indicates why they are eligible for the service, and this does require a counter-signature.

A copy of a local authority certificate of blindness or partial sight is also acceptable for this purpose. Once the application has been accepted the customer will receive a personal membership card with details on how to use the free service.

Registration for free service

So as to offer a personal service we have set up a dedicated registration centre, where our trained operators will gather details and partly fill in the required form prior to posting it out for completion. Forms are returned via FREEPOST. If you feel you may be eligible for this service, or if you know someone who is, call us free on 195 at any time.

Textphone users (New)

If you're a textphone user and want help in finding a UK or international number, you can also register for free Directory Enquiries.

The number to call at any time is 0800 838 363 (textphone using CCITT standard).

Priority fault repair service

Chronically sick and disabled people who are immobile and living alone and whose telephones are a lifeline, may be eligible for our free priority fault repair service. This is available on BT lines and BT rented equipment.

For further information and an application form, call us free on 150.

Disabled Persons Act

The Chronically Sick and Disabled Persons Act 1970 gives local authorities a duty to assess the needs of disabled people for help with the costs of a telephone and any special equipment necessary. You may be able to get help from the local authority with installation costs and rental but call charges are *not* covered. You should apply first to the Social Services Department (Social Work Department in Scotland) of your local council, metropolitan district or London borough. There are a number of charities and voluntary associations which may also be able to provide assistance. These include:

'Telephones for the Blind Fund'
Mynthurst, LEIGH, REIGATE
Surrey RH2 8RJ
Tel: (0293) 862546

The Renate Campbell Trust
Frederick Morfill House
Bounds Green Road
Wood Green, LONDON N22 4DG
(provides textphones for deaf people)

More Information

A Fact Sheet 'Help with telephones' is available on receipt of a stamped addressed envelope from:

Age Concern
Astral House
1268 London Road
LONDON SW16 4EJ
Tel: 081-679 8000

Equipment for employment

Equipment required for a disabled person may be available free of charge under the 'Special Aids to Employment' scheme. For information, contact the Disablement Advisory Service through your local Employment Service.

Text Users Rebate Scheme

Because calls using textphones or keyboard speech synthesisers (*see* below) take much longer, telephone bills are higher for people who use them. The scheme, run by the RNID and funded by BT, provides a rebate, currently 60% of the call charge portion of the phone bill up to a maximum of £160 per year.

For further details of who can claim and an application form please contact:

Text Users Rebate Scheme
Pauline Ashley House
Ravenside Retail Park
Speke Road, LIVERPOOL
L24 8QB
Tel: 051-494 1000
Textphone: 051-494 1085

Braille and large print telephone bills (New)

BT, with the help of the Royal National Institute for the Blind, can send copies of bills in braille or large print to visually handicapped customers a few days after the normal bill goes out. There is no charge for this service.

For further information and an application form, call us free on 0800 400 454.

Talking telephone bills

For people who are blind and cannot read braille, we can phone and read out details of the bill before we post it.

To apply for this service please call us free on 150.

Alarm Systems

How alarms work

You wear a portable trigger which you press in an emergency. It sends a radio signal to the alarm unit which then automatically contacts a special emergency centre or a friend or relative. Most emergency centres are manned 24 hours a day.

Staff at the centre will try to speak to you through the alarm's speech link or by telephone. If they get no reply they will contact someone to visit you. This could be a friend or relative, someone

from the centre or the centre may have called a doctor or ambulance for you.

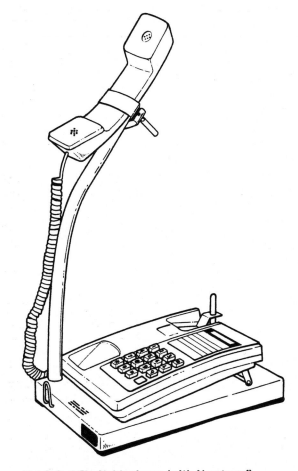

Fig 9.2 BT's Holdaphone (with Vanguard)
Reproduced by kind permission of BT

Disability	Problem	Solution
Partial hearing loss	Hearing the phone ring Hearing speech on the phone	Extension bell/tone caller Extension socket Extension cord Amplifier for incoming speech Extra earpiece Inductive coupler (hearing aid user)
Profoundly or severely deaf	Detecting an incoming call Receiving incoming speech Sending text messages to people with similar equipment Communicating with people who do not have special equipment	Flashing lights Extra earpiece for hearing helper Textphone Fax machine Relay services
Severely deaf *and* blind	Sending/receiving text messages	HASICOM
Partial voice loss	Outgoing speech too quiet to be heard	Outgoing speech amplifier
Total voice loss	No speech	Speech synthesiser Textphone Answering machine
Partial sight loss	Seeing numbers Unable to read phone bill	Enlarged numeral dial ring Big-button phone Large print bills
Total blindness	Dialling numbers Keeping hands free to take notes Operating switchboard Unable to read phone bill	Press button phone with memory Headset Loudspeaker Answering/recording machine Visually handicapped operators console attachment Talking telephone bill service or bills in braille
Mobility impaired	Getting to the phone	Extension socket Extension cord Cordless phone Mobile phone
Dexterity impaired	Plugging in and unplugging phone Dialling numbers Lifting, holding and replacing handset Inserting coins in payphone	Easy grip plug Press button phone with memory Loudspeaker Headset Holdaphone stand Phonecard/BT Chargecard
Severely limited movement	Operating household equipment	Environmental control system
Blindness, partial sight or physical disability	Unable to use the printed Phone Book	Free directory enquiry service
Living alone and at risk	Calling for help in an emergency and unable to get to a phone Help with the cost of a telephone Phone bill unpaid due to circum- stances beyond immediate control Need immediate response for repairs	Alarm system with bodyworn trigger Local authority social services department Protected Service Scheme Priority fault repair service

Fig 9.3 The facilities provided by BT for disabled customers
Reproduced by kind permission of BT

As mentioned briefly above, there is a scheme, run by The Royal National Institute for Deaf People, designed to help deaf and speech-impaired people. This is described more fully in the extract below.

RNID Text Users Help Scheme

The Text Users Help Scheme is designed to help deaf/speech impaired people who can only use the telephone network through text terminals. As it takes longer to use a text terminal than an ordinary telephone, the telephone bills are consequently higher. Text users will receive financial help in the form of a 60% rebate of the call charge portion of their bills to a maximum of £150 per year.

To qualify for help through the Scheme you must: be able to provide proof of registration with your Local Authority as being deaf/speech impaired (or a letter from your doctor); be unable to use an ordinary telephone without someone helping you; have an approved form of text terminal for sending and receiving text over the telephone line; and be over nine years old.

The Text Users Help Scheme is run by The Royal National Institute for Deaf People from its offices in Salford, near Manchester and is being funded by British Telecom and the Department of Social Security. There are currently 2,500 applicants registered with the Scheme.

The Scheme is providing much needed assistance for those with severe communication disabilities and the RNID believes that success in the Scheme's first year will encourage more people to obtain and use text terminals.

(Reproduced from *FAX* magazine No 93 with their kind permission)

Chapter 10

HOUSING FOR PHYSICALLY DISABLED PEOPLE

Physically disabled people should enjoy the same standard of comfort, choice and independence in housing as able bodied people. Existing houses are rarely built to meet the special requirements of a disabled person.

Help in adapting houses is available, as outlined in the piece on Housing Renovation Grants on page 88, which first appeared in *FAX* magazine, No 93 (from the Friedreich's Ataxia Group).

QUESTIONS

(a) Under which Act of Parliament can a Disabled Facilities Grant be made?

(b) What was the intention of this Act?

(c) What has been the result, in practice?

(d) When did the changes come into effect?

(e) What other grant may be claimed if repairs are also necesary?

(f) What do you understand by a 'means test'?

(g) Explain the difference between 'mandatory' and 'discretionary'.

(h) What must be the purpose of any adaptation work?

(i) If the household income is above Housing Benefit level, what percentage of grant will be payable?

(j) What assessments have to be undertaken before any grants are payable?

HOUSE RENOVATION GRANTS

The Local Government and Housing Act of 1989 made many far reaching and dramatic changes to the Improvement Grants given by local authorities. There are three major changes that are best summarised as follows:-

1) A redefinition of the standards of property unfitness.

2) A means test of applicants resources to ensure that grants are not paid to those applicants deemed able to afford the cost of the works.

3) No maximum or minimum amount payable. The objective of the act was to unify the types of grant into one format and to simplify the administration procedure. Without a doubt this objective has been missed, with the whole process being more complex and bureaucratic and resulting in increased staffing levels in local authorities to implement the scheme.

There are four principal forms of grant, each with a distinctly separate application form:-

1. Renovation Grants;
2. Disabled Facilities Grant;
3. Common Parts Grant, and
4. A House in Multiple Occupation (HMO)

Its all rather complex and confusing to deal with just one form of grant, let alone four—particularly with the absence of 'case law' (these changes only came into effect from 1 July 1990). However, here is the gist of the...

Disabled Facilities Grant

This is a grant for adapting a house or flat to make it a more suitable home for a disabled person. The grant is mandatory, (provided certain conditions are met), where the adaptation is to provide access to and around the property. A discretionary element may be available to help adapt a property for the accommodation, welfare or employment of a disabled person.

The applicant should be the joint or sole owner of a property who is the freeholder or leaseholder with more than 5 years to run on the lease, or the sole or joint tenant of a private landlord.

The grant is only for the adaptation works where the local authority is satisfied that such grants are both necessary and appropriate for the needs of the disabled occupant, and that it is reasonable and practicable to carry them out in/on the property.

The adaptation work must be to enable the disabled occupant to have easier access—

—to and from the house or flat;
—to the principal family rooms;
—to a room that is for sleeping;
—to a lavatory, bath or shower and wash hand basin;
—to prepare and cook food;
—to control a source of heat, light or power, and/or
—around the property to care for a dependent relative or to provide or improve a heating system to meet the disabled person's needs.

(if repairs need to be carried out before a property can be successfully adapted, a mandatory or discretionary Renovation Grant may be available) and both Grants would then be taken into account when calculating the amount of contribution to be made by the applicant, (i.e. The Means Test).

If the household has an income sufficiently far enough above Housing Benefit value to be able to afford a loan for all the work, the grant is nil.

This system requires not only a detailed survey of the property to assess the cost and extent of the works (and whether any of the work is of a discretionary or mandatory nature), but also a thorough Housing Benefit assessment

This is only intended as a rough guide, and anyone considering applying for a Disabled Facilities Grant is advised to contact their local Council.

Fig 10.1 Taken from *FAX* magazine, No 93, and reproduced by kind permission of the Friedreich's Ataxia Group

The following material is taken from a booklet entitled *Housing for the Physically Disabled: A guide to adaption or rehousing.*

HOUSING FOR THE PHYSICALLY DISABLED

INTRODUCTION

Physically disabled people should enjoy the same standard of comfort, choice and independence in housing as able bodied people. Existing houses and flats are rarely built to meet the special requirements of a disabled person. This booklet which has been produced by Northern Rock Building Society, The World Health Organisation and Liverpool Polytechnic will help the disabled person to assess the suitability of their existing home or move to a new especially designed house or flat.

HOW TO USE THIS GUIDE

This guide helps to identify common barriers to disabled persons and suggests possible adaptions to remove or alleviate these barriers. Whilst using this guide, please bear in mind that

1 Adaptions usually benefit but sometimes cause problems to other occupants and in that excessive adaption may result in an unsaleable property compromises may be required.
2 Family and friends may not always be able to assist the disabled person.
3 Needs may change over time.
4 Your existing dwelling and situation may be totally unsuitable and a specially built new dwelling or other forms of accommodation may be the only realistic alternative.

INTERIOR OF THE HOUSE

ENTRANCE

- Steps or stairs should be avoided at the main entrance, and there should be a paved level area outside the front door.
- A level entrance area on both sides of the door makes accessibility easier.

- A ramp may be needed to gain entry depending on the disability and on the characteristics of the site and dwelling.
- A threshold which is too high to accommodate a wheelchair can be adapted by using bevelled strips.
- An automatic door opening device is useful.
- The doorway can be widened enough to accommodate a wheelchair user.
- The door handle should be easily reached by a wheelchair user. The handle and locks should be easily operated by one hand, whilst affording proper security.
- To allow the door to swing inwards towards a wheelchair user, the entrance hall should have sufficient space.
- Floor surfaces both sides of the door should be made of slip resistant material.

- The door bell or call button should be within range for a wheelchair user. A light assisted call/doorbell may be installed for deaf occupants.
- The door closer should allow sufficient time to accommodate fragile persons and the door should not need much effort to open and close.

89

KITCHEN

- Easy access by wheelchair from the kitchen to the dining room is essential, and a vision panel in the door will prevent accidents.
- Electricity switches could be relocated to make them more accessible to persons in a wheelchair.
- A cooker with front or side controls is desirable. Controls at the back of a cooker should be avoided because of safety.
- Counter heights should accommodate someone in a wheelchair.
- If knee space is provided under a sink, it should be at standard counter height. Any hot water pipes should be insulated to prevent legs being burnt.
- Taps should be the lever-type.
- Cupboards and storage space should be easily accessible. This can be achieved by making a pull-out cutting board and storage units under the counter top.
- A recessed toe space at the bottom of all floor cabinets allows the wheelchair user to work more comfortably at counters.

- Sufficient turning space is needed in front of and between counters particularly for a person in a wheelchair. Full use of the kitchen for all members of the family is important.

BATHROOM/TOILET

- The bathroom/toilet may be the most important room for any disabled people, and it may present the most serious problems.
- The bathroom deeor could be altered to open outward or replaced by a sliding door, thus increasing the space available.
- Sufficient clear floor space should be provided to allow easy access to each fixture and to accommodate an attendant.
- It is important that light switches, bath taps, razor plug sockets, sliding fixtures etc. should be easily reachable from a wheelchair.
- Grab bars should be provided to allow easy and secure transfer.
- Can a ground floor room be adapted for toilet/bathroom use?
- Sufficient space on one side of the toilet will enable a sideways transfer from a wheelchair.
- A bath tub should be equipped with grab bars.
- Lever-type taps in the bath tub and shower are easier and safer to use. Thermostatically controlled single action taps will encourage independent use.

- Wall cupboard shelving should be accessible from a wheelchair. Similarly racks, hanging rods, cup hooks, etc. should be reachable from a wheelchair.
- It is important that the floor covering should be slip resistant and that carpeting allows the free movement of wheelchairs.

▶

- Wheel-in showers are popular.
- An alarm should be provided.

LIVING, DINING AND BEDROOMS

- In some cases the living and dining areas may be too small for use by a disabled person. It is important that all the rooms are easily accessible by wheelchair and the usual fixtures are within reach of someone in a wheelchair. It is important to consider where doors and windows are placed.
- The dining room may be in the kitchen, but if separate should be directly accessible from the kitchen.
- The general layout of the living, dining and bedrooms should facilitate safety, comfort and convenience for the disabled person.
- A window with a low level cill in a frequently used room will allow a disabled person to see outside from a sitting position. Similarly windows should be able to open and close easily.
- Floor finishes should be carefully chosen. Slippery surfaces should be avoided.

- Surfaces which can be maintained easily are important. Short pile, closely woven carpets can perhaps cater for many situations. The nature of the disability will clearly determine the suitability of floor finishes.
- Visual aids such as strips on stairs will assist partially sighted people.

- Sound insulation should be provided if a room is occupied by someone with hearing difficulties. Fabric wall covering and carpeting may be advisable.

CIRCULATION

- Corridors should be sufficiently wide, have appropriate floor coverings, with changes in level clearly marked.
- Stairs should be avoided whenever possible.
- If stairs are necessary adequate handrails should be provided.
- Stairs to be used by disabled people should have slip resistant finishes on treads, and open risers avoided.
- A stair glide can be fitted to most stairs.
- For people with visual disabilities strips should clearly mark tread edges.
- An interior ramp with a slope no steeper than 1:12 may be appropriate, where level changes are minor for wheelchair users or other persons with limiting disabilities.
- It is important that changes in direction of a ramp are carefully designed.
- Suitable handrails must be provided for ramps. The handrail could have tactile warnings for blind users.
- The ramp must also be well lighted.
- Lifts are best for large changes in levels.
- Turning space in the carriage must be sufficient to allow a person in a wheelchair to turn around.

- An automatic reopening device is important.
- Controls should be accessible from a wheelchair.
- Raised symbols on controls will be useful for the blind.
- An alarm should be fitted.

HEATING, COOLING, AND VENTILATION

- Heating, cooling and ventilation systems are vital for disabled persons who may spend a large amount of time in their homes. Therefore it is necessary to be able to control easily the temperature, and ventilation.
- For persons with serious chest conditions it may be necessary to install air filter systems, air conditioning and humidity control.
- For some disabilities a high relative humidity is required, but it is important to prevent unnecessary condensation and moisture damage.
- Sealing windows and weather stripping doors will help eliminate drafts.
- All heating pipes and radiators should be enclosed to prevent burns.

- For blind people tactile cues at appropriate points to denote changes in level are important. Similarly footpaths must be free from protruding obstacles.
- A ramp may be suitable to allow entry. The suitability will depend on degree of disability and the features of the site and dwelling.
- To determine if a ramp is suitable, the following factors must be considered.
  (a) can the ramp be designed so that it fits in with the dwelling
  (b) can the ramp be kept free of snow and ice
  (c) is there enough space to have a ramp with a slope that is not too steep
  (d) can the ramp give direct access to the main entrance
- The specific design of a ramp will depend on the particular characteristics of the disabled person.
- In general, handrails should be provided and the surface should be slip resistant. It should not be too long, too steep or have sharp corners.
- The use of a chair lift could be considered if a ramp is impractical.

EXTERIOR OF THE HOUSE

PEDESTRIAN ACCESSIBILITY

- Wide footpaths with slip resistant surfaces, drop kerbs and no abrupt changes in level, provide the means by which a disabled person is able to use their neighbourhood facilities.

Vehicular

- Car parking close to the main entrance is important. A wide space may be necessary to allow for transfer to a wheelchair.
- The ideal arrangement is to allow direct access from the car to the dwelling. The pathway from the car to the house should have a hard level surface.

- It is important that a car port is wide enough to protect the disabled person from the weather.
- For blocks of flats it may be necessary to have a parking space specially reserved for a disabled person, which is close to an accessible entrance.
- Appropriate external signs such as the international symbols for access may be necesary for blocks of flats, indicating the way to a specially designated parking area.

SOCIAL SITUATION

PERSONAL INDEPENDENCE/ADJUSTMENT

- Once a person has become handicapped the degree of disability (functional capability) and their attitude to their condition will to some extent help them and their family decide whether they should stay in their present home and adapt it or move to more suitable accommodation.
- If the disabled person is partially or totally confined to a wheelchair, the degree to which they can control it is an important factor in assessing the suitability of their existing home.
- Disabling conditions which immediately or in the future affect the use of the hand or a substitute can have important implications for the person's independence.

- Disabilities which affect a person's capacity to deal with their living essentials such as house cleaning, personal toilet and minor health problems are also of importance.
- Disabled persons will need access to a telephone, or if they cannot use a telephone, other means of gaining assistance in case of emergency.
- If the disabled person wishes to stay in their existing house their ability to use local public transport could be relevant.
- A disabled person's need, ability and desire to use local amenities outside their home will have an important bearing on whether they wish to stay or move to a new house.

FAMILY SITUATION/SUPPORT NETWORK

- Many disabled people's ability to stay in their existing home will depend on the degree of support available from friends and relatives.
- The ability and attitude of the family to offer long term assistance can in many cases be a critical factor.
- Care of a disabled person by their family can involve a 24 hour a day commitment.
- Access to formal assistance programmes supplied by the local authorities can go a long way to enabling a person to remain independent.
- A disabled person's interaction with other residents in the neighbourhood can have an important bearing on their desire to stay or move to a new location.

SURVEY SHEET

This survey sheet will help you to firstly assess the suitability of your existing house situation and secondly to identify possible alternatives.

To assess the suitability of your existing housing situation, each question in each section should be recorded for each room, facility in the home and the disabled person's social situation.

Then count up the number of 'yes' or 'no' answers and put the number in the sub-total box.

Where the grand total shows a higher proportion of 'no' answers, rehousing may be the preferred course of action. However, the cost should also be borne in mind here because even a lot of 'no' answers could mean that it is still worthwhile improving rather than moving.

INTERIOR

Entrance

	YES	NO	N/A
Is the main entrance accessible from the outside without having to use steps or stairs?	——	——	——
Is there a level, paved area at least 1500 × 1500 mm outside the door?	——	——	——
Is there a ramp outside the main entrance?	——	——	——
Are there handrails at the ramp at a height of 800 to 920 mm?	——	——	——
Is the threshold less than 15 mm high?	——	——	——
Is there an automatic door opening device?	——	——	——
Does the door have a clear opening of at least 810 mm?	——	——	——
Are the door handles 760 to 915 mm from the floor?	——	——	——
Are the lock and opening mechanisms operable?	——	——	——
Is there space to manoeuvre a wheelchair in the vestibule?	——	——	——
Are the floor surfaces slip resistant?	——	——	——
Is the door bell or call button lower than 900 mm?	——	——	——
Is there a level floor for at least 1500 mm on both sides of the door?	——	——	——
Do the door closers allow the use of the doors by disabled persons (delayed action)?	——	——	——
SUB TOTAL	——	——	——

Kitchen

	YES	NO	N/A
Do the entries have a clear opening of 810 mm?	——	——	——
Are the door handles within a range of 760 to 915 mm above the floor?	——	——	——
Is the door threshold less than 15 mm high?	——	——	——
Does the dining room door have a vision panel not higher than 1000 mm from the floor?	——	——	——
Are there accessible switches within a range of 835 to 1065 mm above the floor?	——	——	——
Are there accessible electrical outlets at the front or side of the counters?	——	——	——
Are the cooker controls accessible from a seated position?	——	——	——

Is the counter height 840 mm for use by a person in a wheelchair?   — — —

Is there knee space at the sink (min 750 wide × 250 deep)?   — — —

Is there pipe insulation or a baffle for knee protection?   — — —

Are the taps a lever type or other accessible type?   — — —

Are there any pull-out cutting boards below the counter top?   — — —

Are there any pull-out storage units under the counter?   — — —

Is there toe space at the counter 230 mm high and 150 mm deep?   — — —

Is the wall covered shelving reachable from a seated position (lower shelf not higher than 1250 mm)?   — — —

Are the racks, hanging rods, cup hooks, etc. reachable from a wheelchair (1420 mm or lower)?   — — —

Is the floor slip resistant?   — — —

Does the carpeting allow the free movement of wheelchairs?   — — —

Is there adequate space to manoeuvre a wheelchair (1730 mm in front of counters and appliances; 1500 mm if turn-round for efficient operation)?   — — —

SUB TOTAL   — — —

Bathroom/toilet

	YES	NO	N/A

Is the bathroom generally accessible from other rooms taking account of different floors?   — — —

Does the floor have a clear opening of at least 810 mm?   — — —

Are the door handles within a range of 760 to 915 mm above the floor?   — — —

Is the floor threshold less than 15 mm high?   — — —

Does the door swing out of the room?   — — —

Is there a turning circle 1500 mm in diameter in the room? (Note: mark N/A if room is usable without having to turn wheelchair right round.)   — — —

Are there accessible light switches within a range of 835 to 1065 mm above the floor?   — — —

Is there a reachable outlet for plugging in razor, hair dryer, etc?   — — —

Is the mirror and shelf less than 960 mm above the floor?   — — —

Are towel racks, soap holders, and other fixtures in an accessible space, less than 1000 mm above the floor and less than 550 mm from the front of the counter?   — — —

Is the top of the toilet seat 450 mm above the floor?   — — —

Are there adequate grab bars at the toilet?   — — —

Is there a space at least 600 mm wide beside the toilet to allow for a lateral transfer?   — — —

Is there a space for a wheelchair at the front of the toilet (minimum depth 1350 mm)?   — — —

Does the bath tub have appropriate grab bars?   — — —

Does the shower have appropriate grab bars? — — —

Are the taps in the bath tub reachable and easily operable from a wheelchair? — — —

Are the taps in the shower reachable and easily operable from a wheelchair? — — —

Is the toilet flushing device reachable and easily operated from a wheelchair? — — —

Does the room have a device to signal for assistance? — — —

Does the room have space for an attendant assisting someone in a wheelchair? — — —

SUB TOTAL — — —

Living, dining and bedrooms	YES	NO	N/A
Does the door have a clear opening of at least 810 mm?	—	—	—
Are the door handles within a range of 760 to 915 mm above the floor?	—	—	—
Is the door threshold less than 15 mm high?	—	—	—
Are the light switches within a range of 835 to 1065 mm above the floor?	—	—	—
Are the wall receptacles within a range of 450 to 530 mm above the floor?	—	—	—
Is the window cill 760 mm or less from the floor?	—	—	—
Are the window operating devices operable from a wheelchair?	—	—	—
Is the counter height within a range of 835 to 915 mm?	—	—	—
Is there shelving that is reachable from a seated position?	—	—	—
Are the floors slip resistant?	—	—	—
Does the carpeting allow the free movement of wheelchairs?	—	—	—
Is there proper demarcation of differences in level by contrasting colour and appropriate lighting?	—	—	—
Is there adequate space to manoeuvre a wheelchair in the room?	—	—	—
Does a blind person have an unobstructed path without protrusions from walls, floors or elsewhere?	—	—	—
Is the level of mechanical or other background noises low enough to avoid interference with sound reception on a conversational level by persons using hearing aids (less than 85 dB)?	—	—	—
SUB TOTAL	—	—	—

Circulation	YES	NO	N/A
Are the corridors at least 940 mm wide?	—	—	—
Do corridors have slip resistant floor surfaces?	—	—	—
Does the carpeting allow the free movement of wheelchairs, i.e. it is not deep pile or directional weave: does not bunch up or glide, etc.)?	—	—	—
Is there a clear demarcation of differences in floor level?	—	—	—
SUB TOTAL	—	—	—

▶

Stairs

	YES	NO	N/A
Is there an alternative to the stairs?	___	___	___
Are there handrails at a height of 920 mm?	___	___	___
Does the handrail extend at least 300 mm beyond the top step?	___	___	___
Does the handrail extend at least 300 mm beyond the bottom step?	___	___	___
Are the risers less than 180 mm high?	___	___	___
Are the treads more than 265 mm deep?	___	___	___
Do the treads have a slip resistant finish or skid resistant strips?	___	___	___
Are the edges clearly marked for visually impaired people?	___	___	___
Have open risers been avoided?	___	___	___
SUB TOTAL	___	___	___

Ramps

	YES	NO	N/A
Are ramps provided?	___	___	___
Is the length between landings less than 9000 mm?	___	___	___
Is the ramp width at least 900 mm?	___	___	___
Is the gradient 1/12 or less?	___	___	___
Is the surface of the ramp slip-resistant?	___	___	___
Is there a level landing at the top and bottom of the ramp at least 1500 mm long and 900 mm wide and 1500 mm wide if a door swings into it?	___	___	___
Is there a level landing at each change of direction?	___	___	___
Do two wheels of the wheelchair hit the slope or the landing at the same time?	___	___	___
Is there a suitable handrail on at least one side of the ramp 800 mm to 920 mm in height?	___	___	___
Does the handrail extend 300 mm beyond the top and bottom of the ramp?	___	___	___
Does the handrail have tactile warning for blind users?	___	___	___
Are free-standing ramps at least 1500 mm wide and their upturned edges 25 to 50 mm high for safety or protective bars no more than 200 mm above the ramp surface?	___	___	___
Is the ramp well lighted?	___	___	___
SUB TOTAL	___	___	___

Lifts

	YES	NO	N/A
Is there a lift that is accessible?	___	___	___
Is there a 1500 mm turning circle in front of the lift?	___	___	___
Are the carriage dimensions sufficient to accommodate a wheelchair (minimum 1370 × 1300 mm)?	___	___	___
Does the carriage stop precisely at floor level or within 15 mm?	___	___	___

▶

Is the door opening at least 820 mm wide?   —— —— ——

Is the door equipped with an automatic safety re-opening device?   —— —— ——

Are the controls accessible from a wheelchair?   —— —— ——

Are the controls accessible to the blind? (Raised symbols)   —— —— ——

Are there audible signals for the blind?   —— —— ——

Is there emergency communication within reach?   —— —— ——

Is there a handrail in the carriage?   —— —— ——

SUB TOTAL   —— —— ——

Heating and ventilation

	YES	NO	N/A
Are all rooms and internal spaces adequately heated?	——	——	——
Are the drafts eliminated?	——	——	——
Is the humidity at the correct level?	——	——	——
Are all heating pipes and radiators enclosed?	——	——	——
Is the heating system easily operable?	——	——	——
SUB TOTAL	——	——	——

EXTERIOR

Pedestrian accessibility

	YES	NO	N/A
Are the footpaths at least 1500 mm wide?	——	——	——
Do the footpaths have a slip resistant surface?	——	——	——
Does the footpath have drop kerbs?	——	——	——
Are the footpaths on a continuous run without steps or abrupt changes in level?	——	——	——
Are there tactile cues at the top and bottom of stairs, ramps, kerbs?	——	——	——
Are the footpaths free from projecting obstacles (for blind users)?	——	——	——
Is the gradient of ramps less than 1/12?	——	——	——
Is the surface of ramps slip resistant?	——	——	——
Is there a level landing at least 1500 mm × 1500 mm at the bottom and top of the ramp?	——	——	——
Is there a level landing at each change of direction of the ramp?	——	——	——
Is the intersection of the ramp and the landing at a right angle to the direction of travel (i.e. 2 wheels hit landing at same time)?	——	——	——
Is there a suitable handrail on at least one side of the ramp 800 to 920 mm in height?	——	——	——
Does the handrail extend 300 mm beyond the top and bottom of the ramp?	——	——	——
Does the handrail have tactile warnings for blind users?	——	——	——

▶

Are free-standing ramps at least 1500 mm wide, are there upturned edges 25 to 50 mm high for safety or protection bars no more than 200 mm above the ramp surface? — — —

Is the ramp protected from rain, snow and ice? — — —

SUB TOTAL — — —

Vehicular accessibility	YES	NO	N/A
Is there accessible parking space close to your house?	—	—	—
Is there parking space large enough to allow transfer to a wheelchair?	—	—	—
Is the wheelchair transfer space level?	—	—	—
Is the parking area sheltered from rain, snow and ice?	—	—	—
Is there a parking space identified as reserved for vehicles for disabled persons close to an accessible entrance?	—	—	—
Is there an international symbol of access indicating the direction to the designated parking area?	—	—	—
Are there signs indicating the direction to the entrance for disabled persons?	—	—	—
Are the parking spaces 3.7 m wide for persons using wheelchairs or braces or crutches?	—	—	—
Does the designated parking space lead directly to an accessible entrance without crossing vehicular traffic?	—	—	—
SUB TOTAL	—	—	—

PERSONAL INDEPENDENCE/ADJUSTMENT	YES	NO	N/A
Has the client a positive outlook on his/her situation?	—	—	—
Does the client wish to remain in his/her current home?	—	—	—
Is the client satisfied with the current home given his/her present family situation?	—	—	—
Would the client be prepared to move house?	—	—	—
Is the client totally confined to a wheelchair?	—	—	—
Is the client in good control of the wheelchair?	—	—	—
Does the client have the use of his/her hands or a substitute?	—	—	—
Does the client have a major responsibility for his/her hands or a substitute?	—	—	—
Does the client have a major responsibility for his/her living essentials?	—	—	—
Is the client able to keep the house clean and tidy?	—	—	—
Is the client able to see to his/her personal toilet?	—	—	—
Does the client look after minor health problems without help?	—	—	—
Does the client need constant supervision?	—	—	—
SUB TOTAL	—	—	—

▶

FAMILY SITUATION/SUPPORT NETWORK	YES	NO	N/A
Does the client live alone?	——	——	——
If not, are any other members of the family able-bodied?	——	——	——
Is there a member of the family who is willing to engage in a care role on a long-term basis?	——	——	——
Is the care giver willing/able to engage in the care role?	——	——	——
(a) during the day	——	——	——
(b) during the night	——	——	——
Is the attitude of the care giver positive?	——	——	——
Does the client have access to any care support network? viz:	——	——	——
(a) home help	——	——	——
(b) meals	——	——	——
(c) day centre	——	——	——
(d) community nurse/medical services	——	——	——
(e) occupational therapist	——	——	——
(f) othervoluntary support	——	——	——
Is the client part of the local community/immediate social environment?	——	——	——
(a) socially	——	——	——
(b) physically	——	——	——
(c) psychologically	——	——	——
Is the immediate community supportive of the client's disability?	——	——	——
SUB TOTAL	——	——	——

SUMMARY SHEET	YES	NO	N/A
Entrance	——	——	——
Kitchen	——	——	——
Bathroom/Toilet	——	——	——
Living, Dining and Bedrooms	——	——	——
Circulation	——	——	——
Heating and Ventilation	——	——	——
Pedestrian Accessibility	——	——	——
Vehicular Accessibility	——	——	——
Independence/adjustment	——	——	——
Family situation/support network	——	——	——
GRAND TOTAL	——	——	——

Taken from *Housing for the Physically Disabled: A guide to adaption and rehousing*, prepared by Jack Rostron, School of the Built Environment, Liverpool John Moores University, and reproduced with his kind permission. Illustrations by Lynne Lockwood

EXERCISE

Copy out and complete the survey sections using your own accommodation as the model; make a note of all the measurements you will have to make, and make sure you have a suitable tape measure. For the personal information you could use the Moss family (*see* Case 10 on pages 190–1).

What adaptions would you recommend, and why?

Possible modifications are the addition of a lift or an extension; the advantages and disadvantages of these are discussed in the following article which first appeared in *In Focus*, the magazine of the Muscular Dystrophy Group, and is reproduced here with their kind permission. Take into account the advice given here when making your own suggestions in the exercise above.

GROUND FLOOR EXTENSION OR LIFT?

Philippa Harpin reviews the choice.

The decision to choose between a lift or an extension may be governed by the space available, both within the house and garden. A lift is usually the first option to be considered, particularly if a grant application is being made, as Grants Officers usually prefer to approve adaptations that are within the structure of the house.

However, where both are possible structurally, the final decision must depend upon which option will be the most appropriate for the disabled person and the carers, bearing in mind the long-term effects of the particular disability.

A. LIFT

We will cover the different types of lifts in a separate issue of *In Focus*, but for most people with MD it is vital to have a **wheelchair model** installed if a wheelchair is needed now or is likely to be needed in the future.

1 Is there a suitable position for a vertical lift on the ground floor and directly above on the first floor – or are the stairs suitable for a wheelchair platform lift?

2 Are the first floor facilities suitable for a wheelchair, from the point of view of both space and layout?

Space

There is no point in installing a lift if either the bathroom or bedroom are too small. There must be sufficient space for the following:

Bathroom

(a) The installation of either a Mermaid Ranger pillar at the side of the bath with space to cover the arc of the seat – or a floor-level shower.

(b) A counter top, minimum width of 39⅜″ (1000 mm) with an inset basin.

(c) 35″ (915 mm) in front of the basin to allow the disabled person to approach squarely in the wheelchair.

(d) 30″ (760 mm) at the exposed side of the loo pan for the positioning of a wheelchair for sideways transfers.

(e) An additional doorset of between 33½″–35½″ (850 mm–900 mm) to provide direct access from the bedroom.

Bedroom

(a) Wallspace for a 7′ (2110 mm) bed.

(b) 6′ (1830 mm) at the side of the bed to enable the ceiling hoist over the bed to be used for transferring from one wheelchair to another – or from the wheelchair to easy chair or Mermaid Ranger/shower chair.

(c) Standard storage facilities i.e. wardrobe and chest of drawers.

(d) L-shaped working surface 71″ (1800 mm) × 47¼″ (1200 mm).

(e) A doorset of between 33½″–35½″ (850 mm–900 mm) to provide direct access to the bathroom.

(f) Circulation of a powered wheelchair.

Layout

Does the layout of the rooms allow for a double bedroom to have en suite facilities? Boys with

▶

Duchenne muscular dystrophy and other disabled children and adults are often undressed on their bed and then move into the bathroom on a mobile bath or shower chair, or in the case of adults, on an extended track of the ceiling hoist. Adjoining rooms enables this procedure to be carried out in privacy and in the warmth within the rooms.

B. GROUND FLOOR EXTENSION

1. Is there sufficient space in the garden for a bedroom/bathroom extension of adequate size, preferably retaining access down the side of the house? One of the problems may be in getting planning permission but most planning departments will look more favourably and 'bend' their rules where disabled facilities are needed.

2. Internally, can the extension be accessed from the hall or family area and ideally not through the kitchen?

3. In some situations, where a ramp is not possible at either the front or back door, or where a second fire exit is needed, wheelchair access to the house can be provided via French doors or windows into the disabled person's bedroom.

4. An external door from the bedroom is also essential in adaptations where there is no other alternative wheelchair-access into the garden or patio at the back of the house.

5. The basic space requirements are itemized above and are discussed in greater details in the leaflet 'Adaptations for Duchenne muscular dystrophy and allied neuromuscular disorders'.

LIFT-v-EXTENSION

If the house is equally suitable for either a lift or extension there are several factors which should be considered:

Lift – advantages

1. Every room in the house is accessible to the disabled person. This is likely to be very important to a disabled mother who wants to be able to get into her child's/children's bedrooms and wants to maintain responsibility for the housekeeping.

2. The opportunity for the disabled person to sleep on the same floor as the rest of the family. This may be particularly important to families who have a very severely disabled toddler who needs constant attention in the night.

Lift – disadvantages

1. A lift takes up valuable space in a home, is not a thing of beauty, and although it is expensive it does not add to the value of a house.

2. A user with a neuromuscular condition is unlikely to be independent in the use of a lift and having to be helped places an additional burden upon the carers. The result is that the lift is usually used a minimum number of times during the day.

3. The disabled teenager is denied regular and independent access to his or her bedroom which restricts its use as a bed-sit in which to entertain friends.

4. If the disabled person is in the bedroom and needs help the carer has to go upstairs. This may be at an inconvenient time e.g. while cooking a meal.

Extension – advantages

1. Provides the facility of a bed-sit which is likely to be important to a teenager – and with the installation of double-swing doors allows independent access to and from the room in a powered wheelchair.

2. Allows a disabled teenager to move freely between the family areas and the bedroom, adding an independence and freedom that should not be underrated. Those of us who have had teenagers will confirm that they often prefer the privacy of their own rooms and tend to spend much of their free time amongst their possessions.

3. Allows a ceiling hoist installed over a bed to be used to transfer a person from one wheelchair to another during the day, without having to go upstairs – and equally important, allows an easy-chair which is used in the family sitting room, to be wheeled into the bedroom, in order to use the hoist for lifting in and out of the chair.

4. Enlarges a home and provides an additional facility which will add to the value of the house.

5. A purpose-built extension is likely to provide better facilities than adapting existing rooms.

Provides a ground floor wheelchair-accessible loo in a house where there may be no existing suitable cloakroom.

Extension – disadvantages

1. Limits the size of the garden.

2. If the disabled person needs attention in the night the carer has to go downstairs.

I hope I do not make myself unpopular with families who have decided to have a lift installed. I will stick my neck out far enough to say that unless there are special circumstances, I consider an extension is a much more suitable choice for most children, as it will provide them with a much higher level of independence in the future, when in many other respects they have become increasingly dependent.

►

In reaching this decision, I would emphasize that I have been guided by the opinions of the individuals and families who have had first-hand experience of the advantages and disadvantages of either a lift or an extension.

Do please contact me if you wish to discuss any of the issues mentioned. If you feel I have omitted important points – or if you disagree with any of the opinions stated – I do hope you will get in touch. It is only in this way that we can all learn from each other.

In the next issue of In Focus I will be covering the issues involved when making the choice between a bath with an over-bath shower and a floor-level shower.

Philippa Harpin, National OT Adviser MD Unit, Newcastle General Hospital, Westgate Road, Newcastle Upon Tyne NE4 6BE Tel. 0661 842 605
Secretary 091 273 8811 Ext. 22461

Chapter 11

AIDS TO DAILY LIVING

Mobility aids

There are a number of ways in which people move about, and we often use aids of various sorts to achieve this. People with disabilities use a greater range of items such as shoes, bicycles or tricycles (or even tandems), cars, and public transport. They also use the same things as able bodied people, but perhaps with purposeful modifications.

Shoes

These are a necessity for the majority of people in this country. Many of us have oddly shaped feet, and a great many of us have feet of different sizes, so getting shoes to fit can be a great problem, and even more difficult if your needs are not of an everyday nature. Some people need only one shoe; some require attachments such as callipers; others are allergic to the commonly used materials. The problems can be such that shoes have to be individually made. Sometimes these can be obtained from the Health Service, but even when they can, the design will not necessarily be a popular one, particularly with the younger generation.

Information on and catalogues for specialist footwear can be obtained from the Disabled Living Foundation (DLF) in the Useful Addresses section on page 223.

Walking sticks

These are the commonest kind of walking aid, and can be made of wood, metal or plastic. Handles are curved or straight, and the end piece which touches the floor should be covered in a rubber cap, or ferrule to prevent slipping. These ferrules should be checked regularly, and any that are becoming worn should be replaced, to avoid accidents caused by slipping.

Some walking sticks have three or four feet to spread the load and give a better balance; these are known as tripods and quadrupeds. Each foot must have a ferrule fitted.

The white sticks, or red and white striped sticks carried by people with sensory impairments, are not necessarily walking aids. White sticks give a warning to others that the bearer is visually impaired, and are also a useful tool for the carrier to tap ahead and detect potential dangers in the path. Red and white striped sticks signify that the bearer has both visual and hearing impairment.

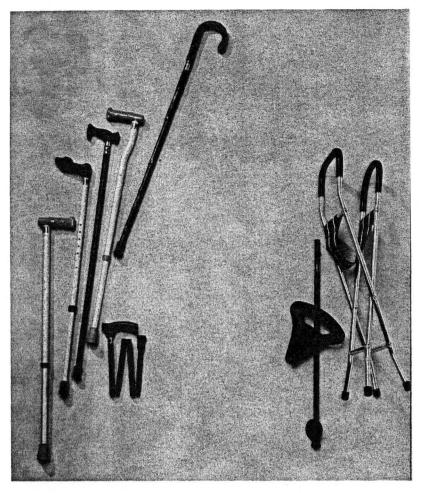

Fig 11.1 A range of walking sticks
Reproduced by kind permission of Boots The Chemist

Crutches

These are a reasonably common sight on the streets. They give more support than a walking stick, and allow for the use of one leg only. There are two main types; the long or axillary crutch which reaches up to the shoulder (or axilla), and the elbow crutch, which is more suited to long-term use.

Once again, ferrules should be checked regularly.

Walking frames

Often called Zimmer frames (after the original manufacturer) these are much more stable, and can give a great deal of support if necessary. Some have four feet, some three; most are made of metal, some fold up for easier carrying in cars or on public transport. Some have wheels, and attachments such as shopping bags or other receptacles to allow things to be carried around can be obtained.

Fig 11.2 A karristick, a product which takes the strain out of carrying heavy baggage
Reproduced by kind permission of Boots The Chemist

Callipers

(Also spelt caliper, or called calliper splints.) These are made of metal rods attached to a padded leather ring which fits to the top of the leg, reducing downward pressure on the leg by redirecting it to the metal supports. They may also be half-length, with a pad at the knee, taking pressure from the lower leg only. The foot end is fitted into holds in the heels of strengthened shoes. Callipers are much less commonly used now that polio has been controlled.

Wheelchairs

There are an amazing variety of styles and designs of wheelchair on the market, manufactured locally or imported – principally from America. In essence, though, there are three basic types: self-propelled; pushed; and powered.

Those chairs intended to be self-propelled increase the disabled person's independence; they have two large wheels with a double rim, and two small wheels. The large wheels are usually, but not always, at the back. The outer rim is a hand grip used to provide the push to move around.

Chairs meant to be pushed by another person have four smaller wheels. Powered chairs will be much heavier than the above two, and may be for indoor or outdoor use; sometimes suitable for both. Controls are most commonly of the joystick type, as supplied with computer games, although a variety of control systems can be supplied to suit individual needs.

Wheelchairs can be provided by the NHS, at the request of a GP or hospital doctor, and they can also be purchased in the same way as any other goods.

Things to bear in mind when choosing a wheelchair are whether the disabled person or a carer will be controlling it; whether it is for outdoor or indoor use, or whether it should be suitable for both. Individual requirements also need to be taken into account; does the user need a reclining backrest, footrests, solid tyres or pneumatic tyres, straps, leg-rests, trays, padding in certain places, or anything else to be custom made? Will it need to fold up for packing into a car, or is it for use in one place only? Is only one chair needed, or one for home and another for work, school, or college? Specialist chairs are also available for sports use.

All wheelchairs need regular maintenance. Brakes and pneumatic tyres need regular checks; small wheels need fluff and dust removing from them, and may need oiling occasionally. Check all nuts and bolts for tightness, and canvas, leather, or plastic parts for wear and tear. Replacement parts should be easily available. Powered wheelchairs need a regular service just as a car does, and should go to the mechanics for this.

There are also vehicles specially designed for disabled children as shown in the photograph on page 108.

EXERCISE

(a) Find out where to obtain wheelchairs in your nearest town, and what the costs are likely to be if you had to buy privately.
(b) Identify other commonly used pieces of equipment and describe them in the same way as the few listed above.
(c) Prepare an information leaflet for your area to advise people with disabilities where they can get equipment from, other than the statutory agencies. Include mail order outlets.

General living aids

Aids to daily living can be obtained through both the Health Service and the Social Services, in both cases via the Occupational Therapist. There is also a growing sector of the commercial world which will provide these items, although the market price will have to be paid. There are local providers, either shops, warehouses, or factories (*see* the *Yellow Pages* directory and exercise on page 22), and national providers such as the Boots chain, and the growing Keep Able supermarket style stores for equipment for Disabled People.

Fig 11.3 A range of vehicles designed for disabled children and young adults.
Front: The Rally Special with good obstacle climbing abilities, most suitable for children with muscular dystrophy and related diseases such as cerebral palsy, spastic paralysis, athetosis and spina bifida.
Top left: The Monarch which also overcomes rough ground is most suitable for muscular dystrophy children and young adults.
Top right: The Mini Comet and Maxi Comet which are practical indoor Go-Karts with limited outdoor use for children. Both are ideal for most physical handicaps.
Reproduced by kind permission of Possum Controls Limited

1 For the kitchen:
- Can openers, both electric and manual which can be operated by people who have the use of only one hand;
- Kettle tippers, for which only slight pressure is needed to pour water out of them;
- Teapot pourers;
- Suitably adapted cutlery and mugs.

2 For the bedroom:
- Easy reachers: these are invaluable for those who cannot bend down or stretch;
- Adjustable bed rests and tables;
- Bed raisers: to increase the height of the bed.

3 For the bathroom:
- Tap turners;
- Bath and toilet support rails and frames (*see* below);
- Raised toilet seats;
- Bath seats: to assist those who experience difficulty in getting in or out of the bath.

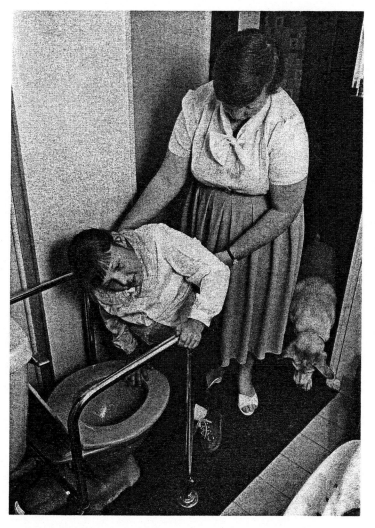

Fig 11.4 Toilet support rails
© John Birdsall Photography

4 General:

- Yale key turner (*see* below).

There are many other items available stocked by specialist companies such as Possum Controls Limited and also by Boots The Chemist. Both these companies publish catalogues containing details of these products.

Fig 11.5 A Yale key turner
Reproduced by kind permission of Boots The Chemist

Chapter 12

UTILITIES

The utilities, as those students familiar with Monopoly may know, are the electricity, gas and water companies. They provide services to just about every household in the United Kingdom, and hence must also provide services to people with disabilities. These are such things as bills in braille, controls adapted for use by people who cannot grip, and the positioning of appliances and mains switches where consumers can reach them most easily.

Local companies should have leaflets giving advice and information for people with special requirements; they all seem to be written for both elderly and disabled consumers with no differentiation between the two groups. Overseeing their work, and monitoring their services are the Consumer Councils.

Gas

The Gas Consumers Council undertook a survey of the services offered to elderly and disabled consumers, extracts from which are reproduced here with their kind permission.

A REVIEW OF BRITISH GAS SERVICES FOR ELDERLY AND DISABLED GAS CONSUMERS

BACKGROUND

1 The role of the Gas Consumers Council and Office of Gas Supply. The Gas Consumers Council and the Office of Gas Supply were set up by Parliament in 1986 when British Gas was privatised.

The Gas Consumers Council campaigns on behalf of consumers about all aspects of gas in the home including appliances (those sold by all companies – not just British Gas). The Council works for consumers at two levels. GCC takes up complaints/enquiries on behalf of individual consumers through its 12 regional offices. At a national level GCC campaigns for the collective interests of all or groups of gas consumers.

In 1988 the Council received over 100 000 complaints and enquiries from gas consumers. Of the 27 000 complaints ten per cent were known to be from older or disabled consumers.

To ensure that the interests of elderly and disabled consumers are represented the Council has two members with special responsibility for elderly and disabled gas consumers.

▶

Ofgas is the regulatory body set up to govern the way in which British Gas and other gas supply companies operate. In carrying out his duties under the Gas Act 1986 the Director General of Gas Supply has a special responsibility under Section 4(3) of the act to look after the interests of elderly and disabled consumers:

'In performing his duty under subsection (2) above to exercise functions assigned to him . . . the Director shall take into account, in particular, the interests of those who are disabled or of pensionable age'.

Condition 13 of the Authorisation (the document that sets out the conditions under which British Gas operates) refers to elderly and disabled consumers. A copy of the Condition is given in Appendix 1. Appendix 2 is the Code of Practice written by British Gas in response to Condition 13 of the Authorisation.

2 The review of services for elderly and disabled consumers. Over ten million people (18%) in Great Britain are of pensionable age (i.e. men over 65 and women over 60 years of age).

Recent OPCS reports have shown that one in four households contains a disabled person – representing around 6.2 million disabled people. About two thirds of disabled people are elderly.

In 1987 the Gas Consumers Council formed a working group, headed by the two specialist Council members, to co-ordinate the Council's work for elderly and disabled consumers. Through liaison with various organisations and analysis of the Council's complaints and enquiries the group identified issues and sought change by discussion with British Gas. Evidence from the working group pointed to the need for considerable change.

British Gas's services to elderly consumers and to disabled consumers were found to be low key and mainly reactive. A good standard of service was available to those who knew to ask for help, but awareness of the services available was low. It was felt that British Gas should be encouraged to up-date and improve its services and to find more effective ways of reaching those who would most benefit.

As a result of evidence from the working group, the Council recognised a need for work on behalf of elderly and disabled consumers to take a higher priority. At the beginning of 1989 the Council therefore established a formal committee with special responsibility for elderly or disabled consumers. The first task given to the committee was to carry out a review of all services to elderly and disabled consumers.

Early in 1989 the Director General of Gas Supply asked the Gas Consumers Council to advise him following receipt of representations about the difficulties of elderly and disabled people who have appliances disconnected following a free safety check. Ofgas was also concerned about reported delays in repairing gas equipment that left elderly people without heating, hot water or cooking facilities for some considerable time.

The Council's committee for elderly/disabled consumers took on this work as part of its review on services for elderly and disabled consumers.

Full copies can be obtained from: Gas Consumers Council, Abford House, 15 Wilston Road, London SW1V 1LT.

QUESTIONS

Having read this information, answer the following questions:
(a) Why do you think that elderly and disabled people constitute one group in the eyes of the Gas Consumers Council (GCC)?
(b) How many complaints did they receive from 'older and disabled gas consumers' in 1988?

(c) How many regional offices does the GCC have?

(d) How many members have responsibility for disabled consumers?

(e) What proportion of households contain a disabled person?

(f) How many disabled people are classified as elderly?

(g) What were the problems associated with British Gas's services to disabled consumers prior to 1989?

(h) What was found to be happening after free safety checks?

In the survey shown above, Condition 13 is mentioned. This is reproduced below, with the response from British Gas to the points made in Condition 13 on pages 114–15.

Condition 13: Provision of services for persons who are of pensionable age or disabled

1 The Supplier shall make arrangements for tariff customers who are of State pensionable age or are registered disabled or are in receipt of State benefit by reason of disability, by which special services in the following respects can be made available where appropriate:

(a) examining free of charge in the case of such customers who live alone the safety of gas appliances and other gas fittings on the customer's side of the meter;

(b) providing where practicable special controls and adaptors for gas appliances and for prepayment meters and repositioning such meters;

(c) providing special means of identifying officers authorised by the Supplier; and

(d) giving advice on the use of gas and the use of gas fittings.

2 The Supplier shall within three months after the date on which this Authorisation comes into force prepare a Code of Practice describing the special services available and any charges made. The Supplier shall consider any representations from the Director or the Gas Consumers' Council about the operation of the Code.

3 The Supplier shall:

(a) send a copy of the Code to the Director and the Gas Consumers' Council;

(b) make available for inspection a copy of the Code to members of the public at each of the relevant premises during its normal opening hours; and

(c) give or send a copy of the Code to any person requesting it.

Services for elderly and disabled customers:
British Gas statement prepared under Condition 13

British Gas plc provides a number of special services for its elderly and disabled customers. These services are listed below. If you would like to apply for any of these services, or would like to know more about them, please contact us. You can call in at any British Gas showroom, or telephone the local British Gas Service Centre – the number is in the phone book under "GAS".

If you know any elderly or disabled gas customers who might find these services useful, please tell them that we may be able to help them.

Free gas safety checks
On request, we will carry out a free gas safety check on your appliances and installation if:

- you are over 60 years of age and you live alone;
- you are a registered, disabled person of any age and you live alone; or
- you receive a State disability benefit, and you live alone.

This check will show whether your gas appliances and installation are safe to use. The check includes any necessary adjustments, and materials up to a cost of £2.50 plus VAT. One free check is available in any period of 12 months.

If any additional work needs to be done, you might have to pay for it. We can give you an official estimate for any repairs that are needed. Some elderly or disabled people may be able to get help towards this cost. You should ask your local Social Security Office or Social Services Department to see if you are entitled to help *before* ordering any work to be done.

Special controls for appliances
If you have a disability which makes it difficult for you to operate your gas appliances, we have a range of special controls and adaptors which could make it easier. We can fit many cookers with tap handles designed to meet the needs of customers with various hand disabilities. We can also fit special controls to many gas fires and some wall heaters.

We can fit braille or studded controls for some ovens, gas fires and central heating systems. These may be helpful for blind customers and those with failing sight.

We can fit special controls to new appliances, or to your existing appliances. We will advise you on the most suitable controls, and on whether we can adapt a particular type of appliance. We make a standard charge for supplying and fitting these controls of £2.20 plus VAT for each appliance.

Coin-in-the-slot meters
Most gas customers prefer to have a credit meter, with a bill sent every three months. This is usually cheaper, and more convenient than finding coins to put in the meter. Many credit customers join one of our easy payment schemes, such as budget plan, so that they are not faced with bills which have to be paid at one go. If you would like further details of the easy payment schemes, please call us or ask at your local British Gas showroom.

If you have a coin meter and would like us to replace it with a credit meter, we will do this free of charge.

If you still prefer to keep your coin meter, but find it difficult to operate, we can fit a special attachment handle to make the coin mechanism easier to use. This is free of charge.

If you find it difficult to reach your coin meter, you could have it moved to a more convenient position. We will move a meter up to three feet from its present position for a standard charge of £3.30 plus VAT. If you want your meter moved further, the charge will be higher. We will give you a quotation.

Paying bills

If you are finding it difficult to pay your gas bill, please let us know quickly. We may be able to help. A code of practice on the payment of bills is available from gas showrooms.

Identity cards and passwords

All British Gas employees who visit your home will carry identity cards, showing their name, photograph and signature. If anyone comes to your door claiming to be from British Gas, ask to see his or her identity card, and examine it carefully. British Gas employees will willingly show you their identity cards. Do not let unexpected callers in if they do not show you an identity card.

Blind customers can arrange for British Gas employees to use a password in place of an identity card when they call. The customer chooses a password, which is known only to the customer and to British Gas employees who need to call at the customer's home. This provides the customer with an assurance that a caller who gives the password is a genuine British Gas employee.

Similar special individual arrangements can also be made, as appropriate, for deaf or severely disabled customers.

Help and advice

British Gas Home Service Advisers will call on elderly and disabled customers at home to provide advice. They are experts in all aspects of the use of gas in the home. They can advise you about the safe and efficient use of gas appliances. They can provide information about the choice of suitable appliances and adaptors. This service is free of charge.

Shown below is an extract taken from the Gas Consumers Council Annual Report highlighting the steps being taken to improve gas services to older and disabled consumers.

HELPING THE OLDER OR DISABLED CONSUMER

The Council's Action Group for Older or Disabled Consumers had a busy year monitoring and encouraging British Gas in its implementation and operation of the GasCare scheme, a new development in the company's special services for older and disabled customers.

1991 saw the full implementation of GasCare in Scotland and its introduction in all British Gas regions in England and Wales. Under the scheme British Gas contacts every customer, inviting anyone over sixty, and disabled people of all ages, to join GasCare. Membership is recorded and any special needs are noted on the customer's individual record. A representative from British Gas then visits each GasCare member to record the member's requirements for any of the company's special

services and to carry out a Free Gas Safety Check if the household qualifies.

The Action Group visited British Gas Scotland in March 1991 to see for themselves how the region was operating GasCare. They liked what they saw and told British Gas headquarters that they hoped the implementation of GasCare in England and Wales would be of the same quality. But GCC Regional Councillors and Managers were soon reporting different timescales for making initial contact with consumers. GCC was concerned that this might cause delays in the follow-up visit and in the provision of the Free Gas Safety Check. The Action Group took the matter up with British Gas which agreed, in July 1991, to remodel its nationwide procedures on the successful Scottish version.

GasCare invitations are now being phased – the whole initial contact exercise is to be completed by 30th September 1992 – so that membership is quickly followed by a home visit and a Free Gas Safety Check for qualifying households.

The Action Group briefed Regional Councillors and Managers on how their gas regions should operate GasCare and on how GCC could monitor it. This monitoring includes discussion with British Gas staff, gathering statistical information and making contact with consumers, caring agencies and statutory bodies. The Action Group used GCC regional information for three policy meetings with British Gas headquarters staff during 1991.

Both regionally and nationally, GCC will continuously monitor the implementation of GasCare and the operation by British Gas of its special services for older or disabled consumers. We shall press for improvements where appropriate.

For its part, GCC has published two new leaflets offering help and advice to disabled or older consumers and a complementary tape for the blind and those who are visually handicapped.

GCC North East installed a minicom telephone system (telephone number 0532 444326), to assist communication with the hard of hearing.

EXERCISES

1. (a) Do you think Condition 13 answers the problems found by the survey?
   (b) Do you think British Gas' response meets the requirements of their disabled customers?
   (c) Can you identify a problem with the criteria for safety checks?
   (d) When was the GasCare Scheme completed in England and Wales?
   (e) What is this scheme?

2. Do the electricity and water companies have anything comparable? Contact those that cover your area (either by writing, visiting or telephoning) to find out.

3. Could you devise a 'WaterCare' scheme based on the GasCare one described above?

Chapter 13

TRANSPORT

Transport – 'a means of conveyance from one place to another' – is something which we all seem to need more and more for all sorts of reasons, whether it is for visiting family and friends, going to work, going out for pleasure, or simply for shopping.

The main methods of transport are walking, cycling, driving, riding, on the bus, on the train or by air, or possibly even by water. With any of these methods, however, there are difficulties for people with a physical disability, and in the main, most means of public transport are problematic for a majority of disabled people. Trains and buses tend to have narrow doorways and aisles; and they also have steps.

Some organisations have made some efforts to improve the facilities for disabled people. British Rail will make arrangements for people with special requirements if notified in advance, and many areas now have a 'Dial-a-Ride' bus service specifically for people with mobility problems.

Fig 13.1 © John Birdsall Photography

For walking, there are a number of aids from shoes and zimmer frames to crutches and walking sticks (*see* Chapter 11 Aids to Daily Living). As a substitute for walking there are wheelchairs, to which people are not 'confined', but get much more mobility from having wheels. For cycling there are stabilisers, three-wheelers and tandems; for riding there are horses (which may need adapted saddles), motorbikes with sidecars or three wheels, and a variety of specially designed vehicles for use indoors or out, on roads or on pavements.

Buses are not the best form of conveyance unless modified in some way to avoid having to take great steps up or down, and with space in front of seating for legs which will not bend, or to leave space to manoeuvre in and out.

There is a whole industry around the supply and adaptation of motor cars, and specific personal allowances to enable disabled people to buy them. Many taxis can now accommodate a wheelchair, and the black cabs are much more spacious to get in and out of than are ordinary cars. There are even some taxi firms which specialise in transport for disabled people, and hold contracts with Local Authorities and Health Authorities to do just this.

Cars themselves may have to be chosen for their size or ease of access, and/or have the controls modified, and if the driver is a wheelchair user, what do they do with this other form of transport when in the car? The options are to stay in the wheelchair and drive, fold it up in the car (which takes up a lot of space), or leave it at home and have another one waiting at the destination. This is quite possible with a regular destination such as work or college, but not for other destinations. Another option is to store it on the roof, but help would be needed to put it there.

An amazing amount of equipment is on the market, including some which will pack the chair away on the car roof. Other mechanical aids transfer the driving from the feet to the arms, and many other modifications and extras are available, the biggest problem for everyday users being the cost.

It cannot be denied, though, that access to personalised transport can transform a person's life, whether they have a disability or not.

Schemes for disabled people

Orange Badge Scheme

This is a national scheme administered through SSDs and SWDs to allow parking concessions for people with disabilities; it is not a licence to park anywhere. Since March 1992 badges with photographs have been introduced to try and reduce their misuse.

EXERCISES

1. (a) What is the Motability scheme?
   (b) Identify a local garage with a Motability consultant, and use him/her as a resource person. Either go to the garage to see what is on offer and ask for relevant literature, or invite him in as a guest speaker. (*See* Assignment 3 on page 202.)

2. Find out if there is a specialist driving school (or instructor) in your area. Are the costs of lessons for disabled people any different from the standard charges?
   (a) What is the reason for this?
   (b) What modifications are required to the cars?

3. Find out what specific facilities are offered by British Rail to disabled people.

4. Find out if there is a Dial-a-Ride or equivalent service in your area; are there any restrictions on its use, such as times of day when it operates, or the number of occasions on which any individual can use it per week or per month?

5. What is the 'Orange Badge Scheme'? Information on this can be obtained from your local Social Services Department, and the Motability consultant.

6. Find out if the AA/RAC and similar organisations have any specific arrangements for their disabled members. Read also the information on the Disabled Drivers Association (DDA) on page 120.

7. If a disabled driver were to break down on the motorway or in a similar awkward situation, and was unable to leave the car, how would they be able to attract attention to their plight? Design a window poster which they could use to ask for help.
   (a) Can you think of any dangers associated with this?
   (b) Does anything similar exist already?

BTEC Common Skills: 1, 2, 6, 8, 9, 10, 11, 12, 15, 17.

Community care

Transport may also be an important component of packages of care; Social Services Departments must arrange a great deal of travel to and from day centres, luncheon clubs, respite care and holiday accommodation or other leisure facilities. Trying to organise everybody's needs with the needs of the service providers is by no means an easy task, especially with time constraints on day centres and luncheon clubs, in particular.

There are also Meals on Wheels rounds to arrange, and laundry service collection and delivery, and the Health Service also has a responsibility to provide transport, particularly with the Ambulance Service.

EXERCISE IN LOGISTICS

Transport is also a service provided by or on behalf of Local Authorities or Health Services. The addresses marked on the map on page 121 all have an individual who attends a Day Centre living there. Work out the most logical and cost effective route to get everyone there as close to 10 am as is possible, allowing the driver a tea-break before he becomes involved in Meals-on-Wheels deliveries.

119

The Disabled Drivers Association

Ashwellthorpe, Norwich NR16 1EX.   Tel: 050 841 449   Fax: 050 841 8409

serving the needs of disabled people

ADVICE

An important service is to guide members and others on problems or concerns about mobility. This function is based upon a confidential telephone and mail answering service provided via the Executive Director and others at National level, as well as the normal flow of information between members at Group level. Matters referred typically include Mobility allowance and Motability matters, driving licences, insurance availability, driving capability and assessment, vehicle and adaptation choices, benefits etc. Local issues such as access and pedestrianisation are also addressed.

FRIENDSHIP

Very many DDA members belong to local Groups throughout the United Kingdom. Members are invited to join such a group where available. This provides a network enabling the DDA to deal with many issues locally, such as advice on driving instruction, vehicle supply and conversion. A focus also then exists for local campaigning activity. Of prime value is the sharing of knowledge and experiences with others. Groups also provide a meeting point through social activities, where real friendships may be forged, and opportunities provided simply for a lot of fun and enjoyment!

HOLIDAYS

The DDA has its own specially adapted hotel, Ashwellthorpe Hall, in Norfolk, totally accessible to wheelchair users and others. Additionally, some local groups have their own facilities. Advice and information on all holiday opportunities are maintained at National level. Such opportunities are a regular feature of 'Magic Carpet' magazine.

BENEFITS

Long established and cherished arrangements exist with car ferry companies which allow full members and their cars to be carried at substantial discounts, both to and from the continent and within the British Isles. This very valuable concession has opened the door to travel beyond the normal means of many members. Other cost benefits also exist, which are regularly reviewed, with a view to extending their range and value. These include RAC membership discounts and cover the purchase of some motoring supplies and services.

CAMPAIGNS

The DDA campaigns constantly to improve the lot of the disabled traveller. It was effective in helping to bring about the Mobility Allowance. The DDA remains highly active today, seeking, for example, improvements that recognise the difference in cost to people with differing degrees of disability. Improvements to the Orange Badge parking scheme have been sought and now, in part, obtained. Access issues including town and city centres, are among areas of continuing action, as are services at petrol filling stations and the provision of usable toilets countrywide. The need for accessible public transport is also recognised.

INFORMATION

Regular dissemination of information is a vitally important function of the DDA. Access, vehicles, jobs, benefits, holidays, care etc. are only some of the topics that the DDA is keen to communicate to members. There is a regular quarterly magazine, published by the organisation and free to members, called 'Magic Carpet'. This presents hard news, reporting of current topics, humour, and news of local group activities. 'Magic Carpet' is widely recognised as the leading magazine for disabled people. In addition to the magazine, broadsheets on matters of information and help to members are produced, including the leaflets listed on the application form.

DDA
INDEPENDENCE THROUGH MOBILITY

Fig 13.2 The leaflet produced by the Disabled Drivers Association
Reproduced with their kind permission

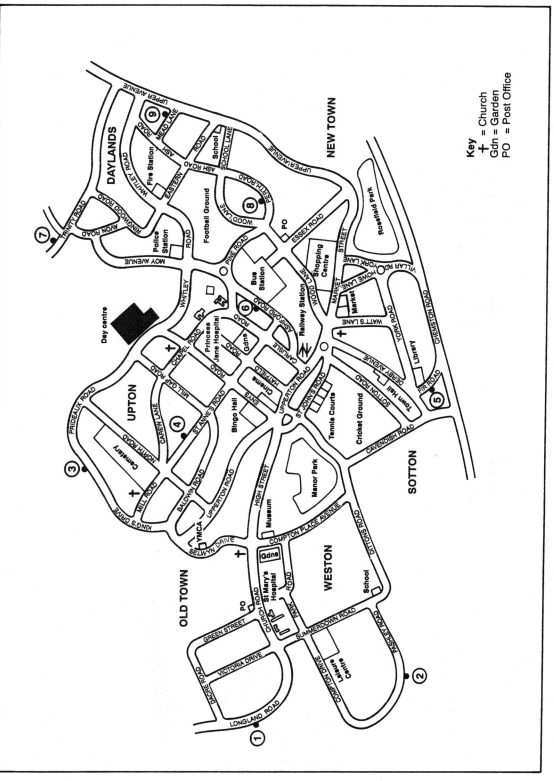

Fig 13.3 Town map

You are the transport controller on duty during the morning when the plan you have worked out is in operation. The driver rings in to report that he has been involved in an accident. He still has four people on board with minor injuries, but obviously cannot leave the scene, even if the vehicle could move.

(a) What would you have to do next?

(b) Who should be notified of the accident?

(c) What are the insurance requirements of your vehicles?

(d) You later learn that the driver suffers from epilepsy, which he did not disclose on appointment, and that this may have contributed towards the accident. What action would you take?

(e) If you decide to dismiss him, what help could he get, for example, from an Industrial Tribunal?

(f) Would his passengers be able to make a claim against him?

BTEC Common Skills: 1, 2, 3, 4, 8, 9, 10, 12, 13, 14, 15, 18.
GNVQ Level 2: 2.1, 5.1, 5.2.
GNVQ Level 3: 1.1, 6.1, 6.2, 6.3, 6.4.

Chapter 14

EDUCATION

Education is something which goes on throughout life, but here we will concentrate more upon the formal variety. In the main this is between four or five years old and either 16 or 18, but with the option of going to colleges, polytechnics and universities, or continuing formal education by another route such as postal courses (including The Open University and The Open College) or with employers.

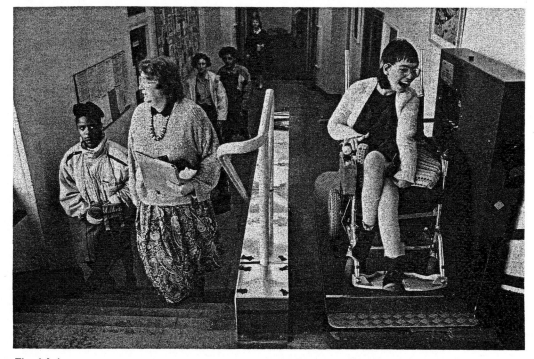

Fig 14.1 © John Birdsall Photography

For people with a disability, this may not be quite so straightforward, and special arrangements may need to be made with regard to both teaching and where it takes place. The 1981 Education Act covers just this situation, and advises Local Education Authorities (LEAs) to assess the specific needs of individual children and make the necessary arrangements for them. This process is known as 'statementing', the details of which are explained more fully in the information leaflet on pages 124–5 produced by ASBAH (The Association for Spina Bifida and Hydrocephalus), and reproduced here with their kind permission. Remember that it was written with a specific group in mind, but that the general information is applicable to all statements.

A GUIDE TO THE STATEMENTING PROCESS

Background

A 'Statement according to the 1981 Education Act' may sound daunting but it is simply a legal document relating to an individual child with special educational needs. It should describe precisely those individual needs and how the Local Education Authority intends to meet them. The process of statementing is expensive and, in the past, not all Local Authorities have chosen to statement children with spina bifida and/or hydrocephalus. Many Local Authorities believe that they can provide excellent education for children with special needs without resort to statementing. Whilst this has been true in some cases, some parents have challenged their Authority to provide a Statement, believing that this is the only way to ensure that their child obtains the most appropriate education.

The importance of a Statement

When a Statement accurately reflects a child's particular learning difficulties, there is reason to believe that suitable provision is more likely. However, provision of the required resources, human and/or material, will depend on whether the Authority has these at its disposal. Once the 1988 Education Act is fully operational, there is no certainty that all Local Education Authorities will have the same support services as they have today. Some may therefore be unable to satisfy fully the specific needs identified by Statements. However, if a child with spina bifida and/or hydrocephalus has learning difficulties or requires special provision because of his or her disability, a Statement of this need should be provided. Although this will not guarantee provision, resources are more likely to be directed towards children with statements. Parents may need to lobby the authority to provide a Statement. The lobbying process can take time and is not always successful.

The importance of accuracy

Statements are meaningless if they fail to specify actual learning difficulties. It is important to ensure that all difficulties are specified. Whilst physical disability can result in learning difficulties, this is not always the case. Therefore, whilst an outline of physical disability is important, it should not overshadow the details of specific learning difficulties. Unless, for example, poor hand-eye co-ordination, left-handedness, dyslexia or poor mathematical ability are specified, it is highly unlikely that additional help will be given to overcome them. Also, the selection of an appropriate school will be related to specified needs given in part A of the Statement. Should these not be fully described, it is likely that a child will be wrongly placed in a school which is unable to cater fully for all his or her educational needs.

General information relating to Statementing

1. The Local Education Authority can instigate the statementing process at any time in a child's school life, that is between 4 and 18 years.

2. Statementing can start before the child enters school at four years. It is then undertaken by the Health Authority. Pre-school nursery opportunities are usually provided as a result.

3. A Statement must be updated regularly—usually once a year. However, it is the Education Authority who decide when re-assessment should take place. It is important for parents to read a new Statement carefully. They should not assume that it is a replica of the previous one or that changed circumstances and newly-identified learning problems have been included.

4. Statements will be discontinued at the Authority's discretion. Parents can put forward a case for this discontinuation at any time. This is best undertaken when the Authority indicates a re-assessment is to be made.

Fig 14.2 A Guide to the Statementing Process, one of the information sheets published by ASBAH

▲ Parental role and rights

1. The 1988 Education Act relating to statementing recommends that parents play a full part in the process.

2. Parents should provide information which they believe should be included in the Statement.

3. Parents must by law be given at least 15 days in which to comment on a provisional Statement. Any modifications which they recommend should be fully considered by the Authority but need not be included.

4. If parents disagree with the Statement, they can challenge it. Appeals should be directed to the Director of Education for the Authority. If this does not result in action, the Secretary of State at the Department of Education and Science should be approached. It is recommended that parents seek advice from their local ASBAH Fieldworker or the ASBAH Education, Training and Employment Officer if they are unhappy about a draft Statement. This should be done as soon as possible so that there is an opportunity to obtain expert second opinions and reports.

5. A child with a Statement has his or her school chosen for them by the local Authority. Whilst, in theory, parents can indicate a preference, they have no right to choose a school for their child. Under the 1981 Act, it is the responsibility and duty of the Authority to specify the school which it believes appropriate for each child with a Statement. This becomes more of a key issue at Secondary level.

▲ Steps in the Statementing process

1. Parents may be told that their child will be assessed by an Educational Psychologist or some other professional. They may or may not be told this is to produce a draft Statement. Technically, parents have 29 days in which to provide evidence which they feel the authority should take into account in the production of the draft Statement.

2. Too often, the first indication parents receive about the process is the arrival of the draft Statement. A final date for the completion of the relevant form and receipt of any proposed modifications from the parents will be given in the accompanying letter. By law, parents have 15 days in which to respond to this first draft. Any details which the parents wish to be taken into account must be sent at this stage.

3. Whether parents sign the Statement or not, it becomes a legal document after the closing date for response has passed. The Authority has the right to ignore any details and modifications which the parents have sent if it feels that they are irrelevant (see Parental Role and Rights, para 4). However, most will incorporate parental ideas providing they are substantiated by relevant facts

▲ Preparation for Statementing

Parents are advised to keep accurate records of their child's functioning and development from birth. Details of age of developments such as starting to speak, crawling, sitting up, and eye/hand co-ordination are all important for statementing prior to four years of age. A diary is by far the best method of keeping such records. Details of medical history are also important. It is strongly recommended that parents keep all relevant letters, especially those relating to the developmental process. An A4 file is, perhaps, most valuable for keeping these in date order.

Such a file and diary are also valuable once the child begins school. School reports and details of progress interviews can then be included.

▲ Final comments

Statementing is usually a process of negotiation between the Education Authority and parents. Every parent should want to obtain the very best education for his or her child and every Authority has to juggle its scarce resources, legal obligations and moral duty to all its children.

Each Authority operates in a different way within the boundaries of the law. So, whilst this leaflet is intended to answer basic questions, it cannot be a comprehensive guide to the statementing process. For further information or help with an individual case, parents are asked to consult both their ASBAH Fieldworker and the Education, Training and Employment Officer at the national office.

(a) What is a statement of educational need?

(b) Why have some parents challenged their LEA to provide a statement?

(c) Why does statementing not guarantee provision?

(d) When is a statement meaningless?

(e) If a specific learning difficulty is not specified, what may be the outcome?

(f) Who undertakes to provide a statement if a child is under 4 years old?

(g) How often should statements be re-assessed?

(h) How long do parents have to comment on a provisional statement?

(i) What should be done if there is any disagreement with the recommendations?

(j) Do parents have to sign the statement in order for it to become a legal document?

(k) How are parents advised to prepare for statementing?

There are, of course, difficulties which arise in the system, and some accolades to be awarded, as shown by the following extracts.

ON THE WINNING SIDE

A family in Wales have just won an appeal to get their child's statement of special needs re-written — thanks mainly to the intervention and support of ASBAH's education adviser, Peter Walker.

The local authority had sent Jane's statement to her parents only two weeks before the end of the summer term, recommending that she attend a mainstream comprehensive school which is designated to integrate disabled pupils from that area. But Jane's parents were not happy with the 'choice' of school: "I just knew the school they'd chosen was wrong for Jane, at this time," said Mrs M. "In such a vast school she wouldn't be able to cope emotionally or educationally but we didn't have a clue about how to get the statement changed". Luckily an occupational therapist, at a unit attended by Jane, suggested the Ms contact ASBAH. The family had always managed on their own before but had now met a problem where they wanted outside help.

"Peter was very helpful, he went through the statement with us and suggested what to say in letters to the authority, he visited the school chosen by the authorities and the one we wanted Jane to go to, and he visited us and spoke to Jane".

The Ms want their daughter to attend Hebden Green Special School for a year to give her time to 'grow up emotionally and to gain more independence' so that she can hold her own in the comprehensive when she's ready.

At the tribunal, which Peter Walker attended, the authority were told to draw up a new statement for the child within two months. In the meantime, Jane is staying at her primary school until things are sorted out. The family will meet with the council again in January.

Mrs M is happy with this result and is full of praise for ASBAH's part in it: "We wouldn't have won without Peter. We are too emotionally involved and didn't understand the procedures involved."

Our Education Adviser has had similar successes in helping families in Essex and Lincolnshire to get the schools they want for their children. Peter Walker feels strongly about parents' rights: 'If we had not challenged the LEAs in these cases children would have been misplaced in secondary school. It is important to challenge a statement that we do not regard as satisfactory'.

If you need help, contact Peter Walker at National ASBAH.

(Note: The names in this article have been changed.)

(Taken from *Link* Magazine, No 197. Reproduced with kind permission of ASBAH.)

SCHOOL WINNER

In a general atmosphere of education cut-backs there is one authority that deserves to be commended for its support and commitment to integrating youngsters with a disability into mainstream schooling.

Prudhoe near Newcastle has recently agreed to spend £50 000 to enable 12-year old John, to stay with his friends and fellow pupils when they transfer from Prudhoe Middle School to Prudhoe High School.

The Director of Education for Northumberland said "If John does well at this school and goes on to the sixth form, we will spend more money again to allow him to study there."

An example to all, and perhaps this story will give hope to those children and parents in a similar situation.

(*Note: John's name has been changed.*)

(Taken from *Focus* (No 50), newsletter of the Muscular Dystrophy Group, and reproduced with their kind permission.)

EXERCISE

Read the piece on the Rosam family on page 75 in Chapter 8 Effects of Disability, taking particular note of Linda's coments regarding her brother's schooling and her son's schooling.

Write a paragraph on the differences you identify between the experiences of brother and son.

Further education

In theory, a wide range of courses are available at colleges, polytechnics, universities, and some specialist establishments such as the Royal School for the Blind in Leatherhead; Hereward College in Coventry, and others.

Some universities and colleges make special provision for students with disabilities.

For those who cannot get to a place of education for whatever reason, there is the Open University (OU) or Open College to consider. There are no entry requirements, and there may be help to pay for the courses. GCSEs and 'A' levels can also be studied by distance learning, i.e. by post, both in writing and on tape – either audio, or video, or both. The National Extension College in Cambridge can provide information about these.

Apart from this academic type of education, there is also Vocational education, aimed at preparing people for work. Your local Jobcentre has a Disablement Advisory Service where specialist staff known as Disablement Resettlement Officers (DROs) can give advice and guidance, and arrange for training courses on such things as how to go about looking for a job, or training for specific jobs. They can also help with the provision of specialist equipment to help do the job; it is also possible that they could help set an individual up in business. (*See* Chapter 16 Employment for further information.)

DOMINIC HUNT, 22, is a 'graduate' of CRYPT's 'Gavarnie' project. In his three years there he studied oil painting, life drawing, sculpture and photography at Chichester College of Technology nearby. He also passed 'A' levels in Art and Art History.

He has always been interested in art and has been encouraged by his mother who is an art teacher. But whilst he was at school, his interest in art took a back seat: 'I didn't really do art at school. I was more involved in other subjects. I didn't really get the chance.'

Subsequently, Dominic found that the artistic environment at 'Gavarnie' did not stretch his artistic development to the level he desired: 'I got a lot of help from a lot of people at 'Gavarnie', but it wasn't on the sort of level I needed.'

He also found the small, group home setting at 'Gavarnie' not conducive to artistic interaction: 'I actually wanted to get to college, and that was more to do with being with other people. It was a bit difficult at 'Gavarnie' because there were only two other artists. I felt I didn't really have enough people of my own age to swap ideas with.'

Dominic has found the artistic stimulation he was seeking in a two year foundation course at Falmouth School of Art. He lives in one of the college's halls of residence and is cared for by community service volunteers.

Dominic has also found increased personal stimulation and responsibility since leaving 'Gavarnie': 'In some ways a lot of things were done for you at CRYPT. Organising carers – you didn't have to do that. But now I'm at Falmouth I've got to assume that responsibility.'

One of Dominic's main artistic interests lies in computer graphics which he hopes may lead to him doing more with animation and computers.

In the same way that cultural and artistic expression was smothered in the old style communist Eastern bloc, so is the personal and artistic development of people with disabilities in institutional life, as these four young artists have confirmed. As they begin to establish their own identity and independence in the communities they will increasingly become a part of, then so too will they find opportunity and stimulation to make their unique artistic statements.

It is to be hoped that the policy of community care in this country will enable people with disabilities to break free from the constraints of institutional life. For young artists like Scott, Nigel, Anthony and Dominic, this presents not only an opportunity for personal development and independence, but also an outlet for their artistic expression.

Taken from *The Search* magazine, 1991, and reproduced by kind permission of The Muscular Dystrophy Group

EXERCISES

1. Fill in the Statement of Educational Needs form on pages 129–31 as for Michael Thomas (*see* Case 1 page 176).

STATEMENT OF SPECIAL EDUCATIONAL NEEDS

I — Introduction

1.   In accordance with section 7 of the Education Act 1981 and the Education (Special Educational Needs) Regulations 1983, the following statement is made by the .... council ("the education authority") in respect of the child whose name and other particulars are mentioned below.

<table>
<tr><td colspan="2" align="center">Child</td></tr>
<tr><td>Surname ....</td><td>Other names ....</td></tr>
<tr><td>Home address ....</td><td></td></tr>
<tr><td>...</td><td></td></tr>
<tr><td>...</td><td>Sex ....</td></tr>
<tr><td>Date of birth ....</td><td>Religion ....</td></tr>
<tr><td></td><td>Home language ....</td></tr>
<tr><td colspan="2" align="center">Child's parent or guardian</td></tr>
<tr><td>Surname ....</td><td>Other names ....</td></tr>
<tr><td>Home address ....</td><td>Relationship to child ....</td></tr>
<tr><td>...</td><td></td></tr>
<tr><td>...</td><td></td></tr>
<tr><td>Telephone No. ....</td><td></td></tr>
</table>

2.   When assessing the child's special educational needs the education authority took into consideration, in accordance with Regulation 8 of the Regulations, the representations, evidence and advice set out in the Appendices to this statement.

▶

II — Special educational needs

(Here set out in accordance with section 7 of the 1981 Act, the child's special educational needs as assessed by the education authority.)

III — Special educational provision

(Here specify, in accordance with Regulation 10(1)(a),

(a) the special educational provision which the education authority consider appropriate to meet the needs specified in Part II.

(Here specify, in accordance with Section 18 of the Education Reform Act, 1988)

(b) any modifications to the National Curriculum necessary to meet the child's special educational needs, in terms of programmes of study, attainment targets and assessment and testing

(c) any exemptions from foundation subjects (specify which)

(d) details to indicate how it is proposed to replace the exempted programme in order to maintain a broad, balanced curriculum.)

IV — Appropriate school or other arrangements

(Here specify, in accordance with Regulation 10(1)(b), the type of school and any particular school which the education authority consider appropriate for the child or the provision for his or her education, otherwise than at a school, which they consider appropriate.)

V — Additional non-educational provision

(Here specify, in accordance with Regulation 10(1)(c), any such additional provision as is there mentioned or record that there is no such additional provision. Where provision is mentioned, state the providing Authority.)

(Signature of authenticating Officer)

....

A duly authorised officer of the
education authority

(Date)

....

2 **Choose one of the following two exercises.**

A *Recorded guide*

Record a commentary for a student with partial sight to guide them from the bus park, or where the taxis stop, into and around the college.

- Remember that they will be listening to it from a Walkman, and will be studying on different courses.
- The first part needs to be a tour of communal areas such as canteen, library, toilets, etc.
- The second part will have to be personalised for an individual to find the rooms required for their particular course.
- The routes from the room used to the communal areas must be included, as should the way to the nearest or most convenient toilets.
- Remember to mention any hazards you come across.

B *Talking newspaper*

Alternatively, find out if there is a local talking newspaper and volunteer your services, either individually or as a group; *or* record your own magazine of local interest for distribution, either through the local talking newspaper, or through your own and college resources.

- Arrange some market research into what your intended customers would like to have included.
- Research the implications for costs, time, distribution and contacting recipients.

BTEC Common Skills: 1, 2, 6, 7, 8, 11, 12, 13, 14, 16, 17, 18.
GNVQ Level 2: 1.2, 2.1, 2.2, 3.1.
GNVQ Level 3: 1.1, 1.2, 2.1, 2.2, 3.2, 5.4.

3 **Survey of college**

(with acknowledgements to Llandrillo College, Colwyn Bay)

You have been contracted by the college management to prepare a survey of the college buildings and grounds in preparation for an advertising campaign to recruit more people with disabilities to courses running there.

Specific questions being asked are:
(a) How many parking spaces are there for disabled drivers?
(b) Are they near entrances?
(c) Do the entrances have a ramp or steps?
(d) How wide is the door?
(e) Is it easy to open?
(f) Which way does it open?
(g) What type of handle is fitted?
(h) Can they travel from there to the rooms without any impediment?
(i) How suitable are the toilet facilities?
(j) Is the signposting adequate, both inside and outside the college buildings?
(k) From where could a disabled visitor get help if necessary? How would she know where to get it from?
(l) Are recreational facilities such as the gym easily accessible?
(m) Are there any lifts (stairlifts or ordinary lifts)?
(n) How accessible are they?

(o) How accessible are the controls once inside or on the lift?

(p) Can these lifts accommodate a wheelchair plus rider plus helper?

(q) How accessible are the academic facilities, such as classrooms, libraries, computer suites, laboratories?

(r) What are the height of benches, and what leg-room is there beneath desks, benches, counters?

(s) Is there room to manoeuvre with walking aids between fixtures and fittings?

Try wherever possible to undertake this survey with somebody in a wheelchair. If the college does not have a wheelchair, and you have to borrow one, try asking the local Red Cross, or an Old People's Home, or possibly a local hospital.

Stage two

(a) How many students with a disability attend the college?

(b) Is there a policy of integration?

(c) What courses are the most popular for people with disabilities?

(d) What courses would they like to be enrolled for?

(e) How many students with disabilities are on your course?

(f) Discuss the possible reasons for your findings; are some courses more popular than others? Can you identify reasons for this?

(g) Is it because they are held in rooms with better access?

(h) How could you encourage more people with disabilities to come to college, and on to your course in particular?

(i) If a student with a disability is on your course, what difficulties are being experienced which are different than those of other students?

(j) If you are a disabled student, what difficulties are you experiencing which differ from your colleagues?

(k) If a wheelchair user wanted to become a member of your course group, what problems would you envisage for them? Bear in mind placement experience as well as college facilities.

BTEC Common Skills: Potentially, there are elements of all of these included in these exercises.
GNVQ Level 2: 1.1, 1.2, 1.3, 2.1, 2.2, 2.3, 3.1, 4.3.
GNVQ Level 3: 1.1, 1.2, 1.3, 1.4, 2.1, 2.2, 3.2, 4.1, 4.2, 5.1, 5.4, 8.1, 8.2.

Chapter 15

SPORT AND LEISURE

A physical disability does not exclude you from taking part in sport or leisure activities, only the range which may be available to you. In some cases the only bar is due to poor access, which can be modified if the will is there.

Many providers of sport and leisure do make their facilities available to disabled people, although some may request prior notice, i.e. disabled people cannot just turn up and expect to take part as could the majority of the population. For example football and other stadia have specified parts of the ground for disabled people, usually concentrating on wheelchair users. Cinemas and bingo halls may make provision for people with specific needs (easier access, or induction hearing loops). Bowling alleys have mechanisms to help those who cannot man-handle the bowls. The best advice for disabled people and their carers is to ask what facilities there are once an activity has been chosen.

In addition, there are organisations which specialise in helping disabled groups. Riding for the Disabled is one such which encourages horse riding; the Terrapins give help with swimming; the British Sports Association for the Disabled help with field, track, and other sports; and there are others.

Some information on what is available and what disabled individuals can achieve is illustrated in this chapter.

CASE STUDY

THE BRITISH SPORTS ASSOCIATION FOR THE DISABLED (BSAD)

What is BSAD?

The British Sports Association for the Disabled was founded in 1961 by Sir Ludwig Guttmann, a world-renowned neurosurgeon, to provide and develop sport and physical recreation for people with disabilities, and to promote integration with the community at large.

Since its inauguration BSAD has established a national remit to provide, promote, co-ordinate and to develop opportunities in all sports and physical recreation for people with any type of physical, sensory or mental disability.

Membership has risen steadily since 1961 and BSAD now has a pyramid structure, with its broad grass roots base in the member clubs, schools and organisations throughout Britain. These groups have a clear input into the policy making of the Association through democratically elected officers at county, regional and national levels.

The Association has its head office in London with ten regional offices around England and close links with the Sports Associations for the disabled in Scotland, Wales and Northern Ireland.

On behalf of its varied membership, BSAD provides recreational opportunities across the whole range of sporting activity at its club and local level; and currently provides competitive opportunities in more than 20 different sports at local, regional,

Fig 15.1 Putting the shot
© John Birdsall Photography

Fig 15.2 Playing snooker
© John Birdsall Photography

Fig 15.3 Playing hockey
© John Birdsall Photography

national and international levels.

In addition, on behalf of its members and non-members alike, BSAD offers a comprehensive information and advice service, as well as leadership, coaching and awareness training in all aspects of sport for people with a disability.

BSAD is recognised as *the* national body responsible for the co-ordination and development of sport and physical recreation for people with a disability. It has created a positive image of our sport and will project the sport into the 21st century.

BSAD's Mission Statement and Objectives

The Mission Statement

The BSAD aims to provide, develop and co-ordinate opportunities in sport and recreation for people with disabilities in partnership with other relevant agencies.

The Objectives

- To provide opportunities for people with disabilities to participate in and enjoy sport and recreation, in accordance with their own wishes.
- To ensure the co-ordinated provision and improvement of coaching, training and education opportunities.
- To organise and develop a programme of sports events and championships at a local, regional and national level.
- To support the membership in the provision of sport and recreation for people with disabilities and to encourage new membership.
- To increase awareness of the objectives and activities of BSAD and the sporting achievements of people with disabilities.
- To provide and maintain an information and advice service for all enquiries concerning BSAD and the provision of sport and recreation for people with disabilities.
- To raise funds at a local, regional and national level in order to fulfil the objectives of the Association.
- To pursue all of the objectives of BSAD in a professional manner so as to enhance the image of sport and recreation for people with disabilities.

BSAD developing sport

by Richard Hunt

Everybody has to start somewhere, even if you happen to be a Linford Christie, a David Bryant or a Desmond Douglas; and everybody, even these elite athletes, needs some help onto the first rungs of the ladder to the top when they are starting out.

However, not everyone wants to be a high achiever. At the other extreme of the sporting scene, there are those who just want to take part but have no real idea of what they want to do or how to go about it.

To help both these types of sportspeople with a disability – the 'stars' of the future and the 'have-a-goers' – BSAD has placed the major emphasis of its work on the development of sport (i.e. the encouragement of more people to take part in more sporting activities at all levels of participation and excellence). In fact, this development of sport is the whole purpose of BSAD but it takes on many guises, with not all seemingly directly related to sport.

In a purely sporting context there are many ways in which BSAD approaches the development of sport at its various levels.

1 **Have-a-Go Days** – at the very grass roots level of sport, BSAD aims to introduce more and more people with disabilities to as wide a range of activities as possible, through numerous 'Have-a-Go' Days or 'Come and Try It' Days. At these, individuals can try a wide and varied number of sports giving them a chance to find out what they really enjoy doing.

2 **Sport-Specific Development Days** – once an individual has found the sport that he/she enjoys, then BSAD encourages them to participate in "Development Days" dedicated to that specific sport. At these days individuals can learn more about the sport and receive good quality coaching and instruction.

3 **Competitions** – Local/Regional/National – once an individual has found their sport and started receiving appropriate coaching, they need a means to test out their new found skills, to compare their ability against others, to set themselves goals and to measure their achievements. For this reason, BSAD sees the organisation of sporting competition at various levels as a vital part of the development of sport. For those who want to compete, the large number of Local, Regional and National Championships that BSAD organises are the next steps on the ladder to the top. The Championships give purpose and direction to those who have the desire and the ability to take their sport further.

The participation in sport and recreation by people with disabilities is the ultimate aim of all BSAD's development work, but alongside just the provision of opportunities there are other important objectives involved in the achievement of this aim.

Coaches/officials

Coaches and officials are of paramount important to the development of sport for people with disabilities. At present qualified coaches and officials from the 'able-bodied' sector are key targets for all BSAD's sport-specific development days. BSAD is working to increase the coach and official's awareness of disability in general, and of the abilities of sportspeople who happen to have a disability. The ultimate aim is to recruit the services of an ever-increasing body of qualified coaches and officials and to convert them to the cause of the wider development of sport.

Sponsorship

None of BSAD's work from grass roots up to elite performance would be possible without the financial support of the generous companies and individuals who donate a large proportion of BSAD's total income.

In recent years, BSAD has sought to interest major companies in sponsoring not just a National Championship but also in making a commitment to a particular sport from grass-roots development all the way up to the National Championships. Major sponsors, such as British Telecom (Swimming) and NatWest (Basketball) have already agreed to cover the 'complete package' giving the necessary resources to the full development of the sport, and so avoiding a continuing emphasis on just the elite.

BSAD is committed to the development of sport for people with disabilities. Through building an ever wider base to the sporting pyramid, and thus pushing the pinnacle ever higher, BSAD is raising standards throughout, in terms of the number of people participating and the quality of their sporting performance.

How can you help

As a charity, BSAD is always in need of help for the continuation of its work and the furtherance of its aims. There are many ways you can help either personally or through a commercial company, local authority, sports centre, club or other organisation.

Financial support

BSAD relies heavily on personal donations and commercial sponsorship, with Sports Council grant aid amounting to only a very small percentage of the total annual turnover. The association is grateful for any financial assistance and you could help by:

- Raising funds for BSAD
- Making a personal donation or a deed of covenant
- Advertising in one of BSAD's publications
- Sponsoring an event

Voluntary help

If you have time to spare, you could help in a local club or BSAD office either on a day to day basis or on special occasions. We need helpers and friends in clubs and at sports events and we also need drivers, as well as help with administration. If you are a disabled or able-bodied sportsperson you could help with coaching at a local club, and physiotherapists can help with classifying athletes and by applying your specialist knowledge to help disabled sportspeople.

Lending facilities and resources

If you belong to a sports club you could encourage people with disabilities to join, or hold a 'have-a-go' day at your club for local disabled groups. You could organise and host sports matches for and with people with disabilities, and if your club or school or work place has sports facilities or equipment, you could offer these free of charge to a disabled group. Office equipment and resources would also be of great assistance to the Regional offices.

Helping to increase awareness

You can also help by increasing awareness of BSAD and of disabled sport in general. Please encourage your local sports centres, schools, and local authorities to provide more opportunities and facilities for people with disabilities to participate in sport. Also, encourage your local newspapers, radio and television stations to report on the sporting achievements of disabled people in your area.

However you help . . . thank you.

(Reproduced with kind permission of BSAD.)

Below are some extracts describing the achievements of three disabled people, two with Friedreich's Ataxia and one with spina bifida.

RONNIE DAVIES

Ronnie is now 47 and FA was diagnosed 22 years ago. A married man, Ronnie was awarded the British Empire Medal in the 1987 New Year's Honours List. Ronnie is also a diabetic.

Ronnie's most conspicuous continuous achievement has been to start and maintain the Rhuddlan and District Sports Club for the Disabled. They now have suitable equipment for all their disabled members including an indoor bowling mat. Ronnie has managed to obtain the services of experts in various sports to give instruction free to disabled people, including Archery, Pistol Shooting, Badminton etc. Also he has raised sufficient money to provide and maintain two buses with lifts to transport club members to their club in the local Sports Hall as well as to sports contests throughout England and Wales — no small job for one person! Ronnie lends the buses out to other disabled groups whenever possible and any time that a flag day is on (for whatever group of disabled people) you can be sure that Ronnie will be there in the freezing cold and pouring rain. Ronnie is a self-effacing person not much given to courting publicity or blowing his own trumpet.

He says: 'I was delighted to receive the BEM in the New Year's Honours List and also feel honoured to be mentioned in this leaflet — particularly if this will help or encourage other FAers. I do not, however, feel that either my achievements or behaviour have been at all oustanding — I am simply pursuing my life by devoting my energies to what I think is worthwhile. The fact that others should also find it laudable is extremely gratifying but coincidental.'

Reproduced with kind permission of the FA Group

Sports personality Alison

We are pleased to report that 17 year old Alison Jennings, an FAer from the Isle of Wight, has won 2 gold medals in the Southern Region Swimming Championships. This qualified her to enter the Junior National Disabled Inter-regional Swimming Competition, where she won a bronze medal for 50 metres backstroke and 25 metres freestyle.

Alison, whose FA was diagnosed five years ago, has been swimming since the age of two, but she only took up the sport competitively when she started to attend the Mayor Treloar College at Alton, Hampshire, in September 1989.

She does a tremendous amount of sport, taking part in athletic championships, including discus, shot put and javelin and has also participated in indoor bowls tournaments where she managed to reach the semi finals.

Alison also won the Sports Personality Cup Of The Year Award for 1990 at the Mayor Treloar College and is to be congratulated as she is only the second girl to have won this in 11 years!

Reproduced from *FAX* magazine No 93, with their kind permission.

Real life rescue for trainee lifeguard

Brian Waugh, a 19-year-old trainee lifeguard, was just on his way home from his shift at the swimming pool when he noticed a little girl in difficulty at the deep end of the teaching pool. "She was under the water and struggling to get back up for air," said Brian. "I was fully clothed as I was about to go home but I jumped in to get her out, before calling for assistance."

The three-year-old child was none the worse for her ordeal and Brian has been recommended for the Friends of Northumberland and Durham Life Saving Society certificate, in recognition of his quick-thinking action.

Brian, who has spina bifida, has been at Consett's Belle Vue swimming centre for a year on a YTS scheme and is hoping to go on to obtain his Teacher's Certificate in swimming, as part of his employment training at the centre.

He's no stranger to the water – having swum for England in the 1987 Disabled Games at Edinburgh where he won two golds and a silver – and hopes to make his career as a swimming teacher.

Reproduced with kind permission of ASBAH

One of the best-known organisations helping disabled people to live a more active life is the Riding for the Disabled Association, whose leaflet has been reproduced on page 140.

© John Birdsall Photography

RIDING FOR THE DISABLED ASSOCIATION

1. What is the Association?
The Association is a nationally registered charity.

2. How is the Association funded?
By voluntary contribution. Fundraising takes place nationally to provide finance for publications, films, insurance, national holidays and training courses and to provide an effective service to Council, Committees and Member Groups.

3. How do we choose our riders?
All riders are referred to us with the approval of their doctors. The majority of our riders come from special schools for the disabled, adult training centres or hospitals.

4. How do we select our helpers?
All our helpers, instructors and physiotherapists volunteer their services free to the Association. Training is given at local, regional and national level. We require enthusiasm, dedication and a willingness to work with disabled people. Prior horse knowledge is not necessary.

5. How can a volunteer find details of local Member Groups
By writing to the Riding for the Disabled Association, at the National Agricultural Centre, Kenilworth, Warwickshire CV8 2LY.

6. Can volunteers who are not interested in horses help in other ways?
Anyone who is interested in fundraising, publicity, secretarial work, administration or simply willing to help at social functions would be welcome to offer their service to a local Group.

7. How often do Member Groups hold riding sessions?
Normally once a week. The larger Member Groups might have sessions three or four times a week, but our numbers are such that it is unlikely that a disabled person will ride more than once a week.

8. For whom is driving provided?
Driving presents an alternative to the heavily handicapped for whom riding is no longer possible. Special vehicles have been designed to suit the more heavily handicapped.

9. Is riding provided for both children and adults?
Approximately one quarter of our riders are adult and clearly have differing requirements from those of child riders. Many Groups are able to cater for both categories, others tend to concentrate on either adults or children.

10. How is riding progress measured?
Progress for the rider depends so much on the nature of his or her disability and the regularity with which they ride. It is possible for riders to take a series of proficiency tests which are a guide to progress. The essential requirement is that riding should give pleasure and fun to all who take part in it. Additionally, we encourage participation in Pony Clubs and Riding Clubs for those more advanced and physically able riders.

Recurring needs
Suitable horses and ponies
Voluntary Helpers
Special equipment for riders
Training of Instructors, Therapists & Helpers
Conference Facilities
Covered Riding Schools
Sponsorships for publications & films
Transportation

Available from the Secretary
List of Member Groups together with Regional and County Structure.
R.D.A. News
Annual Report and Accounts
Films produced by R.D.A.

Chapter 16

EMPLOYMENT

People with disabilities would like a job for the same reasons as everyone else likes to have a job, but are three times less likely to get one.

The Disabled Persons (Employment) Act 1944 states that employers of more than 20 people should have a quota of three per cent of their staff who are registered as disabled by the Department of Employment. (*See* Chapter 5 Definitions of disability.)

In actual fact, by 1990, Department of Employment figures showed that less than one third of employers reached this target. One reason given was that the number of registered disabled people has declined over the years . Prosecutions of companies not employing their quota have reached a grand total of ten since 1944. Disablement Resettlement Officers (DROs) prefer to rely on advice and persuasion rather than court actions.

One problem with the statistics, however, is that it is not compulsory for anybody with a disability to register the fact. Registration is seen as both a positive and a negative step by some people. There are those who do not wish to become labelled as disabled (*see* the section on 'Labelling' in Chapter 8 Effects of disability), and others who wish to take advantage of the training schemes and extra help available by being included on the register.

A new symbol began to appear in job advertisements during 1991:

 An Equal Opportunities Employer welcoming applications from all sections of the community.

Fig 16.1 The symbol denoting companies which are Equal Opportunities employers

This logo commits those organisations using it to abide by the Code of Good Practice on the Employment of Disabled People. They are expected to provide all the help they can, by training, the provision of special equipment, or in any other way possible to recruit or retain disabled people in their employment.

If you should need to help a person with a disability to look for a job, you will use exactly the same sources as you would yourself: newspaper and magazine advertisements, postcards in shop windows, approaching employers direct, or via the Careers Service if it is the first job since leaving school. The Department of Employment and private employment agencies are also available to assist prospective employees. The Department of Employment has Jobcentres and specialist facilities through a Disablement Advisory

Service and Disablement Resettlement Officers (DROs) (for more information *see* Chapter 1 Who are the carers?).

There are also courses to train or retrain for specific jobs, job clubs to help in organising the search for work in the company of other people, and Sheltered Employment in workshops run by Remploy, voluntary organisations and Local Authorities.

EXERCISES

1. Fill out the job application form on pages 143–4 on behalf of Jason Young, who is applying for the job described on page 145.

2. **Job interview: role play**
   Invite Jason to an interview, and organise an interview panel to see him.

   Cast
   - one member of the group is to act as Jason;
   - another as his helper;
   - one as the receptionist at the offices;
   - one as the Personnel Officer;
   - two more as her/his colleagues on the interviewing panel; and
   - one or two more candidates for interview for the same job.

The interview panel should decide who should be appointed, after the interviews have taken place, identifying the reason for taking the decision that they did.

Will these other candidates also be people with disabilities?

If one of these people has a hidden disability such as epilepsy or diabetes, should he or she divulge this? If so, when and how – on the application form, or verbally at the interview? What are your reasons for the choices you have taken about this? If the information about the disability is not divulged, what may be the repercussions of this?

Decide upon the scenario for the candidates' arrival; what difficulties are there, if any, for access? Will you have to move furniture to allow room for a wheelchair? What facilities are there for when a disabled candidate needs a toilet?

The panel should work out the questions they are going to be asking in advance. Did they know of his disability from the application form?

Think what you would be concerned about as an employer – could Jason do the job? Has he any relevant experience? Would he be reliable? Does he need someone with him all the time? How is he going to get to and from work? Would any help be available from the DRO if this was the case?

Jason should anticipate what is to be asked and be ready with his answers. The players should prepare separately, however, as would be the case in the real situation.

The exercise may be recorded on video for discussion afterwards, or use by other groups.

BTEC Common Skills: 1, 2, 3, 4, 5, 6, 7, 8, 11, 12, 16 If video used, 18.
GNVQ Level 2: 1.1, 1.2, 1.3, 2.1, 2.2, 5.3, 6.3.
GNVQ Level 3: 1.1, 1.2, 1.3, 1.4, 2.1, 2.2, 2.3, 2.4, 4.1, 4.2, 5.1, 5.4, 6.2, 6.3.

Application for Employment

Strictly confidential

Please complete in black ink/biro

Position applied for

Source of application

Surname	Date of Birth Sex
	Nationality
First Names	Marital Status
Present Address	No. & Ages of Children
	Work Permit? YES/NO (If not British or from EEC Country)
	Permanent Address (if different)
Telephone No. Home and STD Code Business	
May we contact you at your Business No.? YES/NO	Telephone No.

EDUCATION School(s)	From	To	Examinations Passed	Grade

FURTHER EDUCATION (Full or part time or correspondence course) Name of Establishment	From	To	Examinations Passed	Grade

Please give brief details of honours and/or prizes received, and/or offices held at school/college

SKILLS

Are you an experienced –

Shorthand	YES/NO	Speeds	
Audio typing	YES/NO	Speeds	
Typing	YES/NO	Speeds	

Have you had any other keyboard training? (e.g. word processing etc.) Please give details

Languages – written/spoken/fluency

Fig 16.2 An application form

WORK HISTORY – List the following information giving your present post first or, if unemployed, the most recent

Name of firm and type of business	Period of Employment		Title and nature of your job	Reason for leaving	Salary
	From	To			

How much notice does your present employer require?

REFERENCES

Please give name, address and telephone number of two recent business referees or if none, give two personal referees

We will not contact your present employer without your permission

HEALTH

Are you a registered disabled person?   YES/NO

If 'YES' please give your RDP number

What, if any, serious illness have you suffered during the past two years?

Are you subject to any condition requiring treatment or medication?   YES/NO

If 'YES' please give details

Would you take a medical examination if we required you to do so?   YES/NO

Use this space to state your reasons for making this application, together with any additional information about yourself, your background, or experience which you consider relevant to it

Are you able to drive?   YES/NO

Have you a clean licence   YES/NO

Have you ever applied previously for a position here? if so give details

Have you any relatives here?   YES/NO
If 'YES' specify

Signature

Date

Fig 16.2 continued

Job Description

Post:	Clerical Assistant	**Post Ref No:**	AD9
Department:	Administration	**Salary:**	£8,000 Age 18–25

1. Main purpose of post:

To provide clerical assistance in the Administration Department including mailroom work, Staff Records, Maintenance, dealing with visitors to reception.

2. Reports to:

Office Services Manager

3. Responsible for:

Not applicable.

4. Main duties and responsibilities:

(a) Assisting with opening, sorting and distribution of the company's incoming mail.

(b) Assisting in the despatch of the company's outgoing mail.

(c) Storing and retrieving documents from the paper based filing system. Also, making up new files.

(d) Photocopying documents as required.

(e) Dealing with visitors to reception.

(f) Dealing with telephone enquiries.

(g) Maintaining staff records.

(h) Maintaining stocks of consumerables, including their issue and the recording of stock levels.

(i) Any other general clerical duties which might from time to time be required.

....

Signature   **Date**

Fig 16.3 A typical job description for a clerical assistant

Read the guidelines on inviting guest speakers in the Assignments section on page 202. Invite a local Disablement Resettlement Officer in to speak to the group regarding the problems they can face in their job. Alternatively, you could invite a Personnel Officer from an employing organisation such as a local industry or Local Government Department, or perhaps a private employment agency, about their policy on employing disabled people.

The following *Notes for Employers*, prepared by ASBAH, gives a better idea of the issues involved for people with spina bifida and hydrocephalus, together with general advice relevant to disability and hidden disability.

NOTES FOR EMPLOYERS

Background information – what are the conditions?

Spina bifida occurs very early in pregnancy – within the first 25 days. It is a fault in the development of the spinal column, when one or more of the bones of the spine (vertebrae) fail to close properly, leaving a gap.

This means the vitally important spinal cord and nerves are likely to be damaged, often resulting in paralysis below the level of the fault. Walking may be difficult or even impossible. There may also be the problem of incontinence. Later in life, the spine may curve or twist.

Hydrocephalus is caused by an imbalance between the production and absorption of Cerebro-spinal fluid (CSF) which results in the swelling of the ventricles (cavities) in the brain. An obvious outward sign can be the accelerated growth of the head. The pressure caused by this blockage has to be speedily relieved in order to minimise any damage. This is usually done by the insertion of a valve which drains the excess fluid into the abdominal or heart cavities.

More than 85% of people with spina bifida may also have hydrocephalus but it is also a condition which can occur independently. Because of advances in surgical and medical techniques, many more babies born with the disabilities have survived and taken their place in society. Today, there are more than 15,000 people – children, young people and adults – who, with support, can live fulfilled, independent and enjoyable lives.

The hidden handicaps

Hydrocephalus can also lead to 'hidden handicaps'.

People with the condition can often walk and may look as able as anyone else.

They do not want to appear 'different' and this makes it harder for them to be accepted as having a disability by their peers, tutors and employers. In particular, there continues to be little understanding by some employers of the effect that hydrocephalus may have on an individual's performance.

If hydrocephalus is present in combination with spina bifida, the person may use a wheelchair. For other people, the handicaps arising from the physical disability may be limited to continence management.

There is often no reason why the person with hydrocephalus cannot prove to be a competent and reliable employee with no more than the usual teething problems when settling into a new job. However, in other instances, where the degree of hydrocephalus is more severe, it may require a great deal of understanding and patience on the part of employers and colleagues with whom the individual works to enable him or her to overcome the 'hidden handicaps'.

Results and remedies

As has been explained, the handicaps arising from hydrocephalus will vary from one individual to another depending on that individual and the degree of disability.

The following are some of the more common results and suggested ways of overcoming them:

1 Concentration
People with hydrocephalus may be unable to sustain long periods of concentration on a particular task; they may be easily distracted, having difficulty in focusing their attention on the task in hand.

Allocate a long or complex task in short, separate 'packages'. Tasks should be given individually. For example, papers which need to be photocopied and collated should be given in small quantities at a time; the pages should be numbered clearly to aid collating. As well as verbal instructions on how many copies are required, a clear and concise written instruction should be attached to each piece of photocopying.

2 Short term memory
Some individuals may have difficulty in remembering tasks or details. If instructions are given one day, they may be completely forgotten by the next.

Give instructions to a concise, regular pattern, preferably verbal and written. These instructions may have to be repeated and reinforced if the information is to be retained. Begin with simple messages, with only one or two items, and gradually build up to more complex instructions.

3 Inability to cope with pressure
People with hydrocephalus are often unable to cope with any form of pressure or stress.

Provide a familiar and structured environment. Ideally, the individual should be answerable to one person. If that person is going to be absent from the workplace for any length of time, he or she should ensure that a deputy is nominated and that the employee concerned is notified whom that is.

4 Disorientation
The individual may experience difficulty in relating to a new or altered environment and in transferring skills from a familiar environment to a new location.

Allow time for readjustment and to become orientated to their new surroundings. Some retraining may be necessary.

5 Co-ordination
Hydrocephalus can lead to difficulties with eye/hand co-ordination. This may mean difficulty in using equipment such as a guillotine or stapler.

Ensure that the work station is appropriate to needs. The desk or workbench may need adjustment. Arms may need to be adequately supported to help better control.

6 Tendency to moodiness
Every employee has problems which they bring into the workplace but some people with hydrocephalus can be unduly affected by occurrences in their personal life – for example, a bus running late or an argument at home. This may affect their performance and make them moody and work output may suffer.

On the initial discovery that something is wrong, a sympathetic approach may be appropriate and will often achieve results. However, if the moodiness continues then, as with any other employee, the individual should be asked in a polite but firm manner to give more attention to their work. It can be a natural reaction for an employer to become over-sympathetic because of the employee's disability but often this only makes matters worse.

7 Physical disability
As explained above, hydrocephalus with spina bifida may result in mobility problems and lead to the use of a wheelchair.

Full accessibility to the workplace is of paramount importance. It is comparatively easy to do this through ramps, adequate toilet facilities, a reliable method of transportation to and from work and so on as long as financial resources are available.

Working environment

In a work environment, it is essential that there is someone to whom the person with spina bifida and/or hydrocephalus can relate. This should be someone who is able to supervise their work and give advice and support when required. S/he should also have an understanding of the disability and the possible results outlined above but should not neglect to point out mistakes when they occur. Like anyone else at work, a person with spina bifida and/or hydrocephalus learns by experience and that includes mistakes.

It is not going to benefit the individual or the employer if s/he is over-protected or cosseted. It may be natural for an employer or colleagues to 'mother' the disabled person. For example, although the employee who uses a wheelchair is quite independent in the street, coping with kerbs and so on, in the work environment he or she may not be allowed such independence. There is always someone pushing the wheelchair, opening doors or rushing to pick up papers. Obviously, there may be some who do need help, but the golden rule is to ask first. There may be a need for disability awareness training for other employees – ASBAH can help with this.

Disciplinary procedure

All employees, whether disabled or not, should be subject to the same disciplinary procedure within an organisation. However, more time may need to be taken to help an employee with disabilities to overcome any resulting handicaps. Often a solution can be found through frank and open discussion.

The situation should not be allowed to deteriorate and if an employer is concerned he or she should contact the local specialist Careers Officer, Disablement Advisory Service and, of course, ASBAH, who will be happy to help.

There may be a simple solution to the problem, which may not have occurred to the employer or the employee. Early consultations may well mean that the disabled employee keeps the job and there is better understanding all round. This is the goal to be sought.

Sources of advice

Careers service
Careers Officers, especially Specialist Career Officers, employed by local Education authorities are able to advise employers and young people with disabilities up to the age of 19 years.

Disablement Advisory Service
Is able to offer advice in a number of ways to make life at work easier for the disabled person. It is recommended that employers and employees make use of this service. The people to contact are:
- The Disablement Resettlement Officer (DRO), based at the local job centre

- Disablement Advisory Teams (DAS), regionally based, sometimes at job centres.

The DRO can offer financial help with adaptations to premises, provision of special equipment and grants for fares to work.

The following can also help
- Royal Association for Disability and Rehabilitation
  25 Mortimer Street
  London, SW1
  (for advice on employment).
- Disabled Living Foundation
  380 Harrow Road
  London W9
  (for advice on equipment of all kinds).
- British Computer Society Disability Project (071-637 0471)
  provides a free advice and information service to both the prospective employee and employer. It is hoped to extend this service beyond information about training courses, aids and adaptations using Information Technology to include job vacancies.
- IBM Support Centre for People with Disabilities. (Freephone 0800 269545)
  provides access to a comprehensive data base that addresses all employment questions related to employing a person with a disability.

Reproduced with kind permission of ASBAH

There are also initiatives from the voluntary and private sectors to help people with disabilities. The short pieces opposite on The Shaw Trust, Workable, and C4TV are reproduced from *FAX Magazine*, No 89 (from the Friedreich's Ataxia Group) with their kind permission.

QUESTIONS

1 Hidden disabilities carry additional problems for people seeking jobs; can you identify what these may be?

2 How can employers help overcome the problems of short term memory and short concentration spans?

3 What are your opinions of the Shaw Trust scheme?

4 Do you consider that disabled people suffer from discrimination and prejudice?

5 (a) What do you understand by the term 'positive discrimination'?
  (b) Organise a debate on the advantages and disadvantages of this in relation to disability. (*See* Assignment 6 for guidelines on how to do this.)

The Shaw Trust

The Trust started its operations in 1982 with the objective of helping with the integration of people with disabilities into society through the vehicle of paid and permanent employment.

The Trust found that a powerful aid to its objectives was the Sheltered Placement Scheme which it was able to operate with the help of the Department of Employment. This scheme enabled the Trust to seek out suitable work for its clients and then to employ them itself to do the work it had found on the "host" employers premises.

The Trust pays its clients the same rate for the work done that the host employer would normally have paid to able-bodied workers, but only charges the host a proportion of the wage in relation to the client's output.

This means that compensation can be made for a lack of speed and therefore the pressure to perform at an unrealistic rate is removed. Nevertheless, the Shaw Trust worker remains a cost effective worker to the employing host.

Additionally, the Trust uses its own Development Officers and specially trained Support Officers to provide to both its clients and host employers any advice or assistance that may be necessary at the place of work.

The success of this scheme has resulted in the Trust now being the sponsoring employer of over 1,600 people spread across most of England and Wales, with an increasing number now coming in from the Borders and Edinburgh areas of Scotland.

Shaw Trust and its clients have proved that people with disabilities can fill a wide variety of jobs. From an employer's point of view they are keen and loyal. They can also be highly innovative in devising ways in which a handicap can be overcome.

Since the work sought by the Trust is permanent, the benefits associated with regular employment apply to its workers. They are provided with pension funds in line with those of the host employer and officers of the Trust monitor to ensure that their wage rates and benefits are kept in line with those of able-bodied workers doing the same or similar work.

Many clients enjoy Shaw Trust accompanied holidays. The Trust now escorts parties to a number of Mediterranean resorts as well as to destinations in the United Kingdom.

The Trust is now a leading employer in its field and is pleased to assist whenever it can with any employment matters. It can be contacted at Caithness House, Western Way, Melksham, Wiltshire, SN12 8DZ.

WORKABLE – A new partnership of action on disability and employment

WORKABLE is a new national consortium for the voluntary sector. It has been established to promote joint action in providing training and employment opportunities for disabled people throughout the United Kingdom. Its member organisations include: OUTSET, RNID, RNIB, The Shaw Trust, Mencap, The Spastics Society, I CAN, The London Boroughs Disability Resource Team and The British Deaf Association, among others.

The objectives of WORKABLE are to provide a "one-stop shop" for employers and encourage them to make use of the combined service of disability organisations across the country.

It has already established close links with the Employers forum on Disability, which represents over fifty national employers. WORKABLE is attempting to establish a number of pilot projects between its member organisations and employers. It will focus particularly on areas of employment where disabled people are under-represented. It will also promote a positive image of the talents of disabled people by overcoming stereotypes and promoting the achievements of disabled people. WORKABLE will also be seeking financial support from the public and private sectors to complement the resources already invested by member organisations.

For further information, contact: RNID, or Shaw Trust. Tel: (0225) 707060.

Channel Four initiative for disabled people

Channel Four Television has undertaken an initiative to employ people both within the company itself and within the independent production sector. The company can offer two possible entry routes for people who have a disability and are keen to develop a career in television. The first is at its centre of operations in London. Opportunities exist to join a variety of departments where the roles range from engineering and transmission to accounting, presentation, secretarial and administrative. The other route is through a place on a two-year training course in the independent sector funded and managed by Channel Four. This combines formal college training with placements nationwide in the independent production companies which make its programmes. The course provides basic training in production areas such as camera, sound, editing or research.

For further information contact: Suzanne Jackson, Personnel Department, Channel Four Television, 60 Charlotte Street, London W1P 2AX.

Chapter 17

COMPUTERS

There are a great many aids and adaptations which can help people with the routine of daily living, from the washing machine and vacuum cleaner which are found in just about every home in the UK to the more specialist devices for specific needs, wheelchairs, for instance.

The more specialised the requirements, the higher the price to be paid. Computers are a versatile way of tailoring the specific requirements to individual need. Admittedly,

Fig 17.1 © John Birdsall Photography

the cost of them runs into hundreds of pounds for a basic machine, and then more hundreds for the bits and pieces that go with them, but they are a useful aid to independence and/or communication.

Voice synthesisers are one such aid, as are screens on telephones to allow written communication with deaf people, and controls for household tasks such as opening doors, switching on kettles or whatever, as pioneered by POSSUM (Patient Operator Selector Mechanisms) (*see* the case study on pages 153–6).

Apart from these practical applications, disabled people can derive an increased measure of independence and possibly an otherwise unattainable source of income, as well as great pleasure from the use of a home computer for leisure applications, playing games or even writing programs.

The following extract is taken from a piece by Brian Vallot-Lewis and is reproduced with the permission of *FAX* magazine, the journal of the Friedreich's Ataxia Group (No 96, Nov 1991):

My name is Brian, and I am a professional computer programmer. The programs I write are sent all over the world. They are 'Access Technology', a system of effecting efficient control of a computer by one who is handicapped by the screen, the sound and the keyboard from normal operation.

I have FA (Friedreich's Ataxia) myself, but am clearly not handicapped by computer controls. I use a secretary's wrist rest to steady my aim at the keys. My visual field has a large blind area which has stopped me from driving, but it is no problem with a screen.

I see the computer now as probably the last item I will have control over should the limitations imposed by my disability become very severe. I can still write a few lines, but my hand gets cramp now.

I will still be able to use a computer, however, while I can bat an eyelid, and through it I could write my next letter to you. I have also discovered that I can be artistic – but not with a pen, chisel or paintbrush. My view was, and is, 'do what you can do to the best of your ability, and it will always be the best that can be done'. I had to work with a computer to get it to work for me – I do not find the existing aids desirable or even practical.

The Disablement Advisory Service have supplied me with the best equipment I could get, including furniture to suit a wheelchair. The computer I wanted was the Acorn A540, which is fast and allows me to work on about ten programs together. The control which I can achieve with a computer would be easy for anyone who had spent the same amount of time studying and doing it. With the equipment I have, anyone could design and produce leaflets within a couple of weeks of learning how to tell someone how to plug it in.

You don't need to know the words any more, just point and click. I no longer believe that all disabled people should get themselves a computer. I now believe that it should be supplied by the DSS along with the wheelchair as a required aid, but always the latest or best, not cheap copies of machines dropped eight years before from the original manufacturers list.

The point is that FA does not handicap the mind, and so need not handicap the expression of the mind. In computing, I see FA as an advantage since it gives you time, a lack of expectation, concentration, and a sense of efficiency.

With sensible networking, we could all work together to sell our services and make a living.

The following three extracts describe some of the initiatives being undertaken by organisations to provide computer facilities for disabled people.

Disabled Living Foundation to Join HANDYNET

The Disabled Living Foundation (DLF) has recently opened its newly refurbished equipment centre, which includes DLF-DATA, the most comprehensive database in Europe on technical aids for disabled people. The Government has now nominated the DLF to represent Britain in HANDYNET. This is the network of information on services for people with disabilities, being organised as part of the HELIOS (Handicapped People in Europe Living Independently in an Open Society) project underway in the European Community.

For further information, contact: James McKinnon, Director, Disabled Living Foundation, 380/384 Harrow Road, London W9 2HU.

DESK TOP PUBLISHING COURSES

The Wessex Rehabilitation Association are offering advice, demonstrations and instruction based on 3 years' successful experience in this new technology. It is an exciting and appropriate activity for people who have mobility or dexterity limitations but who are mentally very active. There are good prospects for employment, including self-employment in this rapidly expanding field.

Further details are available from: John Gisby, Executive Secretary, Wessex Rehabilitation Association, Odstock Hospital, Salisbury, Wilts.

Taken from *FAX* magazine No 89 and reproduced with their kind permission

Information Technology and Special Needs

PETER WALKER looks at how useful computers can be as a learning aid for children with special needs and gives some useful contacts in this field.

Many children with spina bifida and/or hydrocephalus experience difficulties in some of these areas: reading, spelling, handwriting, sequencing, visual discrimination, memory, motivation and organisational skills. Computers with the appropriate programmes can greatly assist learners who are struggling to make progress.

Information technology can support effective learning in all areas of the curriculum. Word processors allow the student to produce clear writing and to amend, print, review and revise work. The use of a spell checker can help with spelling difficulties by highlighting words it does not recognise for the writer to check. It may also offer alternative suggestions. Programmes which use 'cloze' procedures – which is essentially a text with words omitted at regular intervals – can help to identify learners' strengths or weaknesses. Such programmes may also help them to improve their recognition of word shapes and common letter strings.

Word processors can enable learners to take notes and organise them more effectively, make work plans using diagrams, flow charts, headings and key words. All these are planning tools which can form an essential part of a successful writing strategy. Specific skills training, using either drill and practice letter recognition or the writing of meaningful and relevant material, can be developed by using a word processor. In addition there are a number of activities that can help in developing memory skills.

For older pupils, in secondary schools, lap top computers and cassette recorders can greatly help with the chore of note taking and the preparation and presentation of school and home work. Technology for many pupils with special educational needs can provide an excellent means of enhancing competence, self-esteem and presentation of work.

Useful contacts

The ACE Centre, Ormond Street, Wayneflete Road, Headington, Oxford OX3 8DD, telephone 0865 63508. This centre assesses children with communication difficulties and recommends suitable technology. They also produce a range of information sheets and publish reports on such topics as: introductory software, word processors and portable computers.

The BDA Computer Resource Centre, Department of Psychology, University of Hull, Hull HU6 7RX, telephone 0482 465388. The BDA centre contains a wide range of software which

▶

learners with dyslexia have found to be of value. Teachers or parents can visit the centre (by appointment) or write/phone with any queries.

National Federation of ACCESS Centres, Janis Firminger, Hereward College of Further Education, Branston Crescent, Tile Hill, Coventry CV4 9SW, telephone 0203 461231. The National Federation is a nationwide group of further education establishments, which assess adult students and recommend suitable software and aids. They undertake assessments for the Open University and for local Education Authorities and have recently begun to help students with specific learning difficulties.

National Council for Educational Technology, Sir William Lyons Road, University of Warwick, Science Park, Coventry CV4 7EZ, telephone 0203 416 994. This Council was set up by the DES in April 1988: "to promote the use of new and existing technologies to enhance learning opportunities in all areas of education and training".

It works with organisations and networks to provide advice, support, information, training and some research. It offers a comprehensive range of information sheets and support materials for teachers and produces a range of packs and other publications. The Special Needs Section tries to monitor and evaluate the use of informative techniques in special needs provision in mainstream, special schools and colleges.

QUESTIONS

(a) What are HANDYNET and HELIOS?
(b) What is desk top publishing? Who can benefit?
(c) What problems do many children with spina bifida experience which can be helped by using computers?
(d) What is a 'cloze' procedure, and what is it used for?
(e) How can word processors help learners?
(f) What does the National Council for Educational Technology do?
(g) Where can you get advice and information from about the use of computers for and by disabled people?
(h) What computer facilities are there available in your school/college for people with disabilities? (Both hardware and software.)

The following case study describes how Possum was set up to help disabled people make better use of computers. The material has been taken from a newsletter sent out by Possum, and is reproduced with their permission.

CASE STUDY

POSSUM CONTROLS LIMITED

BACKGROUND INFORMATION

You may feel that 'Possum' is an unusual name for a Company, but the early systems which were developed were called 'Patient Operator Selector Mechanisms' – hence the initials P.O.S.M., which were soon pronounced Possum. It was then realised that Possum in Latin means 'I can' or 'I am able' – so it was indeed a perfect title. It is also the registered trademark of the Company.

Possum Controls Limited is a unique organisation being totally owned by two British Charities – The Heinz & Anna Kroch Foundation and The Eleanor

Hamilton Educational Trust. The Company is involved with the development and production of equipment to help the physically handicapped, deaf and elderly people.

The Company started over 30 years ago, when engineers working at Stoke Mandeville Hospital in Aylesbury, observed spinal injury patients lying in bed, totally paralysed and unable to attract attention, except by blowing a whistle hanging over their beds.

The engineers felt that if the patients were able to control the air in their mouths enough to blow the whistle, then the same process could be used to operate micro-switches and thereby enable them to control various electrical appliances.

Some early systems were then made available through various charities, and it was quickly realised there was a real need for this type of equipment for use in rehabilitation and in the daily lives of disabled people, giving them a greater degree of independence.

A company to develop and supply these aids was formed and Possum Controls has grown up from this very simple beginning to the pre-eminent position we hold today.

Any profits made by the Company are ploughed back into Research and Development and back-up services, giving disabled and elderly people the chance to use the most modern technology available.

Possum Controls Limited has moved forward in leaps and bounds, both technically and professionally, particularly in the last few years. There is now a very extensive range of equipment covering Environmental Controls, Computer Systems, Communicators, etc., and more recently we have moved into the sensory-handicapped field and have added some exciting new products to our range to help deaf people.

The PSU6 Environmental Control System (*see* below) is available free of charge through the Department of Health to those severely handicapped people who meet their criteria.

Other units are frequently purchased by Social Services Departments, Hospitals, Special Schools, Cheshire Homes and Charitable organisations.

The Possum Trust is a Charity which was formed to assist in the supply of Possum equipment to those people who need it, but are unable to obtain funding elsewhere.

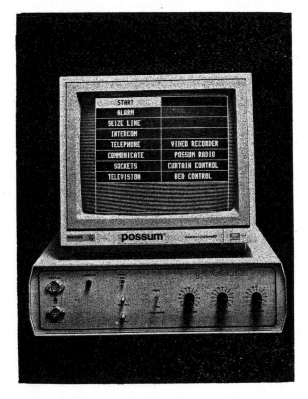

Fig 17.2 The PSU6 Environmental Control System with the following features: door release/close; intercoms; security camera; curtain controls; telephone; up to 20 mains appliances per room; televisions; videos, hi-fi's; computer; remote control of radios; electrically operated beds and chairs; satellite television; teletext; printers; on/off all other electrical appliances; speech synthesiser

Reproduced by kind permission of Possum Controls Limited

DEMONSTRATIONS

We are willing to carry out demonstrations to groups of people at your chosen location, or alternatively, we will loan video films for you to give your own presentation.

There is also a fully equipped Demonstration Room at our Head Office in Slough, where visitors are most welcome by prior arrangement.

SEMINARS

A nationwide campaign of Seminars is constantly under way where we set up the full range of Possum equipment at a suitable venue. We then invite all local professionals and others who are concerned with the welfare and care of disabled and elderly people to spend some time with us to be updated and to try the equipment out for themselves. Please let us know if you would like us to hold one for you.

ASSESSMENT SERVICE

Possum run an excellent Assessment Service throughout the UK, carried out by a professional team of fully trained therapists. This service is free of charge.

Arrangements for Assessor visits can also be made through our Head Office in Slough.

We look forward to working with you to help you enrich the lives of people with all types of disability.

EXAMPLES OF PSU6 USERS

The following people have all been recently supplied with a Possum 2000/PSU6 Environmental Control System.

1 Motor neurone disease patient. Still semi-ambulant – but unsteady, poor hand function, poor motivation and very depressed before installation of PSU6. PSU6 installed 30 November 1988. Now patient has more confidence and interest in life. Relationship with wife improved – she feels he is safer to leave and she has now resumed her part-time job. Patient has returned to reading with the aid of a page turner controlled through the PSU6. Visits to the family by professionals who knew him before say that he shows obvious morale improvements. Although his speech has remained unaffected he uses the communication facility to note messages. Uses a large plate switch.

2 Lady with multiple sclerosis. Resident in nursing home for the last 3 years. She is bed-ridden and in almost fixed extension deformity, no speech. Had very little interest in life until PSU6 installed in January 1989. Now controls TV with channel change, radio, fan, lamp and bed control. Nurse/call system. Makes full use of communication and has recently bought a compatible printer. Uses cheek switch.

3 CP Athetoid boy. Grossly disabled, highly intelligent, no speech. Extremely well motivated. Uses wheelchair – attendant controlled. Can scramble along the floor. PSU6 installed in March 1989 – three room system. Has digital read-out alongside intercoms relaying messages from his PSU6 screen. Family and patient very thrilled with PSU6. Uses foot switch.

4 Friedreich's ataxia patient. Highly intelligent boy, deteriorating slowly. Uses wheelchair, very clumsy hand function. Will need to have compatible computer and operate through PSU6 within a year. Lives with parents, very thrilled to have the ability to use the telephone and to be left alone for short periods – safely. Intercoms particularly useful as he lives in a large Dormer bungalow. Uses large plate switch.

5 Spina bifida patient, 19 year old. Gross physical disability, very weak voice, intellectually 'slow'. Has two room system which provides security and independence that parents never thought possible. Mother no longer has to sleep downstairs on the sofa to be near her. Parents are happy to pop down to the pub for two hours and know she can contact them if necessary. Uses communication facility for note taking. Father feels her reading ability has improved since she has had the ability to type on screen.

6 Multiple sclerosis patient, 36 years old. In wheelchair, well motivated man usually but depressed since hand function deteriorated. Made redundant from work. Since PSU6 installed he has bought a printer and now types thesis for university student. Morale improved. Finds intercom very useful as his wife sleeps upstairs and he often has choking sessions in the night. Uses very sensitive hand switch.

7 Motor neurone disease patient, 34 years old. Very disabled, no active movement apart from slight head movement and eye movement. Was a solicitor before his disability. System installed in December

1988, uses a printer with PSU6 not only for everyday communication but has taken on the correlation of MND research for support group. Uses digital read-outs for intercom.

8 Muscular dystrophy boy, 14 years. Very disabled, has only very weak power in one hand. As well as providing him with environmental control which has relieved a lot of tension at home, the Education Department is buying him an Amstrad computer and printer so that he can do his homework.

9 Rheumatoid arthritis, 71 years old. Very disabled lady, only has limited weak movement of fingers on left hand. Lives alone, daughter across the road. Has electric wheelchair, enjoys going into her garden. Has door opener motor operated through system so that she can go into the garden. Uses all her electrical appliances through PSU6 including bed control. Uses guarded plate switch.

10 Tetraplegia RTA, 25 years old. Has only shoulder movement. Lives alone in adapted bungalow. Has full control of both doors, intercoms and electric appliances. Intends to purchase printer so that she can continue an Open University course. Only nine months since accident.

11 CP Athetoid, 21 years old. Lives in children's home at present, grossly handicapped, no speech. Is still learning how to use system and can control appliances accurately. Is slowly making use of word-store facility. Uses wobble stick input.

12 Motor neurone disease patient, 71 years old. Still ambulant but unsafe, no use of arms, no speech. Was in residential care and very unhappy. Returned home, full nursing support but otherwise lives alone. Uses system to control 2 doors and all appliances. Intercom with digital read-out. Uses communication facility.

POSSUM 2000: FOR EDUCATION AND EMPLOYMENT

- Ken has had multiple sclerosis for 30 years, runs his own accountancy business and also is the Administrator of a charitable trust.
- Christopher has had polio. He trained as a Solicitor and now runs his own business as a Property Developer, employing a dozen or so people.
- Mary has multiple sclerosis. She was a trained Veterinarian and by using the Possum 2000 she continues her work as a Consultant Veterinarian.
- Hassen sustained a spinal injury which left him almost completely paralysed in his mid-thirties. With the aid of a computer, printer and loud-speaking telephone, which he can operate through his Possum 2000, he has gone into business for himself, working from home.
- Danny has cerebral palsy. He has successfully undertaken GCSE and 'A' level examinations using his computer, which is operated through his Possum 2000 by means of a simple foot-activated switch.
- Julie developed multiple sclerosis which as it grew more severe caused her to be made redundant. Since her Possum 2000 was installed, she has been able to take up work from home, using her Word Processor to type students' theses, greatly improving her morale.
- Peter, a teenager with Friedreich's Ataxia, is studying computer technology at College, using his Possum 2000 as a means of operating his own computer. If he decides to move on to University, he will take his Possum 2000 with him and, by adding some additional accessories, he will be able to use the equipment to help him with his studies and maintain his independence in his own room on Campus.
- Michael was diagnosed as suffering from motor neurone disease while at University. He was determined to gain a place at Oxford University to study for his PhD and has used his Possum 2000 to study, with the aid of his computer, and to give him independence in his daily living.
- Vivien was born physically disabled due to thalidomide being prescribed to her mother during pregnancy. She is, however, a professional Music Teacher and is able to use her Word Processor, through the Possum 2000, to set work and keep records of her students' progress.
- Andrew suffers from a rare skin condition which has affected him since birth. He has to exercise great care in his everyday life as the slightest knock can cause blisters to appear, yet in spite of this, Andrew runs his own Desk Top Publishing business and can also control many electrical appliances in his home – all through his Possum 2000.

Chapter 18

FINANCES

Handling other people's money is something that carries with it great responsibility, and many potential problems for carers. Whenever possible, responsibility for cash should remain with the person who owns it, but the mechanics involved may prove difficult for people with physical disabilities – signing names, for example, getting to the bank or the Post Office, and then actually using the facilities once there.

Having to deal with somebody else's financial affairs may fall upon you in your role as carer, you may be expected to act as an agent and collect money on behalf of your client, or pay money into their account. Acting as agent is an informal arrangement between you and the disabled person; many home helps/home care assistants act in this capacity as a part of their day to day work. It is more usual that this task will be delegated to relatives, but this is not always possible. The information given in this chapter is written specifically for the caring student, but can be used to advise others of the options that are available to them.

Where informal arrangements are not feasible for whatever reason, more formal arrangements can be made with the Department of Social Security, or banks and building societies, to become an **appointee**, in which case an interview will be held and references taken up. Medical evidence will also be expected to be made available to prove that the disabled person is unable to do the required things themself. If any problems arise, the appointeeship can be withdrawn. The appointee must keep a record showing money received and money spent on the individual's behalf, which should be available for inspection upon request.

Another legal way of handling other people's affairs with their agreement is by them granting the carer a Power of Attorney. This will give the carer the right to do anything that they would do for themselves, if they could; for example signing cheques, buying and selling shares, taking cash from accounts; even buying and selling property.

What an Attorney can do can be limited by restrictions being written into the original agreement, so it may just allow the carer to draw DSS benefits, pay bills, draw money from accounts, and sign cheques.

If the individual being acted for becomes mentally incapable of taking decisions on their own behalf, then the Power of Attorney will no longer be valid. An Enduring Power of Attorney should be applied for if there is advance notice of this happening, as is the case in certain degenerative disorders; this allows the appointee to continue to act in the client's best interests.

(a) When acting as an 'agent' on behalf of somebody else, what would you be expected to do?
(b) In handling other people's money, what problems can you foresee?
(c) If you wished to become an appointee, what steps would you expect to be taken before this was officially confirmed?
(d) Under a Power of Attorney, what rights would you have?
(e) What is the difference between a Power of Attorney and an Enduring Power of Attorney?

(Further information can be obtained from The Public Trust Office Protection Division, Stewart House, 24 Kingsway, London, WC2 6JX)

Statutory benefits

Some of the benefits available from the Department of Social Security since April 1992 are briefly described below.

Disability Living Allowance

This is made up of an allowance for personal care at one of three rates depending upon need as assessed by the DSS, and an allowance for travel costs to people who have difficulty in walking, paid at one of two levels depending on assessed need. Only for people under 65 years of age.

Invalidity Benefit

This replaces Sickness Benefit after the first 28 weeks of incapacity for work, and is based on having sufficient National Insurance stamps. If there are not enough stamps, then a **Severe Disablement Allowance** is paid.

Disability Working Allowance

May be paid to those whose disability 'puts him at a disadvantage in getting a job', and who is in a low paid job for at least 16 hours a week. The amount payable varies according to earnings and family size.

Other benefits to which individuals may be entitled are the same as those for the rest of us, e.g. **Income Support**, **Social Fund payments**, **Family Credit** and **Housing Benefit**. The Department of Social Security has published *The Guide to New Benefits for Disabled People* and can provide further information. Information can also be obtained from the Citizens Advice Bureaux, Disablement Information Advice Lines, or sources such as a benefits chart published annually and available from Community Care Magazine, Quadrant House, The Quadrant, Sutton, Surrey, SM2 5AS.

EXERCISES

1 Benefits

Obtain copies of the Disability Living Allowance and Disability Working Allowance claim forms, DLA 1 and DWA 1 (the front sheets of which are shown on pages 160 and 161) and fill them in on behalf of two of the people from the Cases section of this book, or any other example you wish to use.

(a) (i) Did you have any problem fillilng in the form; was it easy to understand and complete?
   (ii) What other benefits would the person you have chosen be entitled to?
   (iii) Was any allowance made for non-English speakers?
   (iv) Can braille or audio applications be made?

(b) Using the information you have obtained, prepare an advice booklet for people with disabilities to use to work out for themselves which benefits they should be entitled to, and how to claim them.

2 Financial affairs

Survey your local banks, building societies and post offices, and find out what provision they make for people who are:
- unable to sign documents
- unable to see
- unable to get to the premises.

This exercise could be postal, telephone, or combined with the town centre survey described earlier, looking at access to buildings and the services available to disabled people once inside.

BTEC Common Skills: 1, 2, 3, 4, 6, 8, 10, 11, 12, 13, 14, 15, (16 if computer used) 17, 18.
GNVQ Level 2: 2.1, 2.2, 2.3, 5.2, 6.3.
GNVQ Level 3: 1.1, 1.2, 1.3, 1.4, 3.2, 6.3, 8.2.

Making a will

However unpalatable we may find it, death is an inevitability for all of us. It is unfortunate but true that some forms of disability do shorten the life span of the people affected. Sensible forward planning should include the making of a will. It is never too soon to make a will once you have reached the age of 18 (in Scotland, the age is 14 for boys and 12 for girls); even if you think you own nothing of any value. If there is no will, then all property is shared out according to the Intestacy Rules, which distribute any property and cash according to a complex system which starts with close relatives, and then goes on to more distant ones. There is no doubt that this is a task for a solicitor, and is best avoided by specific wishes being stated in a will.

The rules may or may not distribute things as you would have wished; far better to make your wishes clear than rely on chance. As a carer, you can help those you are caring for to make a will; forms can be purchased at newsagents for personal/private use. It is important, however, that the will states clearly the wishes of the author, and that it is dated, signed and witnessed correctly. There are various books and guides

Your claim for

Disability Living Allowance

benefits
b a
agency

**Date that you asked for a claim pack.
This is the date we take your
claim from.**

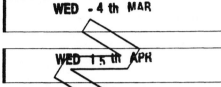

WED - 4 th MAR

**Please send your claim back so that we will
get it by this date here.**
If you wait you will lose money.
Please allow a few days for your claim
to reach us by post.

WED 15 th APR

Remember if you want to ask anything about Disability Living Allowance,
or about filling in this form - phone free on **0800 882 200.**

● Part 1 **Personal details**

If you are filling in this form for a child or for someone else please tell us
about *them* on this form.

Surname

Other names

Any other surnames

Title   Mr / Mrs / Miss / Ms

Address where you live

Postcode

Daytime phone number
This will help us to deal with
your claim quickly

Date of birth

Letters	Numbers	Letter

**National Insurance
(NI) number**

If you cannot find your NI number - do not worry.
And do not wait to send us your claim.

DLA 1

Fig 18.1(a)   Disability Living Allowance claim form (DLA 1)

160

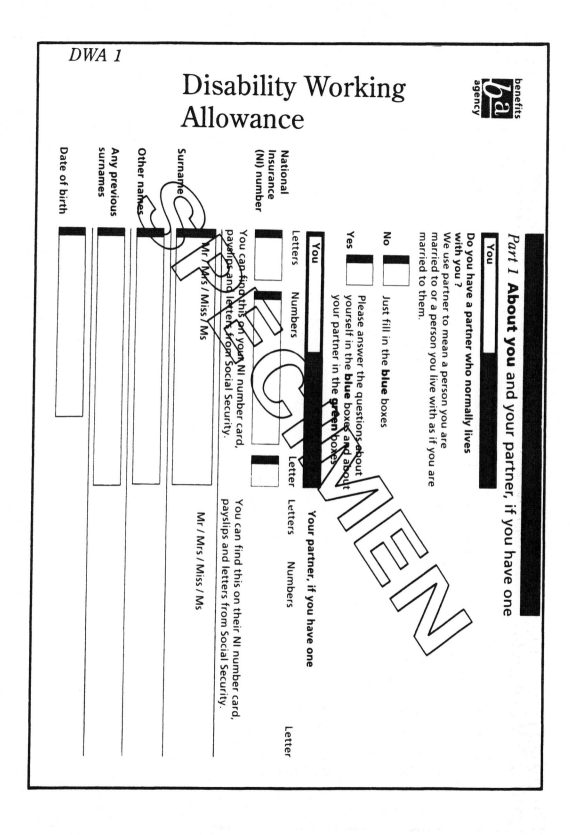

Fig 18.1(b) Disability Working Allowance claim form (DWA 1)

on the market advising on the writing of wills (e.g. The Consumers' Association publication *Wills and Probate*). In your position as an employed, professional carer, it is always wise to advise the use of a solicitor in drawing up a will. They will charge a fee for this service, but it could save a lot more in the long run.

Banks also have a will-writing service, but they tend to be more costly than using the services of a solicitor; and there are also a growing number of independent will writing services in the private sector.

Figure 18.2 shows how a will should be drawn up.

EXAMPLE: Showing how Will should be drawn up.

This is the Last Will and Testament of me ALEXANDER JOHN BROWN, of 133 Forfar Road, Carlisle, Cumbria, Plumber, made this Fourteenth day of January, One Thousand Nine Hundred and Eighty-three.

I HEREBY revoke all Wills and Codicils and other Testamentary instruments made by me at any time heretofore. I appoint my wife, ALICE JANE BROWN, and THOMAS WATT, of Montrose Street, Carlisle, aforesaid Baker, to be my Executors, and direct that all my debts and Funeral Expenses shall be paid as soon as conveniently may be after my Death.

I give and bequeath unto my son Robert Brown, the sum of two hundred and eighty pounds, unto the said Thomas Watt, the sum of fifty pounds, unto my daughter, Alice Brown, all those two houses situate in and being Nos. 3 and 5 Queen Street, Carlisle, and all the remainder of my property unto my wife, the said Alice Jane Brown.

A. Brown

(The Testator's signature MUST follow the last line of writing as above).

Signed by the said Testator
.......................*Alexander John Brown*.......................
who signs..........*A. Brown*.......................
at................*133 Forfar Rd. Carlisle*..............
in the presence of us both, present at the same time, who at his request in his presence and in the presence of each other have subscribed our names as Witnesses.

John Banks
34 Montague Place, Carlisle
Baker
George Shorter
27 Waterloo Avenue, Carlisle
Jeweller

Fig 18.2 How a will should be drawn up

As a carer, you can legally witness a will, but certainly not if you are a beneficiary named in it. This fact in itself may lead to problems with your employer. Some terms of employment (in particular with local authorities and health authorities) state that carers or members of their families are not allowed to benefit from the wills of anybody in their care. Even witnessing a will may be against the rules of the establishment or organisation for which they are working. Carers should always refer such requests to the person in charge, or the administrative offices.

QUESTIONS

(a) At what age can you make a will?

(b) What happens to an individual's property if there is no will?

(c) If a person in your care said they wanted to make a will, what advice would you give?

(d) What facilities are available to help in making a will?

(e) Explain the term 'beneficiary'.

(f) Why can a beneficiary not witness a will?

(g) If you were asked to witness a will written by somebody in your care, what action would you take?

Chapter 19

THE RIGHTS OF DISABLED PEOPLE WHEN ARRESTED

PACE

PACE is the Police and Criminal Evidence Act, which is the police 'bible' as far as how they treat prisoners in their custody; and, among other things, it gives extra protection to people with certain disabilities who have been arrested. The only disabled people mentioned specifically in the Act, however, are blind, partially sighted, deaf and hearing impaired, and those with a speech impediment (also mentally ill and mentally handicapped (sic)).

The Act itself is accompanied by a set of codes of practice which explain in detail what should happen in any given circumstances. General provisions are that in each police station there should be a custody officer who is responsible for all the people detained there. He or she has to keep a custody record of everything that happens to all individuals in his or her care, and inform them of their rights e.g. to have somebody informed of where they are, and to have a solicitor, and to have a copy of the codes of practice. The custody officer must also decide if they are in a 'special group' requiring further safeguards.

It should also be noted that the vast majority of interviews are now tape-recorded, and a small but growing number are being videotaped.

Code of Practice rule C1.6 states that: 'If a person appears to be blind or seriously visually handicapped, deaf, unable to read, unable to speak or has difficulty orally because of a speech impediment, he should be treated as such for the purposes of this code . . .'

C3.6 states that: 'If the person appears to be deaf or there is doubt about his hearing or speaking ability or ability to understand English, and the custody officer cannot establish effective communication, the custody officer must as soon as practicable call an interpreter . . .'

C3.14 states: 'If the person is blind or seriously visually handicapped or is unable to read, the custody officer should ensure that his solicitor, relative, the appropriate adult or some other person likely to take an interest in him (and not involved in the investigation) is available to help in checking any documentation. Where this code requires written consent or signification, then the person who is assisting may be asked to sign instead if the detained person so wishes.'

Other rules forbit interviews without interpreters being present unless the prisoner agrees, and the need for interpreters when the person acting as 'Appropriate Adult' has hearing or speech problems (C13.5, 13.6).

Appropriate Adult

This is the name given to an independent person who will sit in on interviews with prisoners who fall into one of the 'special groups'. This automatically includes anybody under the age of 17 and foreign language speakers. For the other groups mentioned above, it is for the custody officer to decide, for example, whether a person is (*a*) disabled, and (*b*) requires special consideration because of this.

Those who can be asked to act as Appropriate Adults are:

- a social worker, or
- a responsible adult aged 18 or over who is not a police officer or employed by the police.

The Appropriate Adult's main functions are to advise the person being questioned as to what is going on, and what is expected of them, and to observe whether or not the interview is being conducted properly and fairly. They should also facilitate communication with the person being interviewed (but that does not necessarily mean acting as an interpreter, more to explain and clarify). If the carer, or the person being questioned, so wish, a solicitor can also be present, but cannot replace an AA.

QUESTIONS

(a) What do you think is the significance of the word 'appears' in Rules 1.6 and 3.6?
(b) Describe three duties of a custody officer.
(c) Give three rights of a detained person.
(d) What sort of an interpreter do you think is meant in Rule 3.6?
(e) If you were a carer who had been living in for a few weeks with a person with poor speech, and the police wished to interview him, could you be asked to sit in as an Appropriate Adult?
(f) What are the main roles of an Appropriate Adult?
(g) Why do you think a police employee may not be an Appropriate Adult?

EXERCISE

John had been out to the pub with a few friends on his regular Friday night out. He did not have a driving licence due to his epilepsy; he is also deaf. In the taxi on the way back to his parents' house, he had an epileptic fit. This was quite a rare occurrence for him, as he is normally well controlled by drugs. Just before the fit, he vomited, and afterwards he was in a state of confusion. The taxi driver took exception to the mess in the back of his car, and when he was unable to get any money or an address from John, he drove to the police station.

John was arrested for being drunk and disorderly, and trying to get away without paying a taxi fare. He was taken to the police station, where the custody officer felt that he was incapable of being interviewed because he was too drunk. John was put into a cell to 'sleep it off'.

In the morning he was able to get across the message that he was deaf, and the custody officer (a different one by this time) followed the PACE regulations before he would allow John to be interviewed.

Questions

1. (a) Describe what action the custody officer should take to protect John's rights under the Police and Criminal Evidence Act.
   (b) If you were called in to act as Appropriate Adult, what would you be discussing with John and the police before the interview starts? Would you want anybody else to be present at the interview, and if so, who and why?
   (c) Why might the arresting officer have come to the conclusions he did about the reasons for John's behaviour?
   (d) Do you think the custody officer was right to let John 'sleep it off' before allowing him to be interviewed? Give reasons for your answer.
   (e) What advice would you give to John to prevent the same kind of thing happening to him again?

2. **Role Play**
   Organise a role play of the scene in the police station, and the ensuing interview.

   You will need two arresting officers, who will also undertake the interview; the prisoner, and the custody officer. You will also need an Appropriate Adult, and you may also decide to call a solicitor and/or an interpreter for deaf people.

3. **In court**
   Assuming that the story continues, and a court appearance follows, what facilities will be required in court? If you are not already visiting the courts as part of your course, then discuss with your tutors the possibility of arranging this.

   Look at the accessibility (ramps, wide doors, etc. to places such as toilets and canteens, as well as the court rooms, solicitors, social workers and probation offices) and check the acoustics.

   What arrangements can be made for interpreters; is there an induction loop installed? If the outcome is a custodial sentence, then what facilities become available?

   Make some enquires at your local prison or remand centre, and see what they have.

Criminal Justice Act 1991

This piece of legislation came into effect on 1 October 1992, and is the first time a duty has been put on to people working in the criminal justice system (e.g. police, courts and prisons) to avoid discriminatory practice.

Section 95 states that 'persons engaged in the administration of criminal justice have a duty to avoid discriminating against any persons on the ground of race or sex or any other improper ground.' This includes disability.

Chapter 20

BEREAVEMENT

LOST LOVE

Together like climbing trees or vines
The severing of one will cause the other
To die. The world is then empty.
Slowly the interdependence has caused them to combine
Like Siamese twins they have been joined together.

No one else can really fill the vacancy
No matter how well-intentioned the sympathy
The vine without its tree to lean upon.

BRIAN RECK

Disability does not necessarily bring with it death, but it has to be acknowledged that it can mean a foreshortened life caused either directly or indirectly by that disability.

Death is still a taboo subject which most of us would rather not talk about; yet it is a good idea to prepare for the inevitable, no matter how distant or close it may be. What are the individual's wishes? What religious requirements need to be observed? Has a will been prepared? Where should the burial/cremation take place?

Preparation for death is an integral part of the care process. The needs of all the people involved have to be catered for, the carers as well as the person preparing for their own death. Bringing the subject out into the open and talking about it candidly is awkward and embarrassing for many people, but it is important to try to face the issue.

Starting with practical issues may lead on to the more emotional ones. Begin by making a list of such things as the will, insurance policies and where to find them; bank and building society accounts, National Savings, shares, etc., trade union benefits; birth and marriage certificates, NHS and National Insurance numbers; details of regular payments made; and the names, addresses and phone numbers of key people to be informed at the time of death.

No matter how well prepared for, and how much discussion of the issues involved, news of the actual death will still come as a severe trauma. Some of us will experience an emotional response there and then, others will immerse themselves in the practical matters that follow a death; some of us may seek company, and some prefer to grieve alone. Whatever the individual response, the overwhelming requirement of the professional carer is **understanding**. Realise what is happening, and help the grieving person with whatever they want to do. You, in the professional caring situation, will also be affected by death. How are you going to cope? What are your reactions likely to be? Have you had experience of the death of a close relative or friend? If so, how did you react – in both the short term and the longer term? What responses did you find most helpful (and the most unhelpful) from those around you?

The following extract is taken from an article by Karin Weatherup which appeared in the Muscular Dystrophy Group magazine of summer 1991, and is reproduced here with the Group's kind permission.

Elaine's story

Now 18, Elaine was ten when her brother Gary, then aged eight, was diagnosed as having Duchenne muscular dystrophy. She remembers her mother crying on the stairs and then giving her and her sister a children's leaflet which explained what it meant. Because Gary had been born with a club foot, news of the progressively disabling nature of his condition didn't sink in at first.

'I do remember Gary standing in the playground at school though, playing cops and robbers, and everybody knew that you only had to touch him and he'd fall over. I used to stand there and cry, just watching him. People used to tease me about him. But it was when he went into a wheelchair that it really hit me. Gary used to want to come out with me and my friends, but I used to feel ashamed of him at first,' admits Elaine. 'I used to see all my friends with their brothers and sisters and think: Why me? I used to call Gary a spoilt brat and try to get attention by being naughty all the time, just so they'd notice me. I think Mum understood what I was doing, though, because every so often she'd say, "Come here and give me a cuddle". I wanted to talk about how I felt, to ask questions, but it was hard. I had to bottle things up inside me because Mum and Dad used to get so upset.'

As Gary's muscles became weaker and he needed more assistance in the house, and Elaine got older and began to accept her brother's disability and the effect it had on the balance of family life, she found that her feelings toward her brother changed a lot. 'At first, it was a bit of a novelty. I just wanted to fuss round him, but only when I wanted to. Then I wanted to be with him all the time and used to take him everywhere with me and my friends. Gary was a

very caring person, always there for you when you wanted to talk. I still feel he's with me all the time and whenever I want to get something off my chest, I still talk to him. Of course, we used to fight too. I'd hit him but Mum used to say, "Now you stand there, in front of Gary", and he would head butt me back,' giggles Elaine, whose warmth when talking about her brother is infectious: you feel you'd have liked to have known him too.

When Gary became ill at the age of 14, just as doctors had predicted, his parents would spend the night close to him in case he needed to be turned or wanted a drink. It was an intense period with Elaine, her boyfriend John, and her family trying not to let Gary see their distress. Against doctors' recommendations, they insisted that Gary remain in their small, cosy home rather than move into a hospice. Yet when Gary died, Elaine remembers, 'I never expected it. It was never going to happen.'

'I felt that I couldn't talk to anyone because Mum kept breaking down in tears,' says Elaine, 'and I didn't want to upset her. Everybody kept saying "Be strong for your Mum". When we were told that someone would have to go and register Gary's death, I looked round the room at the family and thought, "It's got to be me, nobody else can do it".'

Elaine was sixteen.

Eighteen months later, Elaine can speak objectively and fluently about her brother and her feelings, although at first she found herself breaking down in panic. 'The doctor said I'd had such a burden on my shoulders, being strong for everybody else, so he arranged for me to see a bereavement counsellor. I went during school time, but I used to feel ashamed at having to

►

see a counsellor. I thought everyone would think I was going mad.' The sessions, however, which gave Elaine the space to focus on herself at last, did help, and not just Elaine; 'I used to come home from school, and Mum would tell me how she was feeling and I'd say, "Well, the counsellor says that means . . .".'

As well as teaching Elaine that she is allowed to express what she feels, counselling has also helped her to overcome some of her fear about what has happened to Gary. 'I used to be frightened of death, but now I see Gary as a butterfly, leaving his body behind and being free and happy.'

On a more practical level, Elaine now finds it difficult to get close to people, which has caused some problems in her relationship with her boyfriend. 'John was great with Gary. They were like brothers. He went through the whole thing with me. But since Gary died, I find it hard to be close. I can't talk to anyone, except Gary. John is understanding but I think he feels it's been 18 months now, and I should be over it.'

For someone who has denied their own feelings and emotional needs for so long, Elaine's growing understanding of her experience is a tribute to her strength of character as well as to the skills of those who have helped her along the path.

QUESTIONS

(a) At what age was Gary diagnosed as having muscular dystrophy?
(b) Why was Elaine naughty all the time?
(c) How did she respond to Gary's death?
(d) What did the sessions with the bereavement counsellor do for Elaine?
(e) Why did she not want to go to the counselling sessions?
(f) Why do you think she now finds it difficult to get close to people?

Grieving

There are four basic stages of the grieving process which have been identified; some people will go through them all, others in a different order than shown below, and others miss out one or two of the stages completely.

1 Denial and shock. Denial is the initial reaction of not believing what has been said, or the evidence of the eyes. Shock is the crying, shaking stage when the truth hits home and the emotional reaction takes over all voluntary control.

2 Anger and guilt. These feelings may not be completely rational, and blame is put on to other people, and a string of 'if only's . . .' may be voiced. 'If only I had stayed at home more', 'If only I had called the doctor earlier', 'If only I hadn't taken her into the garden on Thursday' and so on.

Consolation will be difficult, and temper may flare when solace is offered; blame may even be transferred to you as the professional carer for allowing the person to die.

3 Depression and apathy. Loss and despair are a common cause of depression; the effects are that interest in the self is lost. 'What is there to go on for', and self-care ceases. This is the apathetic stage, when nothing is worth doing, and there is no point in carrying on.

4 Resolution. This is when things start to improve; an acceptance of the status quo is reached. Interest is regained in the self and home, and outside activities are considered once more. The feeling of loss will always be there, but the individual is now able to live with that.

You may go through some of these emotions yourself when a person in your care dies, as may other people who have lived with them in a residential setting, or been companions and friends at a day centre.

The length of time each stage lasts will differ with individuals, and artificial props such as alcohol and drugs may be used to try and help. If you are in contact with bereaved people, help them to grieve. Give them permission to cry and talk about things – this does not have to be explicit, verbalised permission, but by listening and encouragement, and by not giving any hint of discouragement such as looking at your watch or looking around while hopping from foot to foot because other chores await your attention.

Practicalities

(*See also* the section on making a will in Chapter 18 Finances.)

Death

Somewhere in the region of 70 per cent of urban deaths occur in hospital; it should be noted that where there are no responsible relatives, and no finances, then the Health Authority has to bear the cost of the funeral. When an individual in the same situation dies at home, then the Local Authority has to bear the costs (Section 50 of the National Assistance Act 1948).

When a death does occur, then the first person to approach is the family doctor. They will come and confirm the death, and issue a Medical Certificate showing the cause of death, plus a notice explaining how to formally register the death at the Registry Office. They will then issue a Death Certificate and a Certificate of Burial or Cremation, which should be given to the Funeral Director.

This straightforward pattern will be altered if the death is sudden, or the doctor has not seen the deceased for some time. The circumstances will then have to be reported to the Coroner, who may order that a post-mortem examination is carried out to determine the cause of death. An inquest will be arranged if the death was caused by accident, violence, industrial disease, or the post-mortem was inconclusive as to the cause. It is only after all these matters have been dealt with that a Death Certificate can be issued, and a funeral arranged.

A leaflet from the DSS entitled *What to do after a Death* (Reference D49) is a useful guide to have. The Consumers' Association publication, *What To Do When Someone Dies* is also available.

Once the doctor has issued the certificate, a Funeral Director can be called in. They will advise on all aspects of the burial and the period leading up to this; one decision to be made is whether to have the body laid out at home or in a Chapel of Rest. The relevant minister of religion will need to be notified, if that was the wish of the deceased, and relatives and friends informed of the death, and date and time of the funeral.

Apart from the practical arrangements, there may be a need for **counselling**. This may be shortly after the death, or a long time afterwards. The Samaritans is one organisation often approached in these circumstances, but a more appropriate organisation is CRUSE, set up specifically in 1959 to provide help for people following bereavement. There are now branches all over the country, and the addresses and phone numbers can be found in the telephone directory.

EXERCISES

1 Booklet design

You have read above that there are guides available on what to do when someone dies. Obtain copies of those that you can, especially the free DSS booklet D49. Obtain also DSS information on financial help for the bereaved.

Could these pamphlets be improved upon? See if you can come up with a better, more 'user-friendly' version.

Alternatively:

Design your own booklet for people preparing for a death in the family; it may be their own death or that of a relative or even a close friend. Cover all the areas which you consider it important for people in such circumstances to think about and make practical arrangements for.

Take into consideration the needs of a multicultural society where there are a great variety of religions and social mores. What are the different requirements for Hindus, Muslims, Jews, Catholics, Mormons, etc.?

In your working life it is more than just a theoretical exercise to be aware of the differing needs and expectations of those around you. It is not necessary to have all the details in your head, but you should know where the relevant information can be found. It is a good idea to make enquiries in your own area as to the contact people and telephone numbers of the various churches, temples, and other places of worship.

If time allows, representatives could be invited in to speak on your course (*see* Assignment 3 on page 202).

2 Making a will

Read again page 159 in Chapter 18 Finances, and then answer the following questions:

(a) How would the Intestacy Rules distribute the estate among the family of somebody who has died without making a will?

(b) Choose one of the cases in this book (*see* pages 176–92) and draw up a will on their behalf.

(c) How would you overcome communication problems when helping people with a disability, particularly a sensory disability, to discuss the making of a will with a solicitor? What if the person chosen is unable to sign? Is the use of a tape recording or a video recording a legally acceptable way to make a will?

(d) Ask a solicitor or a solicitor's clerk to come in and talk to the group about the making of wills.

3 Organise a funeral

Obtain the booklet mentioned above, or other information from appropriate sources.

(a) Contact local Funeral Directors to get an idea of prices for different styles of funeral, and the costs of various parts of the process, such as cars, coffin, burial fees, flowers, etc. Ask also about the different requirements of various religions.

(b) Ask a Registrar to come in and tell you about their side of the work, or just to provide information and sample forms for the Registration of a Death.

(c) Request a speaker from a counselling organisation such as CRUSE to come and speak to you.

(d) Arrange a visit to a Cemetery or Crematorium, and find out how they operate.

4 Euthanasia

There has been some debate over euthanasia for many years, and particularly since medical science has been able to prolong life. Preserving the quantity of life does not necessarily mean maintaining the quality of life, and this is where views differ.

(a) Find out what is meant by 'euthanasia'.

(b) Organise a debate as outlined in Assignment 6 on page 205 to argue the merits and de-merits.

(c) What is a 'Living Will'? (**NB:** The Terence Higgins Trust of 52–54 Grays Inn Rd., London WC1X 8JU is a source of information regarding this.)

(d) What do you think is meant by 'a good quality of life'?

Finally, shown below is an article published in the Muscular Dystrophy Group Annual Review. It relates the story of a couple who, having suffered the loss of their children, are managing to come to terms with their tragedy.

LIVE FOR EACH DAY

The story of Helen and Vic Hearnshaw of Chesterfield seems almost too tragic to be told – until you remind yourself that this is only the story so far, and that hope is on the horizon.

In May 1988 they had a baby boy, Daniel. That December he was diagnosed as having Werdnig Hoffman's disease. The following month he was dead. The chances that a subsequent child of theirs would be born with the condition were put no higher than one in four. Late in 1989 Helen duly gave birth once more; twice, to be precise, for this time she had twin girls, Danielle and Stefanie. Although there was no sign of the illness in the first few weeks of their lives, it was present in both. At the age of 10

months they too were dead, Danielle finally giving up her own astonishing struggle on the very day of her sister's funeral.

'Total numbness, disbelief and then pain'. Although she is highly articulate, these are the only words which 28-year-old Helen can find to describe her and her husband's feelings in the wake of the second and third bereavements. Yet even the awfulness of their loss is not completely unrelieved. She goes on: 'They were very, very happy babies, and they truly enjoyed their lives. We gave them everything. We may not have been able to give them life itself, but we gave them everything that was in our power to give.'

◄

Now Helen and Vic have reason to feel cautiously optimistic. The Jennifer Trust for Spinal Muscular Atrophy put them in touch with Dr. Neil Thomas, a specialist in Werdnig Hoffman's, who told them that next time he would be able to conduct tests on Helen eight weeks into pregnancy, and that within two weeks of the tests she should know whether the foetus was affected. 'He came to see us last March, and took blood from all four of us,' she says. 'I kept calling him every month and finally, in November, he told us that something could be done.'

Far from making them despair, the couple's experience has provided a vivid demonstration of families' and relatives' potential for love and support at a time of unspeakable crisis. To those who have been through a similar trauma, she has these words: 'I say live for each day. Never give up. There have been some who think that all we have to do is have a healthy child and that will wipe away the loss. I suppose you cannot expect people who have not experienced something like this even to start to understand. We haven't come through it yet, but we will. I know we will.'

Helen has been making her first jottings towards a book about what she and Vic have been through. No story can more deserve a happy ending.

Part Four

CASES AND ASSIGNMENTS

CASE STUDIES

1 John and Mary Thomas (cystic fibrosis)
2 June Hatchell (multiple sclerosis)
3 Margaret Hall (incontinence)
4 Jason Young (quadriplegia in residential care)
5 Mr and Mrs Dale (heart and stroke)
6 Betty Church (Bell's palsy)
7 Robert Taylor (package of care)
8 Kay Carpal (abuse)
9 Terry Kelsall (eye problems)
10 Becky and Dave Moss (cerebral palsy with baby)

CASE 1: John and Mary Thomas

John and Mary Thomas are a couple in their late twenties; they have one son, Michael, who has cystic fibrosis. The family run a newsagency and sweet shop, which they took over from Mr Thomas' parents when they retired and went to live in Spain.

Mr Thomas worked in a large car factory in the Midlands prior to taking over the shop, and Mrs Thomas was a sewing machinist in the clothing industry. She left work to have Michael, and then started in the shop when he was a month or two old. She noticed that he was a 'sickly child', very pale, and did not put on weight although he seemed to be eating a lot. He was also very irritable, and cried a lot.

At 11 weeks old, Mary took Michael to the doctor.

Tests were carried out on samples of sweat and faeces, and the diagnosis of cystic fibrosis confirmed. Michael then had to be put on a modified diet, with reduced fat and increased protein and carbohydrate, and extra vitamins A, D and K.

An appointment was made with a physiotherapist, and both parents were taught how to drain the excess mucus from Michael's lungs. A great deal of time and effort has to be put into looking after Michael, and the business kept going at the same time. It is fortunate that they live on the shop premises, and do not have to go out to work.

When Michael was two years old, Mary learned that she was expecting another child. An appointment was made with a genetic counsellor, who advised them of the risk of this next child also having cystic fibrosis. The option of an abortion was made available to them, if they wished it.

QUESTIONS

1 What help is available to them in the care of Michael from:

   (a) the NHS?
   (b) Social Services?
   (c) the Education Department?
   (d) voluntary organisations?
   (e) the private providers?

2 If you were the genetic counsellor, what information would you give to Mr and Mrs Thomas about the chances of having another child affected by cystic fibrosis?

   (a) What can the family do about the new pregnancy?
   (b) What are the arguments in favour of an abortion?
   (c) What are the arguments against abortion?

Organise a debate in class to discuss the issues involved here, with a chairperson and a formal proposer and seconder. For the procedure to adopt, refer to Assignment 6 on page 205.

3 In preparation for Mary going into hospital, design a package of care to help Michael and his father to manage and keep the business open.

Remember to look for possible elements of this package from informal, statutory, voluntary and private sectors of service provision.

Who, apart from Mr Thomas, would ensure that this package was satisfactory?

CASE 2: June Hatchell

June Hatchell had been an unremarkable schoolgirl, and made it through secondary school with average marks, and led an average sort of life.

She lived on a council estate in a three-bedroomed house with her parents, sister, and pet dog. When she left school, she got a job in a local chip shop, which she quite enjoyed, as it meant she could meet people and chat, and not have to work too hard (she said). It was also very near home.

Mrs Hatchell worked as a cleaner at the local doctors' surgery, and Mr Hatchell was a factory worker, and always seemed to be wearing dirty oily overalls. June's sister Linda was younger, and had a lively interest in music and boys. June was quieter, and something of a 'home bird', as her mother called her. The family went to church occasionally, but were certainly not regular attenders. They had occasional Sunday outings, but the main pastime was watching TV.

June was not unhealthy, and had only the usual childhood ailments, which had been and gone in the way these things do. When June started complaining that she could not move her left arm, however, it was considered to be just another minor ailment. No time was taken off work, and the doctor was not consulted.

After about a week, everything was back to normal, and the episode soon forgotten. There were periods after this, over the next few months, when June suffered aches and pains which were treated with paracetamol. The doctor was seen a couple of times, but could find nothing which caused him any concern.

Then, one September morning, June awoke, totally unable to see. The doctor was called in, appointments made with specialists, and nothing definite diagnosed. One consultant suggested that it might be a psychiatric disorder. After a couple of weeks, the family were at their wits' end, and ready to do anything to help June. Her mood varied between tearful depression and seemingly philosophical acceptance of the situation.

So when a faith healer advertised that he was to give a healing session at a local church, the Hatchells went along. Mrs Hatchell said that there was nothing to lose, and they had to try doing *something*.

The Sunday afternoon could not come quickly enough, and the church was very full when they arrived. Local people knew June, and she was allowed with her family to go to the front row. After the service, the healer asked for people to volunteer themselves to his healing touch. June was led to him, seated in the chair, and hands laid on. Nothing very dramatic happened, and the family returned home resigned to having a blind daughter to care for.

The next morning, however, June awoke to the bright sunlight of a frosty day – she could see it all! The local 'miracle girl' was interviewed by the local paper, and soon afterwards, as the word spread, by all the national papers, radio, and television. Attendance at the church soared, the healer could not keep up with the demand for his services. People from far and wide with all manner of disabilities came to him with high hopes.

A few months later, just after June's 18th birthday, she began to lose the use of her legs. Very soon she was in a wheelchair, and remained there for some weeks before some use returned to her lower limbs.

It was at this time that a diagnosis of multiple sclerosis was made.

CASES AND ASSIGNMENTS

QUESTIONS

1 What are June's long-term needs likely to be?

2 If you were taking a history from a patient with multiple sclerosis, what sort of story are you likely to hear?

3 Do you think there is a role for faith healers in a modern society such as ours? Or in any other society? Debate the issues, using the procedure outlined in Assignment 6 on page 205.

4 What is complementary medicine? Find out about other facets of complementary medicine, and prepare a fact-file for reference purposes. (*See* Assignment 13 on page 210.)

5 Which agencies (statutory, voluntary or private) could the Hatchells approach for help?

6 What aids and adaptations would you recommend for June's living accommodation?

7 What beneficial results are claimed from the use of a hyperbaric oxygen chamber for people with multiple sclerosis? What else is such a chamber used for?

CASE 3: Margaret Hall

Margaret Hall is a middle-aged woman who was married to a solicitor, but is now widowed. She lives in a large house in a much sought after suburb of the town. Both her children have left home; her daughter is married with one child, and her son is at university.

Margaret does not work, but is a pillar of the local voluntary network. She helps in the Oxfam shop, makes tea for visitors at the local hospital, undertakes some voluntary driving, and is on various other committees which involve her going out to meetings and generally mixing socially to quite a large extent.

Her main problem is that she suffers from urinary incontinence. This is not something which she will readily admit to anybody, and, in fact, is quite reluctant to admit to herself. She had not even approached her family doctor about it. As he is also a family friend, she does not feel that she could discuss something which she considers so intimate and degrading with him. So she is struggling to cope alone.

She first became aware of the problem a few months ago when she had a touch of cystitis and a cold at the same time. When she sneezed, she wet herself; this also happened when she laughed a little too heartily, as she was wont to do. She is less inclined to laugh at all these days, though the problem has worsened, and no laughing, coughing or sneezing is required to cause the leakage. The whole situation is really getting her down.

At first she would change her underwear three or four times a day, taking a change and some plastic bags with her wherever she was going. Then she took to wearing panty liners and sanitary towels. A great concern for her was that other people would notice, and that she was smelly. This called for frequent baths, and the use of strong perfumes.

People noticed the change in her habits and that she was not the happy, outgoing person she used to be, and some made comments to her about the strong perfume.

Matters did not improve, and she has gradually given up her commitments with all the voluntary organisations she used to help. Visits to her daughter have also ceased, with a variety of excuses being given. She feels safer at home, where she knows she can control things better; a ready supply of pads and clean underwear, bathing or showering twice or three times a day, and not having to meet so many people.

QUESTIONS

1 What are the problems with a 'hidden handicap' that are not so apparent with a more obvious one?

2 From where could Mrs Hall obtain help? What advice would you give her?

3 Is her personal solution to the problem (read again the final paragraph) going to be useful to her in the long term?

4 Do you consider this problem to be common or uncommon? Is it really a handicap? Give reasons for your opinion.

5 Where can you contact incontinence advisers in your area?

6 What psychological and social effects do you think there have been on Mrs Hall?

CASE 4: Jason Young

Jason Young was enjoying himself with his friends on an 18th birthday outing to a pub near the river in his home town when his life changed.

It was a hot sunny day, and he had drunk a few pints of beer. The river looked very inviting, so the group decided to go for an impromptu swim. The pedestrian bridge looked to be an ideal diving board, and one or two of the more adventurous amongst them decided to jump in from there. Jason decided to be different; he would dive in. This he did, but the river was not as deep as it seemed at this point, and his head hit the bottom. He was rescued by his friends, and an ambulance called to take him to the Casualty Department.

X-rays revealed that he had broken his neck, and damaged the nerves: Jason has lost the use of all four limbs, but can use his neck and face muscles. He was transferred to a Spinal Injuries Unit, where he remained for over a year. The unit was quite a distance from home, and meant long journeys for his parents and sister to keep in touch with him. The cost in both time, money and emotion in the early days was very high.

Jason now lives in a hostel with 23 other disabled people. He complains of the shortage of staff, and having to wait until they are able to get him up. This takes two people, and starts with a bed bath as he has usually been incontinent during the night. Next, he is dressed, but is not always allowed a say in what he wears. This depends upon how busy the staff are, and who it is on duty. Some care staff are more caring than others.

The next task is his breakfast and medication. Being fed by someone else is not always a pleasant experience, although you can train the staff to do things to your liking when you get used to them, he maintains.

Jason is then transferred to his powered wheelchair (which has been left plugged in all night to recharge the batteries). The controls are tailor-made to his needs, and are of the blow and suck type. A tube with a mouthpiece has been fixed within reach of his mouth, and Jason now has full control of his mobility when in the chair.

He is then taken to the toilet, and has his teeth cleaned and hair combed before starting lessons on his computer, which is once again controlled by the blow and suck method. Jason's proficiency with this is improving in leaps and bounds, and he is hoping that it will be the answer to his wish for independence. His hope is for a flat or bungalow which can be modified for his needs, and a great deal of computer-controlled equipment. He realises that there will still be a need for human helpers, but hopes that he can keep that to a minimum of perhaps two or three times a day; getting up, a mid-day meal and change of incontinence pads, and going to bed – and that he will have more control of the timing of these.

In the residential unit his day has to revolve around the routine set by the needs of a large establishment. Getting up at the time the staff can get round to it is just the start; after the computer time, Jason likes to read the paper and have a cup of tea. Most days, one of the other residents can help by making the tea and turning the pages of the paper when Jason is ready. On other days, when his more able friends are out, he has to wait until the staff are making a cup of tea in order to get one for himself, and have the pages of his paper turned when people are passing rather than when he is ready. Books are easier, as he has a suck and blow attachment for turning smaller pages.

Dinner time is set by the needs of the establishment, and choice of what to eat is limited. As he and one or two others have to be fed, he has to wait his turn. The food may be lukewarm by then, and somewhat less than appetising.

After dinner, most people doze, watch television or listen to the radio. Sometimes his friends call in to visit, but the number of friends and the number of their visits has been reducing steadily since the accident. Some have genuinely moved away to university or polytechnic, others married and left the

179

area, but Jason feels that others are just plain embarrassed by seeing him in his new circumstances, and prefer to stay away.

The evening meal routine is much the same as the midday one, except more people are there when they come from the day centre, and two or three from work. More television is the order of the day for most, but Jason likes to return to the computer and listen to music if there is nothing he fancies on television. Once again, he is reliant on somebody else to put the music cassettes in the player for him, and occasionally to replace the paper on the computer printer.

At bedtime – again decided more often than not by the staff than by himself – he likes to watch television in bed after he has been undressed, washed and changed. The television has a timer, so it is set to switch off when Jason wants it to. He has to be turned three times a night in order to prevent pressure sores, and changed if necessary, so no night is really undisturbed.

His parents have offered to move house and take him to live with them, but after giving the matter a lot of thought, Jason decided against it.

One of Jason's main complaints is of frustration; frustration at not being able to fully control his own life; the constant reliance on the goodwill of other people, as he puts it. He has been through periods of profound depression, but getting involved with computers and the promise of accommodation by a specialist Housing Association at some point in the future has now given him hope. He has also discovered that he likes writing, and has entered one or two short story competitions. These have brought in a few pounds already, and he is hoping to make more cash in this way, and has asked all his contacts and the local librarian (who visits the home every two weeks) to keep him advised of any new competitions they may come across.

QUESTIONS

1 Why do you think Jason's friends no longer visit as frequently as they did when he first had his accident?

2 Do you think Jason should have accepted the offer of accommodation with his parents?

3 Put yourself in the shoes of a care assistant at this establishment, and write about your daily routine. There are 24 residents with varying degrees of independence, and the most staff on at any one time is four; more usually it is two or three.

4 What role do you see for computers in the care of disabled people in the future? Can you find out what is available now? Find out what you can and invite a speaker in to tell you about what is available and the price you could expect to pay. What is POSSUM?

5 How realistic is Jason's plan to live alone? Find out what is available in your area and design a package of care to suit Jason's needs.

6 Design a bungalow or flat to suit Jason's requirements. Visit a local estate agency and find somewhere which you feel could be modified to Jason's needs; draw a plan of the floor space and equip it appropriately. Work out the costs of purchase and fitting any specialist equipment, or use the plan opposite.

CASE 5: Robert and Hilda Dale

Robert is now aged 58, and lives with his wife Hilda in a ground floor flat on a council estate in the suburbs of a northern town. He was born and brought up in the area, and held a clerical post with a large insurance company for most of his working life. It was here that he met his wife, Hilda, and they worked together until their only child was born. She is now married, and lives in Australia.

Hilda has been something of an invalid for a few years now. She is four years older than Robert, and unfortunately has a heart disorder which means that she cannot exert herself very much without becoming breathless and having to rest.

Robert has a younger sister Dora, who lives on the same estate in a three-bedroomed house with her husband John and their two teenage children. She works part-time as a barmaid at the pub on the estate, the Foresters Arms.

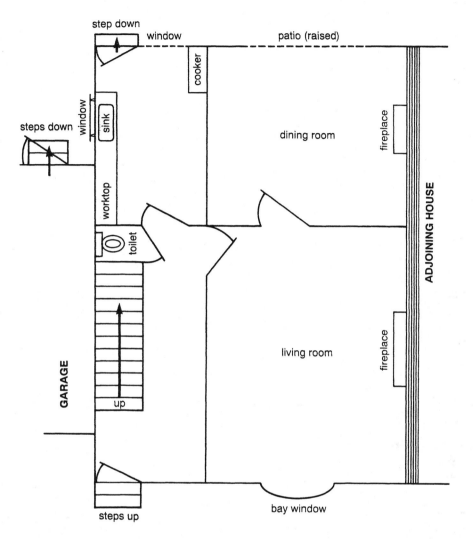

An unmodified plan of a bungalow. Identify any changes required for a wheelchair user.

About three years ago, Robert collapsed at work and was immediately admitted to hospital. He had suffered a stroke and now has a left hemiplegia, and there is no possibility of him returning to his old job.

After the stroke, Robert had difficulty in speaking. Speech therapy has helped him regain much of his speech, but he is still slow to respond, and slurs his words at times. His walking is also quite badly affected, but he can get around the house using a tripod walking stick.

Robert and Hilda do have £7000 savings, and a pension of £45 a week from the insurance company. Robert has loaned his car to his brother-in-law, as he is unable to drive now, and John is not very well off.

Package of care

An Occupational Therapist (OT) from the local Social Services Department (SSD) went to visit the Dales, and made an assessment of their needs.

In Robert's case, the recommendations were for handrails at strategic points (near the front door, in the toilet and around the shower area); a riser chair for the sitting room; a trolley for meals; and, as an aid to mobility, modified eating utensils and other kitchen equipment; and a small ramp to do away with the front door step. The bath has had to be removed to make room to fit a shower with a seat. He has a tripod to help him walk, and a reacher to pick things up. Other things he has bought for himself, such as a new TV with remote control, and a music centre with radio and remote control. A push-button telephone with large buttons has also been supplied. Many of these things are also suitable for Hilda's needs, too, but they never asked for anything when Robert was fit and well.

The daily package of care arranged for Robert and Hilda is as follows:

08.00 Home Care Assistant (HCA) arrives to get Robert out of bed. He is helped to wash, dress, shave, and go to the toilet. Hilda manages without help, but needs more time, so she waits until Robert is finished. Breakfast is prepared, the dishes washed and the beds made. Robert is made comfortable in his riser chair, listening to the radio, and the HCA leaves at about 9.15 am to go to her next visit, after putting the laundry into the washing machine.

11.00 A neighbour from across the road calls in to make a coffee and have a chat. Mrs Burns will also do whatever shopping is necessary, and collect allowances from the Post Office when they are due.

12.30 Meals on Wheels arrives; Hilda makes sure the dinner-plate is on a non-slip mat, the meat cut up, and the adapted eating utensils are within reach. The meal is served on a wheeled trolley in front of his easy chair, which Hilda can push out of the way when he is ready.

In the afternoon, he likes to watch sport on the television, so he likes the remote control unit to be within reach.

15.30 His sister Dora calls on her way home from the pub where she works as a barmaid. She makes a cup of tea for them all, and they have a sandwich and a piece of cake or a biscuit together. Dora will empty the washing machine and do any ironing, before going home to her own family. She will also dust and vacuum around if she has the time, usually once or twice a week. Dora also makes sure that there is something there for an evening meal; soup or a sandwich or a pie, perhaps, which is easy for them to manage themselves.

22.00 The evening HCA arrives to help Robert to the toilet, wash, and go to bed, and the flat is left safe for the night (fires and lights off, doors and windows closed and locked). Robert's radio, book, bedside light and telephone are left within his reach.

The weekly elements of the package are:

Monday: as above.
Tuesday: Robert and Hilda are both collected at 9.30 am to go to the Day Centre, where they stay until 4 pm.
Wednesday: collected by a volunteer driver at 2 pm to go to bingo at the church hall, and home again at 4.30 pm.
Thursday: as Tuesday, plus a District Nurse comes in to give them both a shower and shampoo at 6pm.
Friday: as Monday.
Saturday: as Monday, but no meals are delivered. Dora usually takes something in on her way to work, and Hilda heats it up in the oven.
Sunday: collected by brother-in-law John to spend the day with Dora and her family. Sometimes they go to church; other days they go for drives.

Twice a year they phone their daughter in Australia, and she rings them on another two occasions.

QUESTIONS

Packages of care can be much more complex than this one, or considerably more simple.

The Dales' care manager is the OT, and the package she has arranged has elements of informal, statutory, and voluntary provision. They have also purchased some items from the private sector.

Could you identify which elements come from which sector?

CASE 6: Betty Church

Betty Church is a 35-year old woman who lives with her husband Mark and children Tom aged 11 and Jenny who is 7 years old. She works as a receptionist at a large legal firm in the town, responsible for meeting all visitors to the office, and sitting in the waiting area with them until they can see a solicitor. The family live in a semi-detached house on the outskirts of the town, close to the primary school where Mark Church is a teacher, and near to the Comprehensive which Tom attends.

One morning last January, Betty woke up with a tingling feeling on the right side of her face, and noticed that the pillow had a damp spot where her mouth had been. She went to a mirror, and saw immediately that her mouth was turned down at the right side, and her eye refused to close properly. When she touched her cheek, there was no sensation at all. She became very worried and started crying. Mark went to her to see what was the matter, and also became very concerned. Both were convinced that something was seriously wrong, and that they would have to go to the doctor as soon as the surgery opened.

Betty tried to carry on as normal, but when cleaning her teeth, she noticed that the toothpaste did not taste the same as usual. She checked the tube, and it was the brand they always bought, but it definitely tasted different.

At breakfast, she dribbled tea from the right side of her mouth, and had to eat on the left to avoid losing food while she was eating it. The children noticed something was wrong, and showed a great deal of concern. They were reluctant to go to school, but did so, saying that they would come back home at lunch time to see what the doctor had said, and whether Mum would have to go to hospital. When Mark told her that it was time to go to the surgery, Betty refused to go, saying that she could not let people see her like that, and that the doctor would have to come to her.

Dr Hemmings arrived after her morning surgery. Betty and Mark had both taken the day off work.

She listened to the story and examined Betty thoroughly. The most likely diagnosis was Bell's palsy, she informed the couple. There was no treatment for it, and it may go as quickly as it came.

Mr and Mrs Church were not happy with this, and eventually persuaded the GP to refer them to a specialist at the District General Hospital. Dr Hemmings advised them of the waiting list, and that it may be some weeks before they were seen.

Betty remained very depressed, and rang her mother who lives about 350 miles away to tell her about things. Her mother insisted on travelling down to help them out while her daughter was ill. She arrived the next evening and took over the day to day routine of the house. The children became much more helpful with tidying and running errands, and doing the washing up, and Jenny helped with the ironing.

Betty did not feel that she could go to work, even though she felt physically perfectly well. She did less and less work at home, and they had to cancel their regular evenings out with friends. She also tried to put them off coming to see her, but some still came. They sympathised with her plight, and hoped that she would soon be better. All of this confirmed to her that she was 'poorly', and should stay in and be looked after.

The hospital appointment had still not come through two weeks later, despite Mark phoning to try and hurry things up. They decided to arrange a private consultation, and were seen within a week. More tests were carried out after a longer interview than they had held with the GP, but the results were exactly the same as the GP had stated – Bell's palsy.

As time went on, Betty became more and more reclusive. Her mother stayed as long as she felt she could, but left when she started to get exasperated with Betty not doing anything. Betty was convinced that the facial paralysis was just a small part of a major disability, and that she was bound to get worse. She had, by this time, been to the hospital, and yet a third doctor had told her that she was affected by

Bell's palsy, and to get on with her life as she had before.

After a few months, she had a letter telling her that her job had been given to somebody else, as she had been away for so long, and there was no sign of her returning. Mark was also getting short-tempered, and was going out in the evenings without Betty. The children were staying round at friends' houses more and more frequently, and this just served to confirm to Betty that she was so ugly, people did not want to be near her.

QUESTIONS

1 Find out everything you can about Bell's palsy.

2 Why did Mr and Mrs Church think that Betty may have had a stroke?

3 How did Betty's job affect her reaction to changed appearance? Describe some of the concerns she may have.

4 What effect did the family's reactions have on Betty's own attitude?

5 Why are people seen more quickly when they turn to the private sector than when they use the public sector?

6 What do you understand by the sociological term 'sick role'?

CASE 7: Robert Taylor

Robert broke his neck in a motorcycling accident in 1976, leaving him almost completely paralysed from the neck down. In 1988 he developed his own 'Package of Care', and in 1991 wrote about it in *Nursing Times*. His article is reproduced here with his kind permission.

As a C5/6 tetraplegic I need 24-hour personal care. At first this meant living at home with my parents and relying on community nurses, but I wanted to be independent.

In May 1988 I set up my own 'care scheme' in my specially designed flat in Taunton. I now employ two care assistants on a well-organised rota system.

It is of the utmost importance to get the right care staff, otherwise my independence can be in jeopardy. I advertise in the local press, in the JobCentre, or even on local radio for my carers. It is important to have people without preconceived ideas about what they might be expected to do. The job is basically to be my arms and legs, doing those things for me that I cannot do myself. The job also involves bowel and bladder care.

I find that it is important to employ carers who can become companions as well, as the nature of the job dictates that it cannot be performed by somebody whom you do not like – you may be in one another's company for a considerable time each day and some of that time in very close contact.

The carers must be able to drive, as I work away from home on occasion. They also have to be resourceful because I am involved with disability awareness training courses and this can take us all over the country, which sometimes means spending the night in a hotel.

My funding allows each carer to work 10.57 hours in 24, which is how they are paid. However, it is made very clear at the interview stage that this sum is paid for the 24-hour period and includes time during which they are asleep. I have been awarded 74.75 care hours per week – 'hands-on time', as it is known.

The shift system we find most effective runs over a two-week period – two days on (Mondays and Tuesdays), two days off (Wednesdays and Thursdays), three days off (Fridays, Saturdays and Sundays). This allows each carer to have one weekend off in two. Currently we are trying out a system of four days on, four days off, which is proving fairly successful. Change-over is at 11 am.

▶

It is important to have sick relief and I have a network of carers who will provide cover. I can use the Spinal Injuries Association care attendant agency, but as a fail-safe measure the Local Authority has an augmented Home Care team which would be able to step in for emergencies.

So how did I go about setting up my care scheme which enabled me to become independent of my parents? First, I acquired two books produced by the Hampshire Centre for Disabled Living. I followed the books' advice and put together a detailed list of my care requirements, the 'hands-on' care hours required, and the cost. The next step was to convince my Local Authority that, given financial support, I could arrange my own care. I spent the next 18 months persuading Somerset County Council that operating my own care scheme was a cheap and more efficient alternative to residential care. I was given a green light by the Social Services Committee in May 1988, and I have never looked back.

The largest single problem with running a care scheme is staff selection because, no matter how good your interview technique, the person being interviewed will only tell you what he or she wants you to hear. I emphasise to applicants at the interview stage that the job may not be what they think, but if they seem suitable and are not put off I give them a month's trial. If at the end of that month I like them, and they like me and the job, I give them a six-month contract.

All this may sound easy, but it's not, and there are, inevitably, problems. I have to be fairly assertive regarding my requirements and I find it is important to keep the employee–employer relationship at the back of my mind at all times. I had one carer working for me who expected to go out every night. Once a precedent has been set it is difficult to break, so I have to start as I mean to go on. Once I had a telephone bill of £230, an increase of £75 on my previous quarter, so I now have itemised billing. But that is the down side, and in general my carers stay with me between six months and a year. It is not the kind of job one could do for ever, but most carers have found the job rewarding with a great deal of satisfaction. I have no preference as to the gender of the care attendants; all I ask is an open mind and a willingness to work.

These carers can see that this is the way forward for people with severe disabilities: after all, one is only requesting the right to run one's own life – something able-bodied people take for granted.

There will always be a need for institutional care, but the option of self-operated care should be available. I believe the majority of residents in long-term care could take charge of their own lives, perhaps with a little organisational help from some of us who have been in the community for a while.

My scheme is majority funded by the Local Authority and is the model for other self-care schemes in the community. There is still a great need for community nursing staff, particularly where client's needs are not as clearly defined as mine or where recipients of care are unable to define or organise their personal care.

However, in assessing a client's needs and provision it is of paramount importance that the client be consulted fully in order to take his or her desires into account.

Robert Taylor Disability Consultants can be contacted at: 7 Ladylawn, Trull, Somerset TA3 2LR, Telephone 0823 333802.

QUESTIONS

1 What does 'C5/6 Tetraplegic' mean?

2 What do you understand by the term 'Care Scheme' or 'Package of Care'?

3 How does Robert find his care staff?

4 What does the job involve?

5 How does Robert earn his living?

6 From which groups of providers is help drawn?

7 Who can be called in to cover emergencies?

8 How did Robert go about setting up his Care Scheme?

9 What would have been the alternative if it had not been possible to arrange a Care Scheme?

10 What does Robert say is the biggest problem with the scheme?

11 Who funds the scheme?

12 Before reading on, devise a job description for Robert's Care Attendant; then compare that with Robert's own which is shown below.

Job description for care attendants

It is the job of the support care attendant to assist the person with the disability in all areas of personal and domestic need and to act as an escort and aid in the person's social and day-to-day activities. By providing help at the right time, the person is enabled to lead an individual and independent lifestyle in the community.

The care attendant should always ask what the client's needs are and listen to requests and directions. Care attendants should be able to handle the physical skills of lifting, pushing and bending. One does not have to be a strong person physically to do the job, but it does help, together with general good health.

Personal care requirements
- Bathing in bed/bathroom/chair
- Helping in and out of bed/wheelchair (hoist where applicable)
- Toileting. Bowel and bladder routines. Fitting and care of urinary devices. Dealing with incontinence management
- Assistance in dressing and undressing
- Attention to personal grooming, care of hair, nails, feet, eyes and so on
- Daily exercise, physiotherapy movements of limbs, mainly in the mornings
- Serving and cutting up of food as required

General domestic care
- Making and changing of bed
- Laundry – washing and ironing
- Housework, including cleaning, dusting, vacuum-cleaning of rooms
- Other general areas of household maintenance and shopping
- Preparation, cooking of meals and washing-up

Other duties
- Assistance in and out of car
- Keeping car clean and tidy
- Maintenance of exterior of flat, for instance, clearance of snow from paths, cleaning windows, sweeping outside paths
- Maintenance of equipment such as wheelchairs, hoists and other aids

- Escorting to work, including trips around country. On occasion overnight stops will be necessary. This will also include places of entertainment and leisure
- Assistance with clerical duties, banking, posting letters and opening mail when required
- Answering the telephone and taking messages

Note: All needs will vary from day to day and duties will alter accordingly.

Qualifications and personal qualities required
- Ability to accept responsibility
- Reliability and trustworthiness
- Willingness to learn the job well
- Clean personal habits

Attendant's responsibilities
- As far as possible resolve any questions regarding the job before starting work
- Arrive at the scheduled time ready to work. Notify the person with the disability if you are going to be more than 10 minutes late
- It is important to establish a close working relationship with the person who has the disability. If any problems arise, it is important to discuss and resolve them immediately. Be as open in your communication as possible
- Confidentiality: respect the privacy of the person you are working with. Try to maintain a professional approach at all times
- Attitude: appreciate the stresses and strains involved for the client and the effect this can have on the acceptance of help. Understand that the preservation of dignity and independence is important

Learning of tasks
As far as possibel all areas of assistance can be achieved through the attendant and client working together. Practical assistance and guidance will be available from qualified nurses where appropriate

Nursing Times July 31, Vol 87, No 31, 1991

CASE 8: Kay Carpal

Kay was described as 'a delightful girl with a love of fun, who unfortunately spends a lot of her time day-dreaming' by her primary school teacher. She rarely missed a day from school, and enjoyed the company of her friends.

She is now 13, and attends a comprehensive school. Or rather, she should. Her attendance was initially good, became erratic, and is now virtually non-existent. A letter was sent to her parents, but they did not respond. An Education Welfare Officer, or EWO (Kathy Loughran) was asked to visit, but had trouble making contact. When she eventually did, she prepared a report for the school, extracts from which read as follows:

'My first three visits were in the daytime, but despite writing in advance, and knocking at both front and back doors, I could elicit no response. Despite this, I had the distinct impression that somebody was there.

As these methods had not worked, I called in the evening. On the first occasion there was no car there; I know that Mr Carpal is a sales representative with a company car, so I did not go to the door. On the next occasion, a car was in the driveway, so I knocked.'

It goes on to say:

'Mr Carpal seemed very anxious and under stress; he denied any knowledge of any letters from either the school or myself, and said he spent a great deal of time away from home.

As far as he was aware, Kay was going to school. He would ask his wife, but did not wish to bother her just at the moment as she was ill in bed.

Kay was not to be seen, but loud music was coming from one of the bedrooms. I asked if I could speak to her; Mr Carpal went to her room, but came down the stairs shaking his head as she had refused to come down and see me. I reminded him of the seriousness of the situation, and the legal requirement of his daughter being educated, and asked if I may go up to her room. He shrugged agreement. When I went in, Kay turned up the music, and lay on her bed facing the wall. She refused to look at me or speak to me, even after

I had turned the radio off. I told her that I would be back, and that the matter of not going to school would have to be dealt with.

As I was leaving, a weak female voice asked what was going on. Mr Carpal took me into his wife's bedroom. She was lying in bed looking very gaunt, and was dribbling a little. Her hands were clawed and seemed to have no grip left in them. We told her why I was here and what the problem was. She began crying, and said that it was her fault. She had seen no letters, either, but had asked Kay to stay and look after her when her father was away, and this seemed to be more and more frequently these days. She thought it would only be for a short while, but she seemed to be able to do less and less each day. Kay now did all the housework and cooking.

A District Nurse came in each morning to bathe Mrs Carpal, but Kay usually managed to hide when she arrived.'

The EWO felt she was getting out of her depth, and referred the case to Social Services.

QUESTIONS

1 Why do you think Mr Carpal is spending increasing amounts of time away from home?

2 What happened to the letters from the school, do you think?

3 What is an EWO, and what is their job?

4 Do you think Kay is doing the right thing in staying away from school?

5 Read the description of Kay from the primary school, and compare it with her attitude toward the EWO. What may be the reasons for this?

6 Can you find out how many 'informal' carers are estimated to be school children?

7 If Kay started going to school, what would be the result for:
(a) Mrs Carpal, and
(b) the Social Services Department?

Kay's case (continued)

The SSD allocated the case to a social worker, David Nolan. He went to the house to assess the situation. He discovered that the GP, Dr Rao, had diagnosed Mrs Carpal as having Motor Neurone Disease. This is a progressive disorder, and long-term help was needed by the family. David had as much trouble getting in as did Kathy, the EWO. He decided to call a Case Conference (or a Planning Conference), and invited Dr Rao, the District Nurse, the EWO, Kay's teacher, and Mr Carpal.

A surprising revelation was presented to the conference by Nurse Crowther:

'I had noticed that Mrs Carpal had bruising to her legs for which I could find no reason, and she could not or would not explain. After one visit about 2 or 3 weeks ago, I went on to my next visit, and realised I had left my watch and ring at the Carpals' house. I went back to retrieve them, and let myself in as usual. I was about to shout upstairs that I was there when I heard a young girl's voice shouting and what seemed to be a muffled whimpering. I know I should not really have done it, but I went quietly up the stairs without calling out. I could see through the crack in the door to Mrs Carpal's room. She was lying in bed holding the corner of a pillow to her mouth; Kay had a walking stick, and was hitting the bed at a point I realised was her mother's shins, and repeating over and over again, 'I hate you, I hate you, I hate you.' I had to stop her, and took the stick from her, but she ran away. Mrs Carpal refused to talk about it. I've been wondering what to do ever since.'

QUESTIONS

1 What would you do if you came across this situation?

2 Why do you think Kay was acting as she did?

3 Why is Mrs Carpal refusing to complain?

4 Is abuse of people with a physical disability something which you consider to be widespread?

5 What other forms of abuse should you be aware of? Take into account the section on finances, and relate the question to work with children.

EXERCISES

1 Find out all you can about Motor Neurone Disease.

2 Devise a Package of Care for the Carpal family. (*See* Assignment 7 on page 206 for help.)

3 Organise a role play of the Planning/Case conference with the members as outlined above. (*See* also Assignment 8 on page 206.)

CASE 9: Terry Kelsall

Terry and Jean Kelsall had been married 21 years when the accident happened. Their only daughter Cheryl had left home for university, and Terry ran his own business as a welder, and he travelled quite extensively for his work.

He went off on a contract one morning as usual, but by lunchtime, Jean had received a phone call to go to a hospital in a neighbouring town as Terry had been involved in an accident at work. Getting there was a problem, but she eventually persuaded her sister to drive her.

Terry had damage to his face and eyes, something to do with not wearing goggles and a 'flashback', a term which Jean did not fully understand. He was to be transferred to a specialist eye unit, and there was a danger of some permanent effect on his sight.

Despite medical attention over some months, this is what turned out to be the case. As a result, the Kelsall's lives were in turmoil; Terry was no longer able to work, and had undergone a complete personality change. The pleasant and easy-going husband that Jean had married had become a bitter complainer whom people now avoided.

The relationship between Jean and Terry changed. So much depends on non-verbal communication and the subtle clues of body language and facial expression in transactions between sighted people. Terry could no longer pick these up, and, therefore, could not respond to them. Jean herself was becoming very depressed, and was turning to her sister and to Cheryl for support.

When he first came home from hospital, Terry insisted that he could manage without help, insisting that his eyesight was not as bad as the doctors were trying to make out, this despite bumping into things around the house and in the garden, and never going out alone. He was not foolish enough to try driving, however, and as Jean was unable to drive, this meant using public transport or taxis.

Jean was becoming extremely stressed with having to care for her husband, and his insistence that he did not need looking after. Cheryl was coming home far more often, and this was putting even more strain on the limited income of the family.

On a trip to the town centre one day, Terry said that he wanted to go to the Post Office. Jean knew he would have difficulty in coping, but nevertheless left him at the entrance, and said she would meet him when she had done some shopping of her own.

After about a half hour, she returned to find him still standing by the entrance to the Post Office. He had not been inside, and made excuses such as waiting for the queue to go down, and not being in a rush. Jean was determined, however, and said she would come back for him later, when she had completed the rest of her shopping.

This was the moment when she considered the breakthrough happened. Terry began sobbing, and tears were running down his face – the first time she had seen him cry since the birth of Cheryl. She took him to a nearby bench and held his hand. It was then that he admitted for the first time that his eyes were so bad that he could not do things for himself any more.

They returned home, found all the papers from the hospital, and contacted the family doctor. Terry was referred to the local ophthalmologist, who was of the opinion that Terry was now partially sighted, and form BD8 was completed on his behalf.

The local Social Services Department offered help, which was now accepted. Terry agreed that he would benefit from a training course, and that Jean needed a break. He thus agreed to go into a residential home for a couple of weeks until a place at the Rehabilitation Centre became available.

QUESTIONS

1 In what way did Terry contribute to his own accident?

2 What is the purpose of the Form BD8?

3 What is the legal definition for partial sight? How does partial sight differ from blindness?

4 How is the relationship between Jean and Terry being affected by his loss of vision?

5 Why do you think Terry was reluctant to admit that he could no longer see?

6 Why do you think Terry is so bad-tempered much of the time?

7 What benefits are the family entitled to?

8 How is the situation affecting Cheryl, even though she no longer lives at home?

9 What services can a Social Services Department offer to blind and partially sighted people?

10 What voluntary organisations can you find for this group of people?

11 What differences would you expect to note with Terry after he has completed his rehabilitation course?

12 What advice would you give to Jean to prepare for his return home?

(See also Role Play 2 on page 33).

CASE 10: Becky and Dave Moss

Becky Simpson

Becky Simpson was born in 1967 with cerebral palsy, and is an only child. She spends a lot of her time sitting down. Mostly this is in her wheelchair, but not always, as she also likes to lounge around on her bean-bags when she can. Becky lived at home with her parents until she was twelve, and went to an ordinary school as she can speak reasonably well, and communication problems did not hold her back.

Her father is a Market Manager with responsibilities covering both the indoor and outdoor markets in the town centre. Her mother is a part-time shop assistant in the fashion trade. The family moved to a bungalow about a year after Becky was born, in preparation for making a home which Becky could become independent in. Some minor modifications had to be made, such as ramps, handles, and widths of doorways. In Becky's room the electric points were heightened so that she could reach them from her chair, and plugs with easy grip handles fitted to all the things she may want to use, such as the vacuum cleaner, portable TV, radio and so on.

There is a small garden at the front and a larger one at the back which gives more privacy, and where Mr Simpson grows his vegetables. The paths have been made firm and wide enough for the wheelchair to get about, with curves instead of angles. Becky enjoys being in the garden.

When it came to moving to a secondary school, there was a lot of fuss from the Education Department about not being able to manage her: that there were too many steps in the school; not enough room in all the classrooms; the fire risk; and so on. For a while she was taught at home by a visiting teacher, until the Education Authority then agreed to pay for a place for her at a Residential School which was about a hundred miles from her home.

Mr and Mrs Simpson gave the matter a lot of thought, and discussed it with Becky. They decided to go and look at the school, and see what it had to offer. All three of them were very impressed with the facilities, although Becky was quite nervous about meeting so many new people – and she had never seen so many disabled people together before, as there was only one other at her primary school. This was before the 1981 Education Act, so Becky was lucky to be able to attend the local primary school. Mr and Mrs Simpson went to speak to the primary school headmaster, as they respected his views, and to the Social Worker they occasionally saw. They also got in touch with the Spastics Society to ask their advice.

The outcome was that, in the end, Becky went to the Residential School, but came home every weekend from Friday evening until Sunday night. She was upset at first, as she missed her parents and the friends from where she lived; she also missed Jolly, her pet cat. But she soon made new friends, and got used to seeing her family at weekends. Jolly sometimes came along in the car to collect her, but usually slept all the time.

Becky did quite well at the college, getting pass grades in five GCSEs. She decided to stay on and do her 'A' levels; she enjoyed maths, and had ideas of being a book-keeper or accountant working from home and using a home computer with a Modem.

It was on the Computer Studies course that she met Dave Moss.

Dave Moss

Dave is a year older than Becky, and has spina bifida. He is able to walk with the use of elbow crutches, but does use his wheelchair some of the time.

He comes from another town 50 miles away from the college in the opposite direction to Becky. His father is a nurse and his mother a teacher; his father went on to permanent night-shifts when Dave's needs became apparanet, so that it was easier to share the care between the parents. He has two brothers, one a year older and the other a year younger than him. They went to school together, and so helped Dave complete his schooldays in his home area. His care needs were, and are, mainly with continence and mobility. He had an interest in computers, but there was nowhere suitable in his vicinity where he could take a more advanced course. This is how he came to be at the Residential College where he met Becky. He hoped to become a computer programmer, and started by designing games as part of his course.

Becky and Dave left college in 1985 with the qualifications they wanted and needed to follow their chosen careers. They kept in touch with each other, despite the distance. This was helped a lot when Dave passed his driving test and bought an adapted car through the Motability Scheme.

Both were doing well in their respective careers; Becky was doing the accounts for many of the market traders who knew her father, and her mother brought in some work for her to get started. Business people from a variety of backgrounds were now asking her to do things for them, and she was paying her own way. Dave was also doing contract work for large companies, and his name was getting known in the right circles.

The wedding

Romance blossomed between Becky and Dave, and they decided to get married. All the parents were pleased about this, as they each knew the other family quite well by now. Dave could work from anywhere in the country using his sophisticated communications equipment, but Becky would need to stay in her home area if her business was to continue.

Mr Simpson was due for retirement shortly before the wedding date, and they came to an agreement with Becky and Dave to sell them the bungalow on advantageous terms, and move to a smaller place themselves.

QUESTIONS

1 What is the Motability Scheme?

2 What are the advantages for Dave and Becky of moving into the Simpsons' bungalow?

3 Organise a wedding, bearing in mind the facts that the friends of the bride and groom will include a proportion of people with disabilities, and that Becky and Dave themselves have mobility and access problems.

What special provision, if any, will have to be made in both the church, the reception and the transport arrangements?

Starting a family

Becky and Dave settled into life together, and their combined businesses gave them a decent income even if it would never make them millionaires. They developed a wider circle of friends, partly through going to a PHAB club, and partly through work.

Confirmation of Becky's pregnancy was greeted with great excitement by the families concerned.

QUESTIONS

1 From where could Becky and Dave get advice about overcoming the physical problems of performing the sex act?

2 What are the statistical chances of any of their children having a similar disability to their own?

3 What pre-natal screening is likely to be undertaken; which tests do you consider would be of most use?

4 Can you identify the practical problems this couple are likely to have to face in bringing up a young child?

Parenting

The midwife allocated to look after Becky during her pregnancy and the childbirth is 'of the old school', and close to retirement. She has grave doubts about disabled people having children, and is convinced that they will not be able to look after the child as parents should do. She is concerned about the risks of the child being in danger because neither Becky nor Dave could get to it quickly enough, especially when the baby becomes a toddler and playgrounds and roads become a real problem.

So concerned is she that she refers the matter to the Social Services Department with a recommendation that the child is placed for adoption.

The SSD respond by organising a Case Conference at which all the options available will be discussed. These options are:

- taking no action at all
- going to court for a Care Order on the grounds that the child is likely to suffer significant harm due to a lack of reasonable parental control
- organising a package of care.

TASK

As a class, arrange a role play of this case conference; decide what action to take, and justify that decision in writing. (Read the guidelines in Assignment 8 on page 206.)

People you may consider should be included are the midwife, Health Visitor, family doctor, social workers who know Becky and Dave, former teachers. Don't forget the chair and the note-taker. Would you also include Becky and Dave?

ASSIGNMENTS

1 Locality survey
2 Voluntary organisations
3 Speaker invitation
4 Arranging a visit
5 The media
6 Procedure for a debate
7 Designing a package of care

8 Case conference
9 Organising your own placement
10 Providing a service
11 Organising a holiday
12 Devising a game
13 Complementary medicine
14 Designing a garden

Assignment guidelines

Before commencing work on any assignment, it is wise to prepare the ground by some preparatory work:

(a) Plan a timetable/calendar of work to be done to fit the time allowed.
(b) Identify where you are going to get the information from.
(c) List any books, articles, or other written sources you wish to use, and where they can be found.
(d) Make telephone calls and/or write letters to arrange visits and/or interviews.
(e) Obtain any equipment necessary in advance, e.g. video camera, film, tape recorder and tapes, wheelchair, etc. as appropriate.
(f) Calculate any costs to be met, and make arrangements to meet these in advance.
(g) Prepare any questionnaires, decide which questions to ask of whom, and how.
(h) Decide upon the best way to present the information.

Questionnaire design

When producing your own questionnaire, the following points should be remembered:

(a) Questions should be brief, clear, and to the point.
(b) Wording must avoid ambiguities, e.g. 'tea time' may be different times to different people; specify 3 pm, 4 pm, or 4.30 pm.
(c) Follow a logical sequence in the information you are asking for.
(d) Keep the design of the page open; use larger print if respondents are to fill the answers in themselves.
(e) Leave sensitive questions until later on in the page, e.g. about age or money.
(f) When asking how much would be acceptable to pay, give bands to choose from rather than leave it open, e.g.
10p–50p
50p–£1
£1 –£2, etc.

Questions designed in this way are easier to collate when you have all the replies together.

Test out your questionnaire before using it 'for real'; see if people in the college find it easy and consider it appropriate, and make any modifications necessary before duplicating it.

ASSIGNMENT 1: Locality survey

Read the article opposite entitled *Pete's Patch* about a *Which?* Report on access, and then undertake the following tasks.

Survey the nearest town centre, taking somebody in a wheelchair with you. This could either be a volunteer with a genuine disability, or a fellow student who has taken on the role.

Despite the fact that it is only a minority of disabled people who are wheelchair users, remember that easy access for wheelchairs also eases the way for people who use other walking aids, or who have difficulties in walking (as well as mothers with prams and pushchairs).

A Go to the Post Office, see how easy it is to get in and out, and to move around inside.

(i) How high are the counters in relation to the person sitting down? Look for the same points in the library and banks.

(ii) Do any of the shops make allowances for disabilities (e.g. ramps, wide entrances, wide aisles)?

(iii) Call in for a drink and a snack; was your choice of places to go limited by the wheelchair?

(iv) Did you follow the same route as you would have done if you were alone? If you did not, then why not?

Write about how it felt to be the helper behind the wheelchair, or the person in the wheelchair, whichever role you took.

B When you are out and about, (not just on this exercise, but in your normal day-to-day life) take a little more notice of the things around you. What is there available to help disabled people?

(i) Does the self-service garage have an attendant for disabled drivers?

(ii) In the supermarket, are there any adapted trolleys? Or wider checkouts?

(iii) Are there ramps and handrails at any of the places you go to?

(iv) Does the cinema have an 'induction loop'? What is it for?

(v) Are the public toilets accessible and usable by disabled people?

(vi) How do pelican crossings help people with disabilities?

(vii) What car parking spaces for drivers with a disability are there?

(viii) Do all the cars using them have Orange Badges?

(ix) Could wheelchair users or people with mobility problems get into the buses and taxis you see around?

(x) Would public telephones be easy to use?

(xi) What services are there at the library for people with disabilities? What facilities do they provide?

(xii) Does the Sports Centre cater for people with disabilities? What facilities do they provide?

The trip around the town can be recorded on video, if college facilities permit.

Additional Option 1

When out around the town, ask at the banks, building societies, insurance companies, employment agencies and any other institutions you find about the specialist services they provide for their disabled patrons. Ask for any relevant leaflets in addition to looking for access points, counter heights, etc. Have you collected many pamphlets?

Look back at Chapter 18 Finances and see if any information is available on Appointees, Trustees, etc.

(i) What is the situation with insurance cover for people with a disability?

(ii) Devise a letter to send to the organisations as above (use *Yellow Pages* or the *Thomson Local Directory* for addresses), and ask for any material publicly available on services provided for people with a disability. This part may alternatively be undertaken as a telephone survey.

Additional Option 2

When you are at home, look around and see what would need to be done to allow for people with particular disabilities to live there comfortably.

(i) Is there a step up to the front door?

(ii) Could an arthritic hand get a good grip of handles, e.g. on doors, taps, cookers, cupboards, etc?

Pete's Patch

Peter Bayliss. "Lea Cottage". Withybrook Road. Street Ashton. Rugby CV23 0PJ.

I recollect my very first *Pete's Patch*, about five years ago, was concerned with access problems for wheelchair users. Has anything happened in the meantime to improve the situation?

Well, the main difficulty at that time with regard to new buildings was that access requirements (under the 1970 *Chronically Sick and Disabled Persons Act*) was not enforced. Facilities for disabled people needed to be provided only if it was 'reasonable and practical' to do so. This clause could be exploited by unscrupulous builders to excuse a total lack of facilities.

The way to enforce these requirements was through the Building Regulations. And back in 1983 the Government had decided that these should be used to make sure the provisions of the Act and other legislation were followed. The latest Regulations (known as Part M) came into force in England and Wales in 1987.

In their October 1989 issue of *Which?* the Consumers' Association published a Report on access for disabled people. Aptly entitled *No Entry*, the Report examined the current situation and looked at what effect the new Part M has on building requirements.

The WHICH? Report

The Report began with the findings of 30 disabled people who kept diaries for a typical week in their lives. 'They recorded what happened to them when they did the shopping, went to the bank and so on,' it said. 'Between them, our diarists carried out (or tried to carry out) 293 tasks — and had 300 problems of one sort or another.' They had to give up on one in ten occasions.

FAers will be only too familiar with the sort of obstacles which presented most problems. These included: steps and stairs; cluttered pavements; heavy doors; out-of-reach goods; cars on pavements; roadworks and uneven pavements; reserved parking spaces used by non-disabled drivers.

One wheelchair user complained about the supermarket: 'you either have to bend down to get under the trolley barrier, or wait for the turnstile to be removed.' Later criticism included the lack of baskets to hook onto wheelchairs, and check-outs which were insufficiently wide.

Another diarist complained that escalators were the only means of getting to the 1st and 2nd floors in a particular department store.

New Regulations

The new Part M of the Building Regulations is an improvement. But it only covers buildings built since 1987 — and even then, there are notable exceptions. The worse oversight, in my opinion, is that access shouldn't be made any worse if a building is extended. This means, as the *Which?* Report deftly points out, 'a large extension to a small inaccessible building is allowed to be inaccessible too.'

And conversions are treated in the same way as extensions. 'For example', if a warehouse were to be converted into a shop, access shouldn't be made worse.'

Advice is given to architects on how ramps, steps, doors, etc. can be designed to meet the requirements of Part M. This is good news indeed. In my own experience, architects seem blissfully ignorant of these sort of adaptations. I could write a separate *Pete's Patch* about loos-I-have-known-with-undeserved-wheelchair-access-symbols. Other chairbound FAers will have their own horror stories.

No longer, it appears, can builders hide behind the excuse of it not being 'reasonable and practical' to provide suitable access. 'For example,' says the Report, 'it might not be possible to build a ramp in a narrow busy street — *but alternative access must be provided.*'

It is the Local Authority (through their Building Control Officer) who is responsible for seeing that these requirements are enforced.

And mention is also made of fire regulations which are sometimes used to bar wheelchair users from some multi-storey buildings such as cinemas. 'The new British Standard 5588 Part 8 gives guidance on suitable means of emergency escape from new buildings for disabled people.'

Access in Town Centres

Which? invited several access groups in different parts of the country to 'carry out inspections of their town centres.'

With regard to banks, the criticism included counters and cash dispensers being too high. The aisles in chain stores were often not wide enough. Fixed seating and tables were a big problem in restaurants. In Post Offices, it was the height of counters and stamp machines. And the main problem in cinemas was with regard to steps and stairs.

Once again, access was one of the main problems together with inadequate toilet facilities, especially in pubs, restaurants and cinemas. Other common problems included heavy doores, not enough reserved parking spaces for disabled drivers and not sufficient room to allow someone to get from a car to a wheelchair.

Many of these criticisms serve to emphasize the findings of the diarists at the beginning of the Report. Certainly, none of it is new to those of us in wheelchairs. But it does, however, illustrate the depth of research undertaken by *Which?*

Recommendations

This is especially important because a copy of the Report was sent to the Government departments responsible for the Building Regulations. And a number of improvements were suggested, amongst which was the recommendation that Regulations under Part M should include extensions and conversions (see above).

Which? also suggests that local authorities could do more. In particular, they should employ access officers and consult disabled people at the planning stage. And people (disabled or otherwise) could do more by reporting on access problems to the local authority and by joining or starting up an access group in their area. To find out about such groups or how to start one, write to one of the following organisations:

Access Committee for England, 35 Great Smith Street, London SW1P 3BJ; *Northern Ireland Council on Disability*, 2 Annadale Avenue, Belfast BT7 3JR; *Scottish Council for Disability*, Princes House, 5 Shandwick Place, Edinburgh EH2 4RH; *Wales Council for the Disabled*, Llys Ifor, Crescent Road, Caerphilly, Mid Glamorgan CF8 1XL.

Taken from *FAX* magazine No 89 and reproduced by kind permission of Friedreich's Ataxia Group

(iii) Is there space to manoeuvre in all the rooms, especially the toilet and bathroom?

(iv) Would it be possible to fit a stairlift or other lift?

(v) If you have Ceefax/Oracle on your television set, how do these services help people with a sensory disability?

BTEC Common Skills involved 1; 2; 6–14 inclusive; 16 if videoed; 18.
GNVQ Level 2: 1.1; 2.1; 2.2.
GNVQ Level 3: 1.1; 1.2; 1.3; 1.4; 7.2; 8.1.

ASSIGNMENT 2: Voluntary organisations

This can be undertaken as individual work, or in small groups with task sharing as the second requirement (after choosing the organisation to be studied).

A Choose a voluntary organisation concerned with disabled people. Appendix 2 Useful Addresses at the end of the book is a good starting point.

(i) Find out what is the reason for its existence.

(ii) How and when did it start and what was the reason for it coming into existence?

(iii) How is it funded; are there any contributions from local or central government?

(iv) Who can join? Is it purely for people with a particular disability, or can carers and others join?

(v) What property does the organisation own and why? Are they just offices, or do they run day centres, advice centres, residential homes, holiday centres, or something else?

(vi) Are there any employees (as opposed to volunteers)? Are any of them disabled?

(vii) What services are provided for disabled people, and what are the reasons for providing them?

(viii) Are any of these services the same as the Local Authority or NHS provide? If so, why? Is the statutory service not good enough? Does it not have enough places?

B Imagine that you are the Publicity Manager for your chosen charity, and are offered a stall at a local charities fair.

When members of the public come to you, you will need publicity material available to hand out to them. This should give information about your organisation, what it does, who can join, and (most importantly) how they can help, either with time or money.

(i) Design a layout for the stall, using materials which you can get into the back of a hatchback or estate car (e.g. trestle table and folding screens).

(ii) Prepare eye-catching posters to attract people over to you.

(iii) How much would you need to pay for the printing of a supply of your leaflets or pamphlets? Obtain estimates from local printers: are there any discounts for charities?

(iv) What restrictions are there on the use of volunteers, for example on age range? Can they volunteer if they receive unemployment benefit; and could people with a criminal record be involved?

(v) What different methods are there of donating money to charities?

C Fundraising

(i) What sort of fund-raising events could you hold to coincide with the Charities Fair?

(ii) What restrictions are there on collecting money in the street or from door to door?

(iii) If possible, your group could organise a real fund-raising event either in the college or in the local community.

Use the information gained in the above exercise to contact the relevant people to obtain the permission required.

Choose the charity or charities to benefit from your efforts. Before doing anything else, contact them and advise them of your intentions, and ask for their advice and guidance. If you decide to do something which can be sponsored (a walk, litter pick, pub crawl, abseiling, parachute jump, or whatever), they will probably be happy to supply the sponsorship forms for your use.

NB: When you are undertaking a potentially hazardous activity such as abseiling or parachuting, you will need to arrange insurance cover. The sponsored charity has no responsibility whatsoever for any accidents that occur.

When all the money has been collected, check with your chosen charity whether they will be able to attend a formal presentation. If they are national organisations (such as the RNID), the cost of sending a representative from London may cost more than has been raised by your activity. There should be no problem with local organisations, or those with a local representative.

Option
If enough people are involved, the group can be divided into teams to arrange fundraising for more than one charity on a competitive basis.

If amounts collected are significantly different, was this due to the activities chosen, or to public sympathies toward the group chosen?

Shown below is material sent out by the Winged Fellowship Trust to prospective fund-raisers for the charity.

WINGED FELLOWSHIP TRUST

Winged Fellowship runs five UK holiday centres for severely physically disabled people, enabling carers to take a break from their duties. The Centres are run by a combination of trained staff and volunteers through which 24 hour care is provided. Each Centre is fully equipped for the use of disabled people and also has a shop, bar and garden. Guests are taken out each day to a place of interest and evening entertainment is provided, either at the Centre or elsewhere.

Located in Southport, Nottingham, Chigwell, Redhill and Southampton, the Centres are open between February and December. Prices start at £160 per week (low-season), each week being heavily subsidised by the charity, which is why we urgently need your help. The cost of the holiday is deliberately kept low and the charity subsidises each week by an average of well over £150. Winged Fellowship also organises holidays abroad for groups of nine or so.

Some facts about fundraising:

As a rough guide:
- Every £57 pays for a day's holiday for a severely disabled guest.
- £50 pays for a volunteer's board and lodging for a week.
- £400 is the average true cost of a week's holiday for a guest including fee and subsidy.

Some suggestions for fundraising events
(in alphabetical order)

These include both ticketed and sponsored events.

Babysitting	Dog sit
Bike ride	Fifties night
Book fair	Fill-a-sack
Bring & buy sale	Flower festival
Bus pull	Fun Run
Canteen collection	Garden party
Chess tournament	Gymkhana
Clean up	Hairdressing marathon
Custard pie raffle	Supermarket appeal
Disco	It's a knockout

▶

197

Jail breakout	Scrabble tournament
Jumble sale	Sixties night
Keys – house to house collection	Slim
Magic show	Spring fayre
Marathon/half marathon	Steel can collection
Medieval banquet	Sunflower grow
Mountain climb	Swear box
Pancake race	Swimming gala
Pantomime	Tin collections (full!) outside supermarkets
Parachute jump	Triathlon
Picnic	Trivial pursuit
Pub crawl in fancy dress	Victorian evening
Puppet show	Volleyball match
Rugby match	Walk
Scavenger hunt	Wishing well

Organising the event

Questions to ask yourself:

1 Previous Experience
Have you ever run a similar event before? If not, we suggest that you speak to a Winged Fellowship fundraiser (name on page 1) for advice.

2 Steps to take?
What steps do you need to take to run the event? (It is always helpful to make a plan, with dates). For example, if running a coffee morning at your home, the steps might be:

	Date
Decide on a date	
(and get some friends committed	
to helping you on the day)	
Get invitations printed	25.10.93
Send out invitations	1.11.93
Ring round to see who is coming	26.11.93
Buy provisions	28.11.93
(Borrow chairs/tables)	28.11.93
Organise room on day of event	29.11.93

3 Can you run the event on your own?
If not, you need to gather a group of helpers and give them all specific tasks so that they know exactly what they are expected to do.

4 Budget
How much is the event going to cost to run? How much money do you expect to raise after expenses have been taken off? As a bench mark, a good event usually raises four times the amount it took to put on.

5 Tickets and sponsor forms
If it is a ticketed or sponsored event make sure that tickets are sold and sponsor forms sent out well in advance. Be sure that the legal requirements are complied with. If in doubt, contact the Winged Fellowship fundraiser.

6 Publicity
You can get lists of local media contacts from your local fundraiser. The project sheet on page 7 might help as a prompt.

►

Special Considerations

Make sure that whatever you do is:

(a) safe

(b) legal

(c) cost effective

(d) fun

If you are not sure about any of the above, contact your local fundraiser and he or she will be able to advise.

Budget checklist

It is useful to work out how much you will have to spend when running an event. You could use this shseet as a checklist and jot down how much each item will cost. This might include:

- **Printing**
  Tickets
  Sponsor forms (Head Office has a supply of these)
  Leaflets
  Posters (Head Office can help again)
  Invitations
  (If you are having tickets/invitations printed make sure you shop around as prices vary a lot and printing can add considerably to your costs.)
- **Photography**
- **Provisions**
  Food
  Drink
- **Hire of Equipment**
  Chairs/tables
  Room hire
  Video
  Public announcement system
- **Prizes**
  Raffle or other

  Ask local shops if they can donate raffle prizes or supply provisions either free or at a discount. Offer them publicity at your event.

▶

FUNDRAISING EVENTS FORM

(to be completed by volunteer fundraiser and one copy to be returned to the person named on page 1)

Name: _____

Address: _____

_____

Phone No: (Day) _____ (Eve) _____

Event: (Give short description)

_____

Date of event: _____

I intend to raise: _____

I have already raised: _____

Centre for which funds will be raised/all centres: _____

If this is a sponsored event, the fundraiser is expected to raise the majority of his/her own sponsorship money, although Winged Fellowship will be able to help with publicity if required.

Help required from Winged Fellowship

Item	*Tick or give no as appropriate*
Sponsorship Forms	☐
Leaflets	☐
Posters	☐
Volunteers to help distribute leaflets	☐
Volunteers to help on the day	☐
Publicity	☐
Advice on organisation of the event	☐

FUNDRAISING PROJECT SHEET

Event:

Date of event:

Location:

Organiser:

Anticipated amount to be raised:

Celebrity/local worthy involved:

Local press to be invited: Yes/No

Responsibility:

Any contact names:

Local radio to be invited: Yes/No

Responsibility:

Any contact names:

Local TV to be invited: Yes/No

Responsibility:

Any contact names:

National press (details):

National radio (details):

National TV (details):

Photographer to be present (name)?:

Responsibility for organising photographer/developing pictures:

Press release before/responsibility:

Press release after/responsibility:

Notes:

Thank you

What better way to thank you for helping Winged Fellowship than by letting a guest say it. Here is a recent letter:

Dear Sir or Madam,

Just to say 'Thank You' for a wonderful holiday at Sandpipers once again. Such care and attention one receives at Sandpipers. My husband is in hospital permanently so it is the only chance we have of being together and we appreciate it so much. My husband is not ill in himself it is just his legs that have gone and I have heart trouble so there is no way in which I can lift him about as he must have 2 people at least to move him at all.

He went on all the trips and he even went on the speed boat and in the pool several times which he always enjoys.

Thanking you once again.

Hoping to be able to go next year.

Yours faithfully,

BTEC Common Skills covered: 1, 2, 4, 8, 9, 10, 12, 13, 14, 15, 17, 18, (plus 7 and 11 if done as group work, and 16 if word-processing used).

GNVQ Level 2: 3.2 If choice of organisation is appropriate. Contributions to 5.1, 5.2, 5.3, & 6.3.

ASSIGNMENT 3: Inviting a guest speaker

Use Chapter 1 Who are the Carers? as a reference point, and decide which of the caring professionals, business people, representatives from voluntary organisations, etc. you would like to invite to speak to your group.

Ask your tutors if they have any contacts which would be useful; do you, or other students, have relatives or friends in the caring professions or people involved in caring businesses who may be willing to come and speak to the group? Discuss with the course tutor when the most suitable time for guest speakers to be fitted into the programme might be.

Make initial contact by telephone if possible, and then confirm dates and times in writing on College headed notepaper; or write in the first instance, having all letters checked by tutors before sending them off.

- If there are to be any costs involved, find out if these can be met before confirming anything.

- Check what equipment, if any, the speaker will need, e.g. video player, Overhead Projector, Flipchart and so on, and how they would like the room organised – chairs in rows or a circle; desks for writing on or an informal discussion group?
- Will they be coming alone? Sometimes they may wish to bring a colleague, helper, or professional student on placement with them.

On the day of the talk, delegate one or two members of the group to meet and greet the speaker at the College Reception area. You will need to brief the receptionist beforehand as to who to expect and when, and who to inform of their arrival.

- Offer a coffee or tea if time allows, and show them where the toilets are before they have to ask (which some people find embarrassing).
- Introduce them to the group, and decide in advance who is going to thank them for their time

afterwards. Offer coffee or tea and ask if they need the toilet before they leave.

- Escort them to the car park if they are leaving the college and not spending some time with the tutors, do not just show them out of the room. If they are in a strange place, it may be difficult for them to find the way back to their car.

Write a letter of thanks, and send it as soon as possible after the event. Next year's students may wish to invite the same people, and this is a way of giving a good impression and preserving a useful college resource.

BTEC Common Skills: 1, 2, 6, 7, 10, 11, 12, 13, 16 if equipment used. Possibly 18 depending on circumstances.
GNVQ Level 2: 1.1, 1.2, 1.3, 6.3.

ASSIGNMENT 4: Arranging a visit

An alternative or additional linked assignment is to organise a visit to a community resource.

Discuss with the course tutor when the most suitable time for the visit to be fitted into the programme might be.

- Make initial contact by telephone, and then confirm dates and times in writing on College headed notepaper – getting letters checked by tutors before sending them off.
- If there are to be any costs involved, such as travelling or a visit fee, find out if these can be met before confirming anything.
- There may be a Disability Resource Centre within your area which you could go to and see equipment available which is not very portable (hoists, stairlifts and bathing equipment, for example). Some of these places will charge for student visits, so take this into account with your planning.
- Is there a local manufacturer of equipment for disabled people? Do they have facilities for group visits?

NAIDEX are an organisation which has exhibitions in different parts of the country where not only equipment manufacturers and suppliers have stands, but the major voluntary organisations as well. Keep an eye on the local and specialist press (*Community Care*, *Nursing Standard*, *Care Weekly*, etc.) to find out where these exhibitions are being held, and organise a trip to them.

BTEC Common Skills: 1, 2, 3, 4, 6, 7, 10, 11, 12, 15 if costs involved, 16 if equipment at e.g. Disabled Living Centre used.
GNVQ Level 2: 1.1, 5.1, 5.2, 5.3, 6.3.

ASSIGNMENT 5: The media

The media consists of the newspapers, both daily and weekly; magazines, and radio and television. Disabled people often appear in news stories, human interest articles, or in drama series and documentaries.

A Newspapers and magazines
Choose a week you wish to cover and collect all the different newspapers you can for that week. With weekly publications, collect all that you can for a month. For monthly publications, try to get hold of a three months selection.

(i) Go through them and cut out any items relevant to disability.

(ii) Divide into small groups or pairs, with each group or pair having one paper to research, e.g. local paper, *Daily Mirror*, *Guardian*, etc. Each group or pair could have more than one paper, but keep the findings separate so that comparisons can be made.

Do not look for news items only, but include advertisements as well. Keep them sorted separately.

(iii) Look at what is being written and how it is being written; what impression comes across? Are disabled people being portrayed as helpless; objects of sympathy; people with a

Lessons in road safety

NOW summer is here families will be going out and about as well as taking holidays.

Cheshire County Council's Road Safety Unit believes now is the appropriate time for parents to be reminded of their obligation to protect their children.

[...] on for Life', a leaflet issued by the Department of [...] all aspects of [...] to children [...] covered [...]

use of a zebra crossing and pelican crossings.

Senior Road Safety Officer David Stirzaker said: 'It is all well and good that teachers with the support of the Road Safety Unit instills road safety knowledge into their pupils, but without reenforcement by parents both verbally and in deed, little will be accomplished by children.'

Copies of the leaflet have been circulated to children in the schools, so parents will now have a guide to the areas in which their children need help in their road safety development.

Transplant heroes have golden touch

Special report by JANE DREAPER

WONDER children Kate Law and James Dixon were at their sporting best when they took part in the National Transplant Games at the weekend.

The pair, who have both had heart and lung transplants in the last year, joined 900 other transplant recipients at Exeter for the event.

As well as competing in athletic events, 14-year-old Kate and 10-year-old James were reunited with the Great Ormond Street Hospital transplant team who carried out their surgery.

The dynamic duo have battled with the debilitating effects of cystic fibrosis since early childhood. Their transplant operations have given them a spring board back to normal health.

Kate, of Shay Lane, Oscroft, excelled herself by winning a gold medal in a tricky obstacle course.

She also won bronze [...] in the long jump [...] metre sprint

Soldier tells of IRA bomb blast horror

AN AGENCY which specialises in caring for elderly and infirm people in their own homes has moved into Cheshire.

The Godsall Agency, which provides round-the-clock home care as an alternative to residential care, was founded three years ago by Inger Godsall.

'At least two carers are assigned to the client,' explained Chester-based area controller Bob McConnell.

'A carer will live in for a week at a time, helping with everything from cooking meals, shopping and light housework, to bathing, washing and feeding.

Specially screened staff include a range of nursing auxiliaries and care assistants.

'Not every patient will require the attention of a fully qualified nurse,' said Mr McConnell.

'Sometimes an extra pair of hands is all that is needed to give the sort of care and attention given by a close relative.

He pointed out that clients who receive full attendance allowance may now be able to claim help with the fees.

He said: 'The Government now provides an independent living fund if an elderly or infirmed person has less than £8,000 in the bank.

This fund may pay part of [...] care dependency following [...]

Volunteers call

VOLUNTEERS are needed to deliver books to housebound Chester people. For details phone Mrs Peacock between 9.30am and 2.30pm, Monday to Thursday.

Better services for the deaf

IMPROVEMENTS to services for deaf or hard of hearing library customers have been introduced by Cheshire County Council.

Subtitled copies of 60 feature films can now be borrowed on video. An extensive range of subtitled videos is already available and new titles are being added all the time.

The collection is based at Northwich but videos can be requested from any county library. They can be reserved and borrowed free of charge by adults with hearing difficulties.

Cubs on the penny trail

CUB SCOUTS in Ellesmere Port and Neston laid a trail of pennies around the Rotunda in the Ellesmere Port Arcades as part of the Promise '92 appeal.

They collected cash by filling Smartie tubes full of coins.

Some money will go towards a £10 million national appeal. The rest will be spent locally.

A CHESTER soldier blown up by a IRA bomb in Northern Ireland has spoken for the first time of his horrific ordeal.

Lance Bombardier Kevin Booker, from Blacon, was serving with the Cheshire and Merseyside Gunners when he fell victim of the terrifying attack two years ago.

Two people died and six were injured in the Londonderry blast.

Kevin, who joined the Army after leaving school, said: 'It happened while I was on night patrol in March 1989. Thankfully, though, I can't remember much about it. All I remember was a huge explosion.

'The worst bit was the long time in hospital. I had an operation to remove my left eye and another on my leg. I stayed there for six to eight months recovering.

'At first I was really self-conscious, especially about my eye, but you have to learn to live with what's happened

By CLAIR BEDFORD

and my close friends quickly accepted it.'

As well as losing the sight in one eye, Kevin is partially deaf in his left ear and has limited movement in his left ankle.

He said: 'I was medically discharged from the Army in January. I had originally planned to do 22 years service, but I only actually served 11.

'It's hard to say whether or not I am bitter. At first I wasn't. I was too busy worrying about my injuries.

'But now when I see my mates who are still there going off to Germany and places like that I think that could have been me if all this hadn't happened.'

Following his discharge Kevin went to an Employment Rehabilitation Centre in Preston to learn how to cope with his disabilities in a civilian working environment.

In May he became a student at the Finchale Training College in Durham where he is studying a City and Guilds course in horticulture.

The college is specially equipped to teach disabled people like Kevin new skills and rethink their careers.

He said: 'I like the college. It's good to be able to learn new skills and the lecturers are really understanding, although they do get a bit over-protective sometimes.

'That can be a problem. It's bad enough with your family being so worried about you.

'I would recommend Finchale to anyone who is positive and wants to achieve, but for now I just want to get on with my life.'

Kevin Booker

[...] carol, [...] of the [...] fibrosis [...] said: 'It [...] to see [...] found. [...] was lying [...] her transplant did I think [...] be able to [...] such a high [...] just three [...] after. [...] while, Kate will [...] morning join her [...] Valley High School [...] mates in presenting [...] proceeds from a [...] ride around Oulton Park racing circuit [...] for cystic fibrosis research.

The schoolchildren raised £700 towards the event's expected total of £4,000.

About 60 pupils, including staff, headteacher Chris Marks, pedalled the track in a first rate effort to raise more funds for research into the disease.

positive contribution to make to society; people in need of help (send some money, give some time); or as victims?

(iv) Are there reasons why a particular impression is being given? Is it National Arthritis week, for instance? Has the story been sent in by a voluntary organisation as part of a fund-raising or an awareness-raising exercise?

(v) How are disabled people portrayed in the advertising copy? Why do you think they are portrayed in this particular way?

(vi) Do you think the stories you have found could be improved, and if so, how?

(vii) Re-write one of the news items you have found fault with in what you consider to be a more acceptable way.

(viii) What have you learned from what you have read during this exercise?

(ix) Keep a scrap book of the stories you have found for reference purposes.

Remember at the end of this assignment to recycle the waste paper.

BTEC Common Skills: 1, 2, 4, 6, 7, 8, 11, 12, 16.
GNVQ Level 2: contributions to 2.1, 2.2, 2.3, &
possibly 5.1, 5.2, 5.3 & 6.3.

B Radio and television

Obtain the programme listings for a coming week from *Radio Times*, *TV Times* or a similar publication.

(i) Working in small groups go through the programmes on offer and pick out any which relate to the subject of disability. Decide which members of the group will watch which programmes.

(ii) Report back to the class your impressions of how disability was presented: record the programme for class viewing or listening.

(iii) Evaluate these programmes using the same criteria as for the newspaper and magazine exercise.

(iv) Decide which of those programmes recorded merit a class showing, bearing in mind time restrictions. Those not shown in class can be loaned around the group for home viewing.

(v) Are there any series being broadcast at present which include people with disabilities, e.g. detective series, 'soaps', plays, etc? Are any of the regular presenters disabled people?

ASSIGNMENT 6: Procedure for a debate

First, a 'motion' needs to be decided upon as the subject for debate. Examples could include:

● 'Every family has the right to decide if and when they have children'; or
● 'Abortion is wrong in any circumstances'.

The '**proposer**' then argues in favour of the motion; and the '**opposer**' puts the arguments against the motion. A '**seconder**' for the proposer then answers any points raised by the argument, and the seconder for the opposer points out the weaknesses in the proposer's argument.

The **chairperson** keeps order, trying to ensure that only one person is speaking at one time; and after the formal speeches, s/he opens the debte to the '**floor**' (i.e. everybody else), and ensures an orderly discussion.

At the conclusion of the time allotted, a speaker for each side gives a summing up. This could conclude matters, or you may wish to put the subject to a vote by a show of hands.

BTEC Common Skills: 1–8, 11–14 Inclusive,
possibly 15 and 16 depending upon the
presentations chosen and teaching alds used, 18.

ASSIGNMENT 7: Designing a package of care

Choose one of the people from the Part Four Cases, other than Robert Taylor or the Dales, and design a personalised package of care for that individual or family.

Some guidance on what to include in your thinking is included in Chapter 3 Care in the Community. The following points should also be addressed:

(i) Decide who is to be the Case Manager. It may be a social worker, a district nurse, a physio-therapist, or a relative.
(ii) Identify what equipment will be necessary using brochures such as those available from Homecraft, Boots, Renray, or others you can find.
(iii) Work out the costs, or estimated costs.
(iv) What services need to be involved?

(v) Having decided upon the services, which people will be needed to provide them?
(vi) Write a letter to one of the service providers detailing what part you would like them to play, and asking if they are able to provide a service. It is also important to ask what the cost will be.
(vii) Write up your suggested package of care in a form which can be presented to your clients, and will be readily understandable to anybody picking it up for the first time. Include pictures or diagrams of the chosen equipment, suggested house alterations, and calendars/timetables as appropriate.

BTEC Common Skills: 1, 2, 4, 8, 9, 10, 12–15 inclusive, 17, 18, 16 if word-processing used.
GNVQ Level 2: 5, 6.
GNVQ Level 3: 1, 5, 6, 7, 8.

ASSIGNMENT 8: Case conference

A case conference is a meeting which can be requested by any professional involved in a case, (social worker, doctor, health visitor, district nurse, etc.) and who feels that the sharing of information would be of benefit to the individual concerned. Case conferences are most often, but not exclusively, held in connection with child protection work. They are a useful forum for the sharing of information about an individual or family by professionsals who may be involved for varying reasons, and who otherwise do not have any contact with each other. Also present may be people who do not know the person who is the subject of the meeting, but represent other organisations which may be able to help, or have particular expertise to offer. The subject of the conference may or may not be there, but in most cases, they will have been invited for all or part of the proceedings.

The conference will be chaired by an independent person who does not have contact with the family or individual, and it is his or her job to invite the participants, and keep them to an agreed agenda.

The sharing of information will start with a brief input from each person as to why they are involved,

how often they visit (or are visited, plus written or telephone communication) how long they have been involved, and what they are trying to do.

The reason for the conference being called is then discussed – it is usually a specific matter which precipitates such requests; incapacity or death of a carer, concerns about living conditions, bad behaviour toward caring staff, or concerns about the safety of children.

Decide who is going to attend the conference and assign these roles. Essential members are the Chair and the note-taker; others vary according to the scenario.

Case conference format

The case history of Becky and Dave can be used, if wished (see pages 190–1). Read it once again and decide who should be invited to a case conference. When everybody is there, the chair will ask all participants to introduce themselves, and say what their role is in this matter. He or she will then ask each to give what information they have which is of relevance, starting in the Moss case with the Midwife whose concerns triggered off the procedure. Other professionals with knowledge of the family will have their say, and then the family (if present) invited to make comment.

Once all views have been aired, a decision will be made as to what would be best for the child. This can range from removing the child from the parents to doing nothing at all. A package of care may be organised to give help to the family whilst the child remains at home, or the help of foster-parents arranged. Alternatively, the grandparents could be asked to give greater support, or have the child live with them. The merits of these options plus any others which may arise will be discussed, and a decision reached.

Any decision reached must be justified with reasons why it is felt to be in the child's best interests, not the parents' best interests, as these may differ from the child's.

BTEC Common Skills: 1, 2, 4, 5, 6, 7, 11, 18, 16 if the proceedings are video-taped.
GNVQ Level 2: 2, 3.1, 5.2, 5.3, 6.2.
GNVQ Level 3: 1, 2, 5.1, 5.2, 5.4, 6.

ASSIGNMENT 9: Organising your own placement

This is best done in the second year of two-year courses, when students are more aware of what is involved, and hopefully have some idea of where future caring careers lie.

Try to avoid going back to a place you have been before, take the opportunity a college course offers you of trying different work situations. In this way, you can find out what you like before entering into a long-term commitment. By all means go to a placement in an area of work you have been to before, but try it in a different setting: for instance, if you have been with a physiotherapist in a hospital, arrange to work with one in a school; if you have worked in a day centre for people with disabilities, extend your experience into the community by working with a Home Care Service. If you enjoyed your placement at a playgroup, think about organising one on a children's ward in the hospital.

- Think about the sort of placement you want; discuss this with your tutor if you are unsure what is available either in your area or as a residential placement.
- Check with your tutor that your choice is acceptable and suitable for your purposes.
- Make an initial telephone call to check if a placement there would be possible, and that this could be on the dates dictated by the college timetable.
- Arrange for the college to follow up your initial contacts in a more official way, e.g. by writing on headed paper giving details of your course and who their contact in the college will be.

- Find out the name of the person you should be dealing with, and arrange to visit them at the placement address.
- Take into account the distances involved and travelling times and costs.
- Ask if any special dress is required, or if overalls, work coats, etc. will be provided. Remember that some jewellery such as rings and bracelets can damage people in your care if you have to lift or turn them.
- Determine who your supervisor will be, and check that they are willing to fill in any reports necessary on your behalf.
- See what your working hours will be, particularly starting and finishing times in relation to public transport, if you have to use that.
- Confirm in writing (on college headed paper) the arrangements you have agreed upon between you.
- Check when it would be convenient for your tutor to visit you and confirm this at the placement. Give your tutor instructions on how to find both the place and you, with sketch-maps if necessary.

Suggestions for placements
- Hospitals, both NHS and private: particularly Orthopaedic, Out-patients, Physiotherapy, Occupational Therapy and Speech Therapy departments;
- Residential homes: NHS, private and those run by charitable organisations, e.g. Leonard Cheshire Homes;
- Nursing homes;
- Day centres, as above;

- Warden Housing schemes, either on site with specialist provision run by Housing Associations, or at centralised Local Authority centres on computer control (e.g. Piper Lifeline systems);
- Ambulance services;
- Occupational Health departments of large businesses;
- Personnel offices of large businesses;
- Home Care Schemes;
- Social Services Departments, with specialist social work teams;
- Schools, both specialist and ordinary where there

are pupils with disabilities;
- Holiday centres, e.g. Winged Fellowship, John Grooms, or Camp America or Bunacamp if you are old enough. (Age requirements differ, so read the advertisements carefully.);
- Community Volunteer Service;
- Disablement Resettlement Officers.

BTEC Common Skills: 1, 2, 3, 4, 6, 10, 11, 12, 14, 15, 18, plus 16 if word-processing used.
GNVQ Level 2: 5.

ASSIGNMENT 10: Providing a service

Is it possible for you as a group to provide a service for people with a disability? Could the college/school premises be used as a part of this? Examples of services that could be considered include:

- coffee mornings where people with a disability could spend some time while the carer goes shopping;
- a shopping service whereby you help the person with the disability do their own shopping by helping them around and/or carrying the goods; or possibly going shopping on behalf of people unable to get out and about; is it possible to do this with a telephone ordering service followed by home delivery?
- A home sitting service to allow the carers to have an evening off;
- a laundry and/or ironing service;
- a meals service, either by inviting people into your college/school facilities or by a delivery service;
- starting a PHAB club if none already exists in the area;
- a taped news service, or recording specialist information on to tapes for students with disabilities; or
- a play scheme and/or a Mother and Toddler group for children with a disability.

Before embarking upon the provision of any service, you should look into any legal requirements (e.g.

regarding space needed, staffing, fire precautions, health and hygiene regulations, insurances, etc.).

When you have decided what service is the most appropriate:

(i) elect a management committee;
(ii) decide upon the time limits for your project;
(iii) undertake research to find what is available already in the area;
(iv) design a questionnaire to find out what the consumers want. Include a question about how much the potential users would be prepared to pay toward your scheme. Think about how you are going to conduct your research – door-to-door visits, or a postal survey? Via the local statutory services; or through voluntary organisations? Advertising in the local press; or by postcards in shop windows; or through local radio?;
(v) organise a publicity/advertising campaign. Allocate tasks and roles to group members.

BTEC Common Skills: 1–8 inclusive, 11–15, 17, 18, also 16 if word-processing used.
GNVQ Level 2: 1, 2, 3, 4, 5, 6.
GNVQ Level 3: 1, 2, 3, 4, 5, 6, 7, 8.
Potentially all competences can be covered.
  Teaching teams will need to monitor the activity chosen in order to identify those covered more accurately, and arrange assessment.

ASSIGNMENT 11: Organising a holiday

You can carry out this assignment either as a college/school exercise, or offer your services to a family with a disabled member, or a group of disabled people who may appreciate help in arranging a holiday. If it is an academic exercise, you can make all the decisions as to where to go and when; if it is a real task you have volunteered for, then full consultation must take place – where do your customers want to go? When do they want to go? What sort of holiday do they want – beach, activity, touring? Will they need carers travelling with them, or will they be independent, or perhaps need some help for certain things which couriers or hotel staff can provide?

Decide whether the holiday will be in the UK or abroad. (Trips abroad will need a valid passport.)

(i) Visit some travel agencies and collect information including brochures covering holidays which would be suitable for your chosen group. How much will the chosen holiday cost? Would disabled travellers have to pay more than able-bodied ones? If so, why?

(ii) Look in Appendix 2 'Useful Addresses' on pages 223–5 for specialist holiday providers and write to them for information.

You could also get information on specialist providers from your local SSD or SWD, Citizens Advice Bureau, Tourist Information Centres and voluntary organisations concerned with disability.

(iii) Investigate travel requirements from the holiday maker's home, not just from the tour operators' pick-up points. Will you need a taxi or other specialist transport (e.g. tail-lift coach), or is the rail station/bus station within walking distance?

(iv) What is required in the luggage? Do you need to take incontinence pads for the whole holiday or will they be available on-site at the destination? Are any specialist adapted items such as eating utensils required? If medication is needed, is there enough for the whole holiday plus extra to cover for unforeseen eventualities such as airport delays or mechanical breakdown of cars or coaches? Do you need travel games, books, tapes, portable radio, alarm clock?

(v) Does any advance notice need to be given to stations, airports, cafes en route, hotels? (If it is, you could also ask why, but nevertheless do so in writing, well in advance.)

(vi) If helpers are needed, where will they come from? Will they need paying? Or are they supplied as part of the holiday deal (as at the Winged Fellowship hotels)?

(vii) Present your plan in a folder with information easily available and readable, together with costing and an itinerary.

BTEC Common Skills: 1–18 potentially if a variety of visual forms are used, and the result is word-processes, otherwise omit numbers 9 and 16.
GNVQ Level 2: potentially all competences 1–6 are covered.
GNVQ Level 3: 1–5, possibly 7 & 8.

ASSIGNMENT 12: Devising a game

In small groups of three or four, devise a game connected with the subject of disability in some way or another. Think of the games you have seen already, the ones you have at home, or have seen on computers.

You can use any style you like, the only limitations are your imagination and ability. It can be a board game in the style of Snakes and Ladders, Monopoly, Game of Life or perhaps Trivial Pursuit. It may be a card game or require only pencil and paper; if you are able, and have the facilities, why not a computer game?

You could, for example, devise a dice game about a trip to town, in which players go back two spaces if no access to the hairdressers, miss a turn when the helper rather than the disabled person is spoken to; go ahead two spaces when the toilets are easily accessible, etc. Alternatively, it may be a game for people with disabilities to play, e.g. specifically for blind and partially sighted with an emphasis on sound, or a variation of blow football, or a tactile game.

If your game has an educational bias, and is intended to raise disability awareness, so much the better – who is the target audience, children or adults? This should be clearly stated in your introduction, which should include full instructions on how to play, in either written or audio-tape form, braille, computer graphics or whatever you feel would be most appropriate.

Look around toy and game shops to come up with your own ideas, and design the whole of the project from scratch, practising your artistic and design skills as well as problem solving skills.

BTEC Common Skills: 1, 2, 4, 6, 7, 11, 14, possibly 15 and 16, 17, 18.

ASSIGNMENT 13: Complementary medicine

Complementary medicine is the collective phrase used to describe those medical or quasi-medical techniques which are not fully accepted by the mainstream of the medical profession. It is also known as 'fringe medicine'. The methods include some which are very old and some which are very new; some are practised by conventionally trained doctors, and some by people who are no more than enthusiasts and believers.

One aspect which should be remembered is that belief in itself is a great healer, and it would be a good idea to familiarise yourself with the 'placebo effect' before researching complementary medicine.

Either as individuals or in small groups, choose a facet to research, and prepare a fact-file for reference use by other members of the class. Some suggestions of headings to look under are:

- Acupuncture;
- Bio-feedback;
- Aromatherapy;
- Faith Healing;
- Hyperbaric Oxygen;
- Reflexology;
- Naturopathy;
- Osteopathy;
- Hypnosis;
- Homeopathy;
- Naprapathy;
- Chiropractice.

In addition to collecting the facts, analyse your findings and give your opinion as to the usefulness of these methods in relation to disability.

BTEC Common Skills: 1, 2, 5, 6, 7, 8, 10, 11, 12, 18.

ASSIGNMENT 14: Designing a garden

Like the rest of us, many disabled people enjoy gradening, or just spending time in the garden. In order to make this possible without a great deal of trouble for all concerned, certain modifications can be made to the layout of gardens, and some thought given to the choice of plants to be included.

There are also a variety of modified and labour-saving tools on the market which can help.

(i) Re-read Case 10 (Becky Moss) as a starting point.

(ii) Identify a garden or a piece of land which could be converted into a garden. This may be in the college or nearby; at a placement, or at your own home, or home area. Draw a scale plan and duplicate this, and take photographs.

(iii) On one of the scale plans, design a garden which you feel would be suitable for people with disabilities. Remember to cater for both wheel-chairs, mobility problems, and visual difficulty.

(iv) If at all possible, this could be a class project and the garden modified in reality. If this is the case, permissions will have to be obtained, and fund-raising may be involved. A committee will have to be set up, and roles and responsibilities allocated.

Fig A14 A garden modified for wheelchair gardeners that has been paved and furnished with raised beds and planters. Note the ramp from the patio doors to give good access for wheelchair users.

Reproduced by kind permission of David Hollinrake, Mary Marlborough Lodge

CROSS-MODULAR ASSIGNMENT

Scenario

Carole lives on the seventh floor of a block of flats on an inner city estate with her partner, Pete. They have a four-year-old son, Simon; and also living with them is Carole's mother, Molly.

Carole is in her mid-30s and is pregnant again, so will soon be having to give up her part-time cleaning job. She is worrying about this, as it is the only earned income in the family. The number of cigarettes she is smoking is subsequently increasing.

Pete is 29 and has epilepsy; he has not worked for some years. He drinks quite a lot, and has a tendency to be violent.

Simon is a very active child, difficult to control at times, and does not have enough scope in the flat to wear himself out properly by bedtime.

Molly is aged 70 and hard of hearing, her memory is not as good as it was, and there are lots of arguments in the household, particularly between Molly and Pete. Molly tends to try to be the boss, and this upsets both him and Carole.

Task 1 (Simon)

(a) What sort of toys do you think would be suitable and affordable for Simon?

(b) Design a simple toy which you think he would enjoy playing with.

(c) What would you suggest to help him use up some of his excess energy?

(d) What safety measures should there be in the flat to protect Simon?

(e) Suppose Simon gets hold of a container of toilet

211

cleaner which contains a high percentage of bleach. He is able to remove the top and actually drinks some of it.

Describe the signs and symptoms that may be present, and describe the correct stages of first aid which should be followed in this situation.

(f) What effects may the family arguments be having on him?

Task 2 (Carole)

(a) List the factors causing the stress that you think Carole would be suffering by living this lifestyle?

(b) How could this stress be showing itself in Carole's behaviour?

(c) What could be done to reduce this stress?

(d) How would you advise her to look after herself during her pregnancy?

Task 3 (Pete)

(a) What would you have expected somebody of Pete's age to have achieved in life?

(b) What effect could the epilepsy have on his lack of achievement?

(c) What are the signs and symptoms which may be present when a major seizure attack occurs? Describe the first aid treatment which ideally Carole should be able to carry out should Pete suffer a major epileptic fit.

(d) What do you understand by the term 'hidden handicap'?

(e) What may be the reasons for Pete's violent outbursts?

Task 4 (Molly)

(a) Why should Molly be trying to dominate the household?

(b) What are the possible causes of her failing memory?

(c) What do you think her relationship with Simon will be like?

(d) If she should decide to go and live somewhere else, what effect will this have on:
   (i) Carole and Pete;
   (ii) Simon; and
   (iii) Molly herself?

Part Five

APPENDICES

Appendix 1

GNVQs, NVQs AND BTEC COMMON SKILLS

General National Vocational Qualifications (GNVQs)

GNVQs were introduced into British education in Autumn 1992 for use in schools and colleges for students aged 16–19 in the main. Together with NVQs, they will form a progressive vocational scheme of education similar to GCSEs, A levels and university/polytechnic degrees.

At the time of writing, only the GNVQs in Health and Caring at levels 2 and 3 have been finalised. Students must gain units of achievement rather than of competence, and during the pilot year (1992–3) there are six mandatory units at level 2, usually to be undertaken over one year, together with the three core units of communication, application of number and information technology. Level 3 has eight mandatory units which will normally be taken over two years together with four optional units and the three core units as above. There are also Optional units which can be taken alongside the mandatory units and the choice will differ from college to college.

All the necessary evidence of achievement will be kept in a student portfolio, and success can be awarded with a merit or distinction if performance justifies this.

There will also be Unit Tests for each individual mandatory unit, for which a pass must be reached in order to achieve that unit. Continuous assessment, however, remains the main form of evaluation of student performance.

Health & Social Care GNVQ Level 2
summary of units and elements

1   Provide Emotional Support
1.1 Employ conversational techniques to maintain social interaction
1.2 Identify self-esteem needs in others
1.3 Demonstrate supportive behaviour in social interaction

2   Social Influences on Health and Well-being
2.1 Identify ways in which individuals are affected by social factors
2.2 Provide examples of social discrimination and its effects on well-being
2.3 Identify client rights in health and care

3   Health Promotion
3.1 Identify risks to health and social well-being
3.2 Describe leisure activities which promote health and social well-being
3.3 Plan a nutritional programme

4   Health Emergencies
4.1 Identify emergencies
4.2 Respond to emergencies
4.3 Explain health and safety principles relevant to emergencies

5   Health and Social Care Services
5.1 Explain the structure of health and care services
5.2 Examine the roles of different health and care services
5.3 Identify the roles of health and care workers in the community

6   Collect and Monitor Information
6.1 Investigate recording and measuring techniques
6.2 Design a plan to monitor an event
6.3 Use information systems

Health and Social Care GNVQ Level 3
summary of units and elements

1   Access to Health and Social Care
1.1 Describe the ways in which environment and culture influence experience
1.2 Identify ways in which individuals and groups are discriminated against
1.3 Investigate how anti-discriminatory practice operates
1.4 Analyse purposes of legislation and equal opportunities policies

2   Interpersonal Interaction
2.1 Develop understanding
2.2 Identify interpersonal approaches for the maintenance of choice and independence
2.3 Investigate and analyse the importance of confidentiality
2.4 Analyse client rights in health and social care

3   Physical Aspects of Health and Well-being
3.1 Describe anatomical and physiological aspects of health and well-being
3.2 Investigate factors which affect health and well-being
3.3 Identify dietary requirements of different client groups

4   Interaction Between Social, Psychological and Physical Well-being
4.1 Investigate social and psychological aspects of well-being
4.2 Describe ways in which health and social well-being are abused
4.3 Analyse the development of psychological and social well-being

5   Health and Social Well-being Promotion
5.1 Investigate health risks in different contexts
5.2 Explain health and social well-being advice to others
5.3 Propose health promotion methods for different groups
5.4 Review health, safety and security requirements

6   Structure and Practices in Health and Social Care
6.1 Identify the ways in which systems of health and care provision are structured
6.2 Investigate legal and economic frameworks which determine health and social care provision and priorities
6.3 Investigate ways in which services within health and social care operate
6.4 Investigate systems of accountability within health and social care

7   **Health and Social Care Delivery Plans**
7.1 Explore the function of care plans
7.2 Propose methods of assessing client need
7.3 Prepare a plan for a programme of care delivery
7.4 Design monitoring and evaluation approaches for a programme of health or social care delivery

8   **Collect and Evaluate Information**
8.1 Evaluate information gathering techniques
8.2 Operate information systems

The mapping of GNVQs within this book is based on the six pilot mandatory units at Level 2, and allowances should be made for this.

From September 1993, the requirement will be for *four* mandatory units at Level 2. These will be:

2HSC1 Provide Emotional Support
2HSC2 Influences on Health and Well-being
2HSC3 Health Emergencies
2HSC4 Health and Social Care Services

plus two Optional units and additonal units, as decided by individual colleges.

As these courses are so new, there could well be other changes within the foreseeable future. The choices of Optional and additional units will undoubtedly increase, and the knowledge specifications within units may be modified.

Tutors should make sure that they are on the GNVQ Health and Caring mailing lists from BTEC and GNVQ.

National Vocational Qualifications (NVQs)

NVQ STANDARDS

What are standards?

Occupational standards can be seen as *'quality specifications'* for people at work: they specify the quality of performance required in the workplace. Standards are comprehensive yet precise descriptions of what people need to be able to do in the work environment − not only the routine and technical aspects but also the way in which tasks have to be managed, the necessary inter-personal relationships and the values which the organisation wishes to be expressed in action. Standards are expressed in terms of the *outcomes* people are expected to achieve, rather than the tasks they will have to carry out, or the skills they need to do those tasks.

Nationally recognised standards have a number of uses. They can be used:

- as the basis of job descriptions or skill profiling
- to identify training needs
- to develop training programmes
- as a basis for assessment
- as benchmarks for development
- to form vocational qualifications.

Individuals and organisations are free to use the standards as they wish. This publication details the standards which have been developed for those who deliver hands-on care and the way in which these have been grouped to form vocational qualifications.

In the care sector, the overall purpose for developing standards has been seen as increasing the quality of service for all who *receive* care, by specifying the quality of performance required of those who *provide* care.

The care context should be one which recognises the equal value of all individuals, provides an anti-discriminatory framework for practice and recognises that individuals have the right of confidentiality for personal information. Care is not an activity which can be split down into a number of tasks which have no reference to each other. A worker is expected to perform her/his role in a manner which continually promotes each individual's identity, rights and personal beliefs and preferences, and enhances effective communication.

The Care Sector Consortium believes that the vocational qualification model developed must reflect the holistic view of care held by those who deliver the service within the sector and be supportive of the values or concepts which are essential for a quality service to all individuals. The model adopted in the work is designed to:

- indicate the way in which the value base of the sector runs through all of the activities undertaken in any particular work role, and
- recognise that such values are also expressed as specific functions within their own right.

Both of the levels have 'others' signalled at the end of the list to indicate that further qualifications will be developed over time as the standards framework is extended. At level III further work is taking place during 1992 on the standards and qualifications relating to supporting communication and caring for feet.

The connecting lines between the qualifications at level II and level III in the diagram shown overleaf and the matrix shown in the figure on page 219 are designed to indicate potential progression routes which individuals may take. These are only 'potential' as there is no prerequisite for candidates to take a level II qualification before they take a level III or to take the ones which are indicated.

Described on page 217 are the requirements of the Care Sector Consortium National Occupational Standards for Care as they stand at the time of publication. They are still in the process of development, and more are to be added over the next year or two.

The requirements have not been linked to the exercises and assignments in the book, but this can be done using the following outline as a guide. The full list of standards and detailed requirements can be obtained from the Local Government Management Board, Arndale House, The Arndale Centre, Luton, Bedfordshire LU1 2TS.

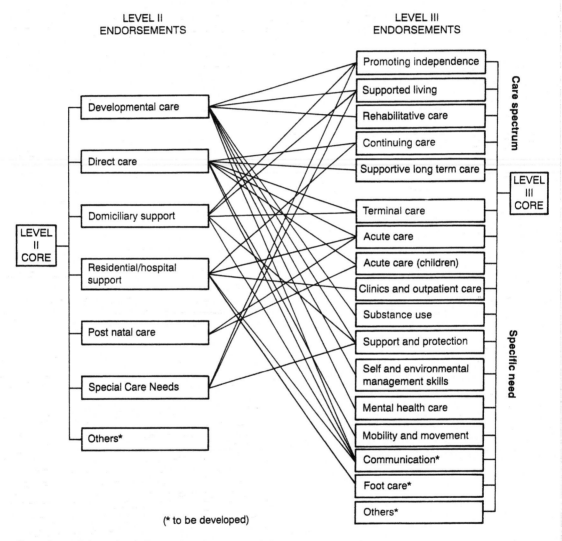

Overview of Awards in Care showing potential progression routes

Crown Copyright © 1992. Produced by the Care Sector Consortium

Awards in Care

NVQs/SVQs – Level II

Level II Core

| O   Promote equality for all individuals |

Z1 Contribute to the protection of individuals from abuse

W2 Contribute to the ongoing support of clients and others significant to them

W3 Support clients in transition due to their care requirements

U4 Contribute to the health, safety and security of individuals and their environment

U5 Obtain, transmit and store information relating to the delivery of a care service

| Others to be developed |

Endorsements

Developmental care
Z5 Enable clients to move within their environment
Z13 Enable clients to participate in recreation and leisure activities
X1 Contribute to the support of clients during development programmes and activities
W8 Enable clients to maintain contacts in potentially isolating situations
U2 Maintain and control stock, equipment and materials

Direct care
Z6 Enable clients to maintain and improve their mobility
Z7 Contribute to the movement and treatment of clients to maximise their physical comfort
Z9 Enable clients to maintain their personal hygiene and appearance
Z10 Enable clients to eat and drink
Z11 Enable clients to access and use toilet facilities
Z19 Enable clients to achieve physical comfort

Domiciliary support
Z7 Contribute to the movement and treatment of clients to maximise their physical comfort
Y1 Enable clients to manage their domestic and personal resources
W8 Enable clients to maintain contacts in potentially isolating situations
U1 Contribute to the maintenance and management of domestic and personal resources

Residential/hospital support
Z7 Contribute to the movement and treatment of clients to maximise their physical comfort
Z10 Enable clients to eat and drink
Z11 Enable clients to access and use toilet facilities
U1 Contribute to the maintenance and management of domestic and personal resources
U2 Maintain and control stock, equipment and materials

Post natal care
Z10 Enable clients to eat and drink
Z11 Enable clients to access and use toilet facilities
Z16 Care for a baby in the first ten days of life when the mother is unable
Z19 Enable clients to achieve physical comfort
W6 Reinforce professional advice through supporting and encouraging the mother in active parenting in the first ten days of babies' lives

Special care needs
Z9 Enable clients to maintain their personal hygiene and appearance
Z10 Enable clients to eat and drink
Z13 Enable clients to participate in recreation and leisure activities
Y1 Enable clients to manage their domestic and personal resources
X1 Contribute to the support of clients during development programmes and activities
W8 Enable clients to maintain contacts in potentially isolating situations

Awards in Care

NVQs/SVQs – Level III

Care Spectrum Endorsements

Level III Core

O   Promote equality for all individuals

Z1   Contribute to the protection of individuals from abuse

Z3   Contribute to the management of aggressive and abusive behaviour

Z4   Promote communication with clients where there are communication difficulties

Z8   Support clients when they are distressed

Y2   Enable clients to make use of available services and information

U4   Contribute to the health, safety and security of individuals and their environment

U5   Obtain, transmit and store information relating to the delivery of a care service

Promoting independence
Z2   Contribute to the provision of advocacy for clients
Y3   Enable clients to administer their financial affairs
Y5   Assist clients to move from a supportive to an independent living environment
X2   Prepare and provide agreed individual development activities for clients
W5   Support clients with difficult or potentially difficult relationships
V2   Determine the ways in which the service can support clients

Supporting living
Z18   Support individuals where abuse has been disclosed
X2   Prepare and provide agreed individual development activities for clients
W1   Support clients in developing their identity and personal relationships
W5   Support clients with difficult or potentially difficult relationships
V2   Determine the ways in which the service can support clients

Rehabilitative care
Y4   Support clients and carers in undertaking health care for the client
X2   Prepare and provide agreed individual development activities for clients
X16   Prepare and implement agreed therapeutic group activities
W1   Support clients in developing their identity and personal relationships
W5   Support clients with difficult or potentially difficult relationships
V1   Contribute to the planning and monitoring of service delivery

Continuing care
Z12   Contribute to the management of client continence
Y4   Support clients and carers in undertaking health care for the client
X2   Prepare and provide agreed individual development activities for clients
X13   Prepare and undertake agreed clinical activities with clients whose health is stable in non-acute care settings
X16   Prepare and implement agreed therapeutic group activities
V1   Contribute to the planning and monitoring of service delivery

Supportive long-term care
Z12   Contribute to the management of client continence
X10   Support professionals by assisting with and carrying out agreed physiotherapy movement programmes
X12   Support professionals with clinical activities
X13   Prepare and undertake agreed clinical activities with clients whose health is stable in non-acute care settings
V1   Contribute to the planning and monitoring service delivery
U3   Prepare and maintain environments for clinical procedures

Awards in Care

NVQs/SVQs – Level III (continued)

Specific Need Endorsements

Level III Core

O   Promote equality for all individuals

Z1   Contribute to the protection of individuals from abuse.

Z3   Contribute to the management of aggressive and abusive behaviour

Z4   Promote communication with clients where there are communication difficulties

Z8   Support clients when they are distressed

Y2   Enable clients to make use of available services and information

U4   Contribute to the health, safety and security of individuals and their environment

U5   Obtain, transmit and store information relating to the delivery of a care service

Communication To be developed later in 1992

Foot care To be developed later in 1992

Others To be developed

Terminal care
Z6   Enable clients to maintain and improve their mobility
Z14   Support clients and others at time of loss
Z15   Contribute to the care of a deceased person
X13   Prepare and undertake agreed clinical activities with clients whose health is stable in non-acute care settings
U3   Prepare and maintain environments for clinical procedures

Acute care
Z12   Contribute to the management of client continence
Z14   Support clients and others at times of loss
X12   Support professionals with clinical activities
X19   Prepare and undertake agreed ongoing clinical activities with clients in acute care settings
U3   Prepare and maintain environments for clinical procedures

Acute care (children)
Z20   Care for and promote the development of babies in the first year of their lives
X12   Support professionals with clinical activities
X19   Prepare and undertake agreed ongoing clinical activities with clients in acute care settings
W7   Support and encourage parents and others to care for babies during the first year of their lives
U3   Prepare and maintain environments for clinical procedures

Clinic and out-patient care
Y4   Support clients and carers in undertaking care for the client
X12   Support professionals with clinical activities
X19   Prepare and undertake agreed ongoing clinical activities with clients in acute care settings
U2   Maintain and control stock, equipment and materials
U3   Prepare and maintain environments for clinical procedures

Substance use
Z14   Support clients and others at time of loss
Z17   Support clients who are substance users
Y4   Support clients and carers in undertaking health care for the client
X2   Prepare and provide agreed individual development activities for clients
W1   Support clients in developing their identity and personal relationships
V1   Contribute to the planning and monitoring of service delivery

Support and protection
Z2   Contribute to the provision of advocacy for clients
Z18   Support individuals where abuse has been disclosed
Y4   Support clients and carers in undertaking health care for the client
X2   Prepare and provide agreed individual development activities for clients
W5   Support clients with difficult or potentially difficult relationships
V1   Contribute to the planning and monitoring of service delivery

Self and environmental management skills
X14   Support clients and professionals during occupational therapy
X15   Assist occupational therapists in supporting clients to develop self and environmental management skills
X16   Prepare and implement agreed therapeutic group activities
W4   Assist occupational therapists in the provision of support and equipment to clients and carers is the community
V1   Contribute to the planning and monitoring of service delivery

Mental health care
Z2   Contribute to the provision of advocacy for clients
X2   Prepare and provide agreed individual development activities for clients
X16   Prepare and implement agreed therapeutic group activities
W1   Support clients in developing their identity and personal relationships
W5   Support clients with difficult or potentially difficult relationships
W8   Enable clients to maintain contacts in potentially isolating situations

Mobility and movement
Z7   Contribute to the movement and treatment of clients to maximise their physical comfort
X8   Prepare and restore the client and the environment prior to and following physiotherapy programmes
X9   Support professionals by assisting with and carrying out agreed physiotherapy programmes
X10   Support professionals by assisting with and carrying out agreed physiotherapy movement programmes
U2   Maintain and control stock, equipment and materials

BTEC Common Skills

THE COMMON SKILLS OUTCOME STATEMENT

Common Skill	Outcome
Managing and Developing Self	1 Manage own roles and responsibilities 2 Manage own time in achieving objectives 3 Undertakes personal and career development 4 Transfer skills gained to new and changing situations and contexts
Working with and Relating to Others	5 Treat others' values, beliefs and opinions with respect 6 Relate to and interact effectively with individuals and groups 7 Work effectively as a member of a team
Communicating	8 Receive and respond to a variety of information 9 Present information in a variety of visual forms 10 Communicate in writing 11 Participate in oral and non-verbal communication
Managing Tasks and Solving Problems	12 Use information sources 13 Deal with a combination of routine and non-routine tasks 14 Identify and solve routine and non-routine problems
Applying Numeracy	15 Apply numerical skills and techniques
Applying Technology	16 Use a range of technological equipment and systems
Applying Design and Creativity	17 Apply a range of skills and techniques to develop a variety of ideas in the creation of new/modified products, services or situations 18 Use a range of thought processes

Appendix 2

USEFUL ADDRESSES

When writing to any of these organisations, remember that they are charities, so include a stamped self-addressed envelope of a sufficient size and with sufficient postage for whatever you expect to receive in return.

Arthritis & Rheumatism Council
41 Eagle St.
London WC1R 4AR
Tel: 071-405 8572

Association for Research into Restricted Growth
5 Plover Road
Milbourne Port
Dorset DT9 5DA
Tel: 0963-250175

Association for Spina Bifida & Hydrocephalus (ASBAH)
42 Park Rd
Peterborough
PE1 2UQ
Tel: 0733-555988

Association for Speech Impaired Children (AFASIC)
347 Central Markets
Smithfield
London EC1A 9NH
Tel: 071-236 3632

Association to Combat Huntington's Chorea
34a Station Rd.
Hinckley
Leics LE10 1AP
Tel: 0455-615558

Blind (*see* Royal National Institute for)

British Diabetic Association
10 Queen Anne St.
London W1M 0BD
Tel: 071-323 1531

British Epilepsy Association
Anstey House
40 Hanover Square
Leeds LS3 1BE
Tel: 0532-439393

British Limbless Ex-Servicemen's Association
185–187 High Rd.
Chadwell Heath
Romford
Essex RM6 6NA
Tel: 081-590 1124

British Polio Fellowship
Bell Close
West End Rd.
Ruislip
Middx. HA4 6LP
Tel: 0895-675515

British Sports Association for the Disabled
34 Osnaburgh St.
London NW1 3ND
Tel: 071-383 7277

Brittle Bone Society
Unit 4, Block 20,
Dunshane Est
Carlunie Road
Dundee DD2 3QT
Tel: 0382-817771

Chest, Heart & Stroke Association
Tavistock House North
Tavistock Square
London WC1H 9JE
Tel: 071-387 3012

Deaf People (*see* Royal National Institute for)

223

Disability Alliance
25 Denmark St.
London WC2H 8NJ
Tel: 071-240 0806

Disabled Drivers Association
Ashwellthorpe
Norwich NR16 1EX
Tel: 050-841 449

Disablement Income Group
Millmead Business Centre
Millmead Rd.
London N17 9QU
Tel: 081-801 8013

Disablement Information and Advice Lines (DIAL UK)
Tel: 0302-310123

Disabled Living Foundation
380–384 Harrow Road
London W9 2HU
Tel: 071-289 6111

Disabled Living Services
Redbank House
4 St Chad's Street
Cheetham
Manchester M8 8QA
Tel: 061-832 3678

Disabled Persons Information Centre
Wimpey House
382–384 Newport Rd.
Cardiff CF3 7UA
Tel: 0222-488184

Dogs for the Disabled
Tel: 0926-889103

Employers Forum on Disability
5 Cleveland Place
London SW1Y 6JJ
Tel: 071-321 6591

Friedreich's Ataxia Group
Copse Edge
Thursley Road
Elstead
Godalming
Surrey GU8 6DJ
Tel: 0252-702864

Haemophilia Society
123 Westminster Bridge Rd.
London SE1 7HR
Tel: 071-928 2020

Head Injuries Association (Headway)
200 Mansfield Rd
Nottingham NG1 3HX
Tel: 0602-622382

Holiday Care Service
2 Old Bank Chambers
Station Rd.
Horley
Surrey RH6 9HW
Tel: 0293-774535

Hydrocephalus (*see* Association of Spina Bifida &c)

Invalid Children's Aid Nationwide (I CAN)
Allen Graham House
198 City Rd.
London EC1V 2PH
Tel: 071-608 2462

John Grooms Association for the Disabled
10 Gloucester Drive
London N4 2LP
Tel: 081-802 7272

Lady Hoare Trust for Physically Disabled Children
37 Oakwood
Bepton Rd.
Midhurst
West Sussex GU29 9QS
Tel: 073081-3696

Leonard Cheshire Foundation
26–29 Maunsel St.
London SW1P 2QR
Tel: 071-828 1822

Medic-Alert Foundation
11–13 Clifton Terrace
London N4 3TP
Tel: 071-833 3034

Mobility Information Service
Unit 2a, Atcham Estate
Shrewsbury SY4 4UG
Tel: 074375-889

Motor Neurone Disease Association
61 Demgate
Northampton NN1 1UE
Tel: 0604-250505

Multiple Sclerosis Society
25 Effie Rd.
London SW6 1EE
Tel: 071-736 6267

Muscular Dystrophy Group
Nattrass House
35 Macaulay Road
London SW4 0PQ
Tel: 071-720 8055

Parkinson's Disease Society
36 Portland Place
London W1N 3DG
Tel: 071-323 1174

PHAB (Physically Handicapped and Able-Bodied)
Padholme Road East
Peterborough
PE1 5UL
Tel: 0733-54117

RADAR (The Royal Association for Disability & Rehabilitation)
25 Mortimer St.
London W1N 8AB
Tel: 071-637 5400

Remploy
415 Edgware Rd.
Cricklewood
London NW2 6LR
Tel: 081-452 8020

Riding for the Disabled
Avenue 'R' National Agricultural Centre
Kenilworth
Warks CV8 2LY
Tel: 0203-696510

Rowntree Trust (The Family Fund)
PO Box 50
York YO1 2ZX

Royal National Institute for the Blind
224 Great Portland Street
London W1N 6AA
Tel: 071-388 1266

Royal National Institute for Deaf People (RNID)
105 Gower Street
London WC1E 6AH
Tel: 071-387 8033

Scottish Council on Disability
Princes House
5 Shandwick Place
Edinburgh EH2 4RG
Tel: 031-229 8632

Spastics Society (Cerebral Palsy)
12 Park Crescent
London W1N 4EQ
Tel: 071-636 5020

Spina Bifida (*see* Association of . . . & Hydrocephalus)

Spinal Injuries Association
76 St James Lane
London N10 3DF
Tel: 081-444 2121

SPOD (Association to aid the sexual & personal relationships of people with a disability)
286 Camden Road
London N7 0BJ
Tel: 071-604 8851

Thalidomide Society
Southville, Water End Rd.
Potten End
Berkhamsted
Herts HP4 2SG
Tel: 0442-872875

Wales Council for the Disabled
Caerbragdy
Bedwas Road
Caerphilly
Mid-Glamorgan CF8 3SL
Tel: 0222-887325

Winged Fellowship Trust (Holidays)
Angel House
20–32 Pentonville Road
London N1 9XD
Tel: 071-833 2594

Appendix 3

GLOSSARY

This glossary is meant as a brief guide only; for more detailed information refer to a Medical Dictionary.

Abortion: the removal or expulsion of a foetus from the womb before it is capable of existing independently.

Agnosia: a disorder of the brain in which the information from the sensory nerves is not interpreted properly. Auditory agnosia affects the ears; tactile agnosia affects the skin.

Anaesthesia: loss of the sense of touch.

Anosmia: loss of the sense of smell.

Amputation: the removal of parts of the body, especially the whole or part of a limb.

Amputee: a person who has had an amputation.

Ankylosis: the fusion of two bones at a joint due to disease.

Ankylosing spondylitis: the most common form of spondylitis, affecting men between 20 and 40 years, in the main.

Aphasia: the loss of the power of speech due to a brain disorder, and associated with difficulty in understanding speech.

Aphonia: the loss of the power of speech due to a localised problem in the mouth or throat.

Apoplexy: an old name for a stroke.

Arteriosclerosis: hardening of the arteries.

Arthritis: inflammation of the joints.

Arthrodesis: a condition where joints are deformed at birth; hands and feet are the most commonly affected areas.

Asthma: a condition which causes difficulty in breathing.

Ataxia: shaky movements and unsteady walk due to a lack of co-ordination in the locomotor system.

Athetosis: involuntary movements especially affecting the hands, face and tongue. Often found in association with cerebral palsy.

Atrophy: wasting away; in this context the wasting away of muscles due to lack of use or diseases such as poliomyelitis.

Bell's palsy: the paralysis of the facial nerve causing weakness in the muscles on one side of the face.

Blindness: an inability to see. There are various degrees of visual impairment classed as blindness for administrative purposes, and so the term does not necessarily mean a total absence of sight.

Bronchitis: inflammation of the tubes in the lungs (the bronchi), causing coughing and shortness of breath. People badly affected are unable to walk very far.

Caliper: metal supports for weakness in the lower limbs (legs, ankles or feet); they can be full length or knee length.

Cardio-vascular diseases: those that affect the heart and circulatory system. People affected can be very short of energy, and unable to move very much without becoming breathless and tired.

Cerebral haemorrhage: the rupture of a blood vessel in the brain. *See also* Stroke.

Cerebral palsy: a developmental abnormality of the brain causing weakness and uncoordinated limb movements. The cause may be birth injury, faulty development, or infections. Those affected were once called spastic. It is estimated that some 1:2500 adults are affected in this way.

Colostomy: an artificial opening in the abdomen. Surgery is performed to bring a piece of the colon (or large intestine) out through the abdominal wall in order to drain the contents before they reach a diseased or damaged area. Colostomies may be permanent or temporary. It is usual for a drainage bag to be worn, held in place either by adhesive or a belt, although some people can retain control as they would with a normal bowel opening. Where the opening is from the ileum (or small intestine), this is known as an **ileostomy**. The product is of a more liquid nature.

Colour blindness: a variety of conditions in which colours are confused with each other. The most common is red–green confusion. The condition affects mainly men (some eight per cent of the UK population, as opposed to 0.4 per cent of females.)

Congenital: i.e. present from the time of birth.

Cystic fibrosis: a hereditary disease which causes the excessive production of thick mucus in the body, particularly affecting the lungs and intestines.

Deafness: total or partial loss of hearing in one or both ears.

Diabetes mellitus: a disorder in which the body is unable to regulate the use of sugar due to a lack of insulin. **NB**: There are two other types of diabetes which are much more rare than this.

Disseminated sclerosis: *see* Multiple sclerosis.

Dwarfism: abnormally short stature from any cause, the most common being an inherited disorder called **achondroplasia**, when a normal body has fore-shortened arms and legs, and **hypopituitarism** where growth is proportional, but on a small scale.

Embryo: a baby developing in the womb from conception to eight weeks.

Enuresis: bedwetting (*see* Incontinence).

Epilepsy: a nervous disorder in which an individual suffers seizures (petit mal) or convulsions (grand mal). For the majority of people affected, this condition is not handicapping.

Flaccid paralysis: 'floppy' paralysis in which the muscle tone is lost, and the limb falls about uncontrolled.

Foetus or fetus: a developing baby from the beginning of the third month of pregnancy until birth. Before this, it is referred to as an embryo.

Friedreich's Ataxia: an inherited disorder of the nervous system, appearing in childhood or early adolescence. In the early stages walking is unsteady. As the disease progresses the muscles become weak, there is a lack of control of movement and vision is impaired.

Haemophilia: a hereditary disease in which the bood clots very slowly, so that minor cuts and bruises cause major haemorrhage (bleeding). It is a disorder of males passed on by females, and affects one man in 3500 in the UK. In severe cases, there can be bleeding into the joints which affects mobility, possibly leading to wheelchair use.

Hemiplegia: paralysis of one side of the body.

Huntington's chorea: a progressive hereditary disease in which the symptoms of involuntary movements, slurred speech, and deterioration in mental functioning only appear during middle age.

Hydrocephalus: an abnormal accumulation of fluid in the brain; often associated with spina bifida. In children it causes a noticeable enlargement of the head.

Ileostomy: similar to a colostomy, but the opening is made further up in the bowel (into the ileum). The product will be more fluid than that from a colostomy.

Incontinence: inability to control the bowel and/or the bladder.

Kyphosis: curvature of the spine, causing a hunchback.

Monoplegia: paralysis of a single limb.

Motor Neurone Disease: a progressive disease of the nervous system, usually starting in middle age. It causes muscle weakness and wasting.

Multiple sclerosis: a disease of the nervous system. Sclerosis means hardening, multiple refers to the many places where the sheath covering the nerve has become hard and stopped it working properly. (Disseminated means 'spread out'.)

Muscular dystrophy: there are actually three types of this hereditary disease. All cause progressive muscle weakness.

Myasthenia gravis: a disease of uncertain cause in which the muscles become very tired very quickly, and act as though they were paralysed.

Orthopaedic: concerning the bones and joints.

Paraplegia: paralysis of both legs.

Parkinson's Disease: a chronic disease of the brain mainly affecting middle-aged and older people. Characterised by tremors, shuffling walk, and rigid facial muscles.

Polio, or poliomyelitis: an infection affecting the nervous system, causing paralysis of the muscles.

Polydactyly: having more than the usual number of fingers or toes.

Prosthesis: an artificial replacement for a natural part of the body, including teeth, eyes, breasts or limbs. (Plural – prostheses).

Quadriplegia: *see* Tetraplegia.

Rheumatism: a descriptive term for aches and pains affecting the muscles and joints.

Rubella, or German Measles: an infection which can result in babies being born disabled when contracted by pregnant women during the first three months of pregnancy.

Scoliosis: a sideways curve of the spine.

Spastic: an outdated term for cerebral palsy.

Spastic paralysis: rigid paralysis where the limbs are tightly bent and resistant to movement (*see* Flaccid paralysis).

Spina bifida: a congenital disability resulting from deformity of the spine and spinal cord.

Stroke: an interruption to the flow of blood to the brain for a number of reasons; often causing a hemiplegia.

Tetraplegia: paralysis of all four limbs.

Thalidomide: a drug prescribed to help morning sickness in pregnant women between 1959 and 1961. It was found to cause severe deformities in babies, often leading to them being born without fingers, or arms or legs.

Appendix 4

SELECTED ANSWERS

QUIZ ANSWERS (*see* page 41)

1 (a)	**11** (b)
2 (b)	**12** Ignore parking restrictions.
3 (b)	**13** To help people with visual problems know
4 False	when it is safe to cross.
5 (a)	**14** 400 000
6 False	**15** 14%
7 (b)	**16** True
8 False	**17** 31%
9 Social Services Department/Department of	**18** Blindness
Social Security/Occupational Therapist/	**19** Spastic is rigid; flaccid is loose and floppy.
Multiple Sclerosis/Home Care Assistant.	**20** False
10 Deaf and blind	

DIAGNOSIS (*see* Chapter 7 pages 59–60)

When haemophilia is known to be present in a family and a woman is identified as a carrier, prenatal **diagnosis** from a foetal blood sample is possible. Alternatively a **blood** sample from the new-born baby can be used to make a diagnosis. This applies to mild, **moderate** and severe cases. In some **30%** of cases of haemophilia there is no known **family** history and the occurrence of **haemophilia** is presumed to be the result of a spontaneous genetic mutation. Cases of severe haemophilia may become apparent and be diagnosed at an early age as a result of **surgery** or injury. For example, prolonged bleeding may follow circumcision or routine blood sampling. More often the first **symptom** of a bleeding tendency is in the form of extensive bruising as the child learns to crawl or **walk**. Unfortunately this is sometimes suspected to be a result of non-accidental **injury**, but increasingly in such cases it is automatic that coagulation tests are used to **investigate** the possibility of the child having a blood disorder. Cutting teeth is another stage at which the **condition** may become apparent.

Moderate and mild haemophilia may not be diagnosed until later in **childhood** or in some cases even adultdhood. Because there is some **clotting** factor available more minor injuries will heal normally and it may not be until a major injury occurs that the deficiency is **revealed**. The process of diagnosis involves many **complex** laboratory tests on blood samples and takes several days to **complete**.

Index